2002

Seeking Light In Each Dark Room

Buscando Luz en Cada Cuarto Oscuro

Seeking Light in Each Dark Room
Buscando Luz en Cada Cuarto Oscuro

Por los Abrecaminos

Those who make a way
Young Latino Writers in Yakima

Edited by Jim Bodeen

Photographs by Rob Prout and Jim Bodeen

Blue Begonia Press   Yakima, Washington

Acknowledgments

The stories and poems in this book were written by writers who call them-selves abrecaminos, enrolled in a year-long Latino literature and writing course at Davis High School in Yakima, Washington using bilingual texts from the great works of Latin American writers.

Jorge Rodríguez, Julie Salatino, Juan Plata and Jim Rigney did extensive proofreading with the Spanish in the parent interviews. In addition, Linda Brown, Barry Grimes, MaryAnn Piñon, Kerry Chama, Becky Mineard also provided abrecaminos with editorial and proofreading assistance. Four abrecaminos, Eloisa Gonzalez, Martha Gamboa, Daisy Hernandez and Blanca Flores, put in extra hours typing the manuscript. Eloisa Gonzalez assisted in an editorial capacity in the selection of the poems for the Macchu Picchu Section and the Letter Poems to Latin American Women Section.

Terry Martin from Central Washington University read the entire manuscript, proofreading, shaping, editing.

Rob Prout went with me into the homes to photograph the mothers and fathers for the interviews. His sense of humor helped all of us relax and that is evident in the photos. We ate well in the homes. We acknowledge the Mexican cooking.

Partial funding of Seeking Light/Buscando Luz is made possible by grants from the Yakima Schools Foundation and the Davis High School Parent-Teacher-Student Association. Patty Dion, Peggy Ludwick, Mateo Arteaga, thank you.

Responsibility for authentic documents rests with the writers. They own their own stories. The editor's is job to maintain authenticity. This involves the responsibility of resisting changes as well as making them.

Copyright 2002 by the writers. All rights reserved.
Division Pages, *Late Night Jazz,* by Rob Prout and Jim Bodeen
Book Design by Karen Bodeen and Rob Prout
Front cover photograph, *Gamboa Dining Room Window,* by Rob Prout
Back cover photograph by Jim Bodeen
Photographs by Rob Prout and Jim Bodeen.

ISBN: 0-911287-48-5

Blue Begonia Press   225 South 15th Avenue   Yakima, Washington 98902

Para los padres
Los primeros abrecaminos

Table of Contents

Part V — Interviews with Our Mothers and Fathers

Part VI — Testimonios

Part VII — About the Authors & Vocabulario de los Abrecaminos

Seeking Light / Buscando Luz

The abrecaminos, the ones who make way, who look into themselves, who look beyond themselves. *Abre*, open. And *camino*, way. Open the way. Open the ways. One who opens one path opens many.

Making way and giving testimony. *Testimonios*. One of the traditions in Latino culture, telling the stories, bearing witness, giving testimony.

Oscar Rosales is a *luchador*, a wrestler. Most of his friends probably define him this way. I know him as a writer. In 36 weeks over a two-year span of time, I often spent time wondering about Oscar's work, the source of his *ganas*, or desire, and his ability to think like a writer and be a source of inspiration for others. One of our writers, writing an essay on being an abrecaminos, wrote about Oscar, calling him the "writing wrestler."

Oscar transferred into our class from another school in the middle of his junior year. I got to know him first as a writer. He didn't talk much in class, but he always went to the podium to read. He was always interesting on the page. I've never seen a place he wouldn't go in his writing.

"It's the podium more than anything," he said one day when we were talking after class, "going to the podium." Oscar likes telling the story as much as the writing itself. The podium in front of the class is a symbol of power. We stress the deep work of listening, and the energy that listening takes.

Telling our stories. Giving testimony. Carlos Maldonado visits us from Eastern Washington University and talks to us about the *testimonio* tradition. Being listened to. Maldonado says, "The farmworker does not know how to write his story. It takes two people to do a *testimonio*. The interviewer finds a story that reflects the lives of others and finds a common experience, a universal….The person telling the story is the story. It's a story shared by others."

Eloisa Gonzalez is at her computer writing an essay on her editing of the Machhu Picchu poems. I'm talking to the abrecaminos about their writing. Looking at each of them, I tell them which ones have not missed one assignment, large or small, all year. I ask them to verify if I'm right. They represent more than half the room. Before they can feel too good, I point to Eloisa. "Eloisa hasn't missed an assignment in four years."

Eloisa has a story. She writes a good story. She's the soul of this book. One of them. She insisted on it. She interviews her parents. She listens, and as she listens, she opens opportunities for them. It's a shared story, *testimonio*. Interest and need. Interviewing involves two people. She listens and writes, listens and organizes. She returns a year later and asks more questions.

One of the themes in our writing is breaking silence. Writers break silence at the podium reading their stories. Going to the podium is more important than safety and silence.

Carolyn Calhoon-Dillahunt sends me a page on "sharing, privacy, and safety in exploring the writing process" from a book by Peter Elbow. Carolyn teaches writing at Yakima Valley College. Susan Luppino, a teacher in a writing workshop explains, "I realized that as a member of a minority group, the line between safety and self-respecting survival is frequently blurred. The oppressive powers that foster one's feelings of being unsafe count on fearful silence as a means to continue the oppression ...I give myself voice and demand that society acknowledge my existence—I become visible in a world which might otherwise choose to ignore me."

Another connection. Inés Hernandez-Avila, from the University of California comes to read with the abrecaminos at Yakima Valley College. She gives us a paradoxical truth from *Alchemy of Erasure*. "Somos tan invisibles que somos visibles./We're so invisible we're visible." She says, "When a woman has to be made invisible, it is because she is powerful, and her presence reverberates, touching everything in its path."

The truth is confirmed daily by the abrecaminos. Every day. It's a truth confirmed not only by the women for themselves, but by the men, too. Not only for what it says about women, but for what it says about us all. The men want some of this power. We, too, want some of the visibility inherent in the invisibility. As Inés says, *Parece contradicción, pero no lo es.* It seems like a contradiction, but it's not.

As we write our way up the mountain, studying Pablo Neruda's transformational poem, "Las Alturas de Macchu Picchu," we're discovering our resources, learning together where we've been in our lives. Uncovering where we've been, we arrive at a new beginning point. When you read the Macchu Picchu poems in this book, read them as one story, written individually and collectively by a writing community on a journey. That's how they were written. Making the ascent, we also make the descent. Making the journey we give our *testimonios.* We tell where we've been. For most of us we're hearing it for the first time ourselves.

Seeking light in each dark room. The title comes from Estakio Beltran. Looking over his writing this winter he has some finished poems with some unfinished poems. A line stands out on the page. "Every dark room has a secret." Estakio looks at the line, and looks at me. "My brother gave me that line," he says. *Each dark room.* We say it over and over to each other. "It would make a good title, wouldn't it?" We say it to each other. As good as it is, it's not quite the truth.

Writers go into the unknown seeking truth, looking for answers. Dark rooms. The unconscious. *Seeking light in every dark room. Buscando luz.* The light that's in here. *En cada cuarto oscuro.*

Young men become men, and write about themselves as men. *Puntos de vistas cambian.* There is a paradigm shift. Becoming visible to themselves in writing and reading their stories, something else happens, too. They see themselves in solidarity with the young women. The women are also making this journey. When we finish our month-long study of Neruda and arrive at the *cima/*summit of Macchu Picchu, we are really at a beginning point.

"Yo soy principiante," I tell them. I'm a beginner. And I am. Writing stories and telling them is exhilarating work, but it's also the work of humility. *Principiante. Abrecaminos.*

I've been living with the word *abrecaminos* for more than ten years. Given as one word. One word only. I couldn't live without it. I couldn't say it enough. When I couldn't say it enough, I had to teach it. The word became a lesson plan. It became a unit and finally what I began calling my students. *You are the abrecaminos.* You are the ones. You are the ones making a way, making ways. The word became a *principio*, a principle around which a group of principles were constructed. *Principios para ser abrecaminos.*

The word is a calling. Abrecaminos are those of us who have been called to a word. Called to a word with a promise large enough to take us through the impossible. If the word is visionary it must also be practical. Make a way where there is no way. I asked the writers to write about the *principios* as I saw them operating in their lives.

Carlos Maldonado's words echo like Juan Rulfo's in Pedro Páramo. Not everything is going to be in order here. "Life is not in order. Memory is not in order. *Testimonio* opens the way for those who have been left out of the story. *Testimonio* opens up the story for everybody. It's democratic."

Where is my grandfather buried? What makes a citizen?

Start this way, by asking questions.

Jim Bodeen
Yakima
November, 2001—April, 2002

Part I

Unknown Passage: A Poem and a Story

"I want to be there for my people, especially for those who are afraid and don't speak up."

Josie Guapilla
Abrecaminos

The Unknown Passage Beginning June 25, 1989
On the Tijuana River Near the U.S.-Mexican Border

We hear commotion
then waken by shouting
telling us we're leaving,
to pack what we can carry.
A car waits outside.
After a couple of hours,
we stop walking
for a while,
meet other folks.
Then we are led by a man.
I am carried.
We are put in a boat.
The next thing I know,
I am in a new world
and different language
and see things
I have never seen before
at home.
I don't know if there's a home for us
until my uncle shows up.

I still don't understand
what happened.
I am told it is our future and a better life.

Arturo Obispo

The Beginning of Aguililla, Michoacán

María Guadalupe Barriga

I was born in Yakima, Washington. When I was five years old, my parents and I went to México. We started a new life in Aguililla, Michoacán, México, where I grew up.

How did God make Aguililla?

On a sunny morning of June, God sat under a tree and he looked around. He was thinking, "What a beautiful town I could make on this place." God started to make a garden and a plaza with a *kiosco* in the middle of the plaza where the people could walk around. "Walking around the *kiosco* in the garden, and hearing the music is a good thing for the people," God thought.

Then God made a temple where the people could go to church every Sunday. He called this temple *Nuestra Señora de Guadalupe*. Then he made a beautiful town with a few buildings, and houses with many trees, including some fruit trees, like mangos, *pinzanes* and *ciruelas*.

In Aguililla we celebrate the *12 de Deciembre*, because that's the *Virgen de Guadalupe's* day. Many girls wear Indian style clothes, like long skirts with huaraches y trenzas en su pelo and white blouses. We call these girls *Huares*. They also carry a *canasta* or basket with many kinds of fruit. They take them to the temple to offer it to the *Virgen*, and that's like an honor to her. We sing *Las Mañanitas* to the *Virgen* and it goes like this: "Buenos días, paloma blanca, hoy te vengo a saludar, saludando a tu belleza en tu reino celestial." After the song, las huares bailan y danzan, like the Indians Maya danced many years ago, and still do. Because we are Maya, too.

Exploring America

This room, it's a square. It has too many pictures and posters on the wall. The pictures are of the students who are the abrecaminos. It has many chairs in it, too. This is my classroom. Here is where we learned to break chains and climb mountains. We are trying to climb la montaña de Macchu Picchu.

This school is a big school. It has many stairs. It doesn't have a color, because it's just the gray color of the material that it's made of. It has three big buildings, and a fuente among the buildings with water and a few green trees. I like the fountain. Sometimes it's loud at Davis, but not too much. I like the way our teachers speak to students. Davis is never quiet. When I am at my school I hear music inside of me all the time. I guess that is because I love to be here learning. The music that I hear is the music of my future, telling me how much I will be helped by attending school.

I am glad to be American.
I am glad to live in America.
I know what I want, and I work hard for that.
I want to graduate from Davis, and I am sure I will.
I have an American family. I have a big family. We live in Yakima,
where I was born. Yakima. It's a small city,
but I think it's pretty and quiet.
We have the Yakima River. I think it's beautiful.
We also have many orchards with apple trees, which reminds me
of my Mexico where I was raised, in Michoacán.
Mexico is America, too.
My family and I are glad to live in Yakima.

Letter to America

America quiero darte gracias por todo lo que me has dado. Si, a tí
America. *Why? Because* me diste unos padres lindos. *You gave me my
wonderful parents.* Tú, America quien me miró y me conoces, desde niña.
Tu quién le dio un trabajo, a mis papás, para que me dierán de comer,
para que me vistierán, de tí. *You gave a job to my parents, so that they could
feed me, so that they could dress me. Thank you.* Yo no he aprendido mucho
de tí seguré aprendiendo y alimentandome porque tú siempre estarás
conmigo, a donde quiera que yo vaya. Tú me diste mi color, mi
lenguage. Tú serás mi compañera por siempre. *I haven't learned much of
you, but I will follow you and I will always be learning from you and you are
always with me. Mexico is America just as the United States is. I was born here,
but I was raised in Mexico, and I'm glad for that because that way I get to be
multicultural.*

Part II

Three Voices

*"Every room has a secret.
That's a line I got from my brother."*

Estakio Beltran

Kunayaya / Abre Caminos
My Life Story

Manuh Santos

Part One:

My name is Manuel Santos. I am going to talk about my life and how I came to the United States.

It was early in the morning on July 12, 1996 when I was working with my mom and two of my little sisters in the countryside far away from my home. At that moment I told my mom I wanted to come to the United States. I came with Onorio, my cousin, because he invited me to come with him.

Before I came I hugged my mom and my two little sisters. They said good-bye to me and good luck. I told them not to worry about me. I know how to take care of myself.

The reason I came to the United States is because I wanted to have a better life. My family is very poor. When I was a little boy, I did not go to school. I was the youngest of my family. I used to work all the time with my mom. My mom and I spent most of the time working with other people. They used to pay us around 50 Mexican pesos for five months.

I arrived in the United States in 1996. At that time it was very hard for me because I did not know how to speak English or Spanish. I only spoke my native language, Mixteco. I also did not know many people. I only knew my cousin Onorio. He knows the United States because he came here before.

At the time of my arrival I did not know how to write or read. One time my cousin Onorio and I went to look for a job. Guess what? We did not get the job because we couldn't speak English.

At that moment, I decided to go to school. That was the first time I started going to school in my life. I went to the MAS program, which at that time was located in southeast Yakima. The first day of school I began to study. I started to learn some lessons in English. The next day I began to practice my English. Two months passed and I decided to come to Davis High School. At first when I came to Davis High School I met Mr. Rigney. He started to talk about my education. After that, he sent two students to show me the classrooms. Many days passed and I met a lot of friends. I began to talk with different people and gained new friends.

Now I am a successful student. I am learning a lot of English and Spanish, I am also learning how to write and read.

The reason I am successful is because I want to help my mom to have a new house and raise many pigs. Also, I want her to have a grinder to grind corn.

Part Two:

"Kunayaya nuha Yuhvi chen"
(I went among the forest and mountains)

It was early in the morning on January 12, 1996 when I was working with my mom and two of my little sisters in the countryside far away from my home. At that moment I asked my mom permission that I wanted to see the immense mountains close to my village because I wanted to discover how immense it is. My mom let me go see the immense mountains, I just wanted to speak with them. When I reached the top of the mountains, to me it was something very beautiful, because on the top of the mountains I could see most everything in the atmosphere around the mountain. I felt blissful because finally I visited it. I waited for years to reach it.

Part Three:

La Muerte de una Niña Inocente

La niná se llamaba, María. Ella era una niña sin padres, muy pobre. También era una niña honrada y muy trabajadora.

Pero un día algo horrible le sucedió con ella. Había un hombre viejo en mi pueblo que le gustaba a la niña, pero la niña nunca supo por que no habló con ella.

Un día la niña salió para ir a jugar con sus amigos. En ese día el hombre estaba cuidandola que estaba haciendo por que ella queria. (Según la gente contaban.)

El hombre pensó que la niña tenía un novio.

En realidad la niña tenía el animo para jugar con sus amigos porque tenía todavía sentimiento como una niña, no como una niña adulta. Un día triste y sucia.

Cuando la niña decidió irse a la barranca para collectar nueces que caían de los árboles de nueces. El hombré ya sabía que la niña iba ir a ese lugar. Él se escondió adentro do los árboles de walnut.

Cuando, la niña llegó a la barranca. En ese momento la niña empezaba a recoger las nueces, cuando el hombre y tenía las piédras en sus manos para matarla.

Según el cuento indicaba, minutos después, el hombre mató la niña con las piedras porque les pegó las piedras en la cabeza de la niña.

En su pensamiento, dijó ¿Porque me hicieron esto?" La niña nunca supó porque lo han assesinado.

Cuando ella murió se preguntó en si mismo ¿Cuáles eran las razones? ¿Porqué me han matado?

El hombre se huyó.

Ese fue algo muy horrible para la vida de una niña inocente que nunca supó. ¿Por qué?

Part Four:

Monte Alban

Dime, Monte Alban, ¿Cómo has estado todos los años que has enfrentado aquí sólo y triste? ¿Dónde están tus hijos que han estado aquí contigo durante su hera de Mesoamérica?

¿Por qué se huyeron de ti?

Dejandose soló en un lugar valdillo y montañoso.

¿Cómo te sientes quedandote solo en este lugar sin hijos, sin habitantes?

Ahora que estás sólo ¿No te da lastima que sus hijos te abandonaron? Tus hijos están sufriendo mucho por sus culpas y ahora ya no te quieren.

Muchos de sus hijos están perdiendo su honor, su idioma, sú tradición, su costumbre porque los desparramase por todos lados de la tierra por está razón.

Muy pronto sú cultura, se va a desaparecerse en este mente. Porque otras culturas nos están debilitendo y la gente también. Yo tengo la esperanza que no acurra esta cosa.

Part Five:

Monte Alban

Fui al Monte que está lejos de mi pueblo pero nunca fui a ese monte.

Mi corazón latía por no ir a ese monte que nunca alcanjé de conocer. Mi poder me hace que vaya a ese monte tan olvidable. Yo todos los días deseo como voy a poder ir a ese monte.

No puedo estar sin calmar de conocer ese monte. Pero todos los días estoy cada día más preparado, entenando para yo poder ir a ese monte, mi ritmo de mi corazón cada día está más contento y feliz porque ya es hora de conocer a ese monte que tantos días he esperado.

Es muy interesante conocer a un monte. Me llamo Monte Alban. Mi vida es muy triste, porque estoy abandonado por mis hijos que me han protejido por muchos años.

Part Six:

My Father

My father, I send this letter to you to say how are you? I hope you receive this letter father.

I did not meet you because you left this world 18 years ago. I miss you a lot, father.

Tell me, where are you? Why did you leave me with my mother? We are suffering a lot because of you. My mother does not know how to do many things that you used to do for us.

Come see me when I sleep because I want to meet you. I want to be with you to talk to you and I want to hug you.

One night my father came to see me when I was sleeping. In my dream I was holding his hands, trying to ask him to carry me because never in my life did I see my father carrying me.

He inquired, "What do you like me to bring next time when I come back?"

I told him. " I would like you to bring me a little white toy horse."

My father said to me, "Good bye my son. Take care of yourself. Be a good boy all the time and say hello to your mom."

"I am still liking her a lot."

"Father, don't leave me alone father. Take me with you."

"No, you need to stay with your mom!"

"She needs your help, son."

When I woke up, I was laying down on the bed.

Part Seven:

My Slave Pencil

I want to write, but my pencil makes me think. My pencil is my weapon, but it is also my power.

My pencil is my knowledge and it is my process.

My tuchacha is my slave and prisoner but it is also without hope to be free in my hands.

Querido Amigo, José,

Le mando está carta para ti. La presente es con el fin de saludarle y darle las gracias por la ayuda que me ha ofrecido y su experiencia de correr. Lo he apreciado mucho su ayuda y no se imagina el lindo efecto que me hace sentir, muy alegre todos los días porque me disfruto corriendo.

Espero verle pasado mañana en la práctica de cruzado y en el campo, la cual parece que va a ser muy importante en mi futuro.

Deseo que esté bien con la compánia de los suyos.

Yo sin novedad. Le saludo como, su amigo, Manúh.

Final Part

Today we talked about the most important issue. How the

rules are in this college. Do not spend a lot of your money and do not party a lot.

Manuel!! Can you hear me?? Where are you at this moment? Don't hide from me, please. Show up. I want to know you so we can become good friends and have a good relationship with each other you know. Since I heard, you have not spoken to me anymore. What is going on with you? Speak up. Don't be shy. I am a human being, too. Don't be afraid to face me. Be self-confident you know. Well, I know ma'am, I hope to talk to you next time.

I can feel the potential energy inside you that you can do the things you wish to discover. I know that you have big dreams and you also are a dreamer. Don't stop. Keep going with your motivations and have a lot of confidence in yourself. You have to motivate you. Do what you have to do and don't look back to the past things that you have done. There are things to explore in this world. Talk to you later, okay?

The Way Where the Path Lay

Michelle Martinez

And I watched the Sun beat on his body, as it always did. It's a ritual from sunrise to sunset. He tried to beat the Sun, but somehow it always came out on top.

He climbed those stairs that almost reached to Heaven, as he picked the forbidden fruit. He grabbed, twisted, and bent. Then he dropped it over and over again. But it never did fill up his bag of what he considered those helpless dreams.

The Earth was his mother and the Sun was his father. His mother gave him the dirt from which he came. But his father the Sun was the one that made him grow.

He sees me staring at him. I am at the foot at the tree. I look up at him with my sinful eyes. I open my mouth and my words fly out.

"Are you ever going to beat your father, the Sun?"

He looked at me. His mouth looked like it had been tied with roped chains. He started to chew.

"My time will come when I rise above the Sun. Then my words will no longer be contained. I will be able to rise above the Sun and rule it." he said.

"That will be good. Then, the Sun will no longer beat you down," I said.

"Aye, it will be good. But answer me a question. Where did you come from?" he asked with dim eyes.

"I really don't know where I came from. I guess the Wind blew me here or I got lost and I really don't remember where I came from. It's been a long time. But the one thing I do remember is the smell from these fruits. Wherever I go the scent chases me. On those lonely nights it actually haunts me," I said with sad eyes.

So we stared at each other. It was like looking into a lake that showed you what you've missed. We both watched as our souls interlocked. Then we both beat each other. He showed me what I missed and I showed him what he needed. I finally saw that he was my Sun, my father. I've been so blind in the dark that I didn't know where I was. I showed him how to set himself free from the Sun because the Sun wasn't his father. It was him holding back. So then to get back where we belonged, we both tore a sleeve from our souls, exchanged the sleeves and sewed them back up without tears.

Now Entering Terrace Heights

He's driving his red Beretta car, now entering Terrace Heights. He keeps on going straight until he turns to the left.

"We're going to visit an old friend."

"Okay."

He drives along the paved streets. Never beginning. Never ending. He stops. He opens the door. They both get out. He walks straight to her. Then he looks down on her and her husband.

"She was like a mother to me. Two years ago, I gave her Mother's Day flowers." I told her, "…Even though you aren't my mother, I consider you that."

She is lost for words. And the only comfort she can give him is a pat on the back.

"They only died a couple of months in between. She went first. Then he went next. Let's leave."

They both get in his red Beretta car. They leave the paved streets. Never beginning. Never ending. They go back out to the road that heads home for the both of them.

"Look there's a quail."

"Where?"

"There."

"Oh, I missed it."

"I am always looking out for things like that."

She knew exactly where she had to go. All she had to do is follow this paved street where it led exactly to the local supermarket. But she wanted to take the short cut. So she did. But the short cut wasn't what she thought. Instead of finding the supermarket, she got lost. She never did find her way off the shortcut.

Birth Ritual

He always had a ritual to his walk. He always walked with his head up, too. But the problem with that was, he never knew what he was stepping into.

"I heard that he is like that because he wants to be the same as everyone else."

And every night he cries, because he is so confused. He doesn't know whether to throw his mask away or to surrender to it.

"Too bad, he was a nice guy. He could've changed things. But I will never understand why he changed himself."

He prayed to whatever was supposed to be up there. And he cried out, asking was he doing things right.

.

And that's what she waited for every Sunday. She loved it when her grandma made fresh hot tortillas. Every Sunday resulted in a high pile of tortillas, that she imagined could touch the sky.

Inside out

It took her thirty-six years to see that the world was open to her. She had been so contained and limited in what she wanted to do. It haunts her even though she has this freedom.

"Yeah, they called me to go back to school and get my G.E.D. at YVCC."

"Hey, that's great! You should go and get it."

"What for? I don't even know what I want to do."

"Who cares? You could still go there and then along the way, you can figure out what you want to do."

She was afraid. She dropped out of school when she was in eighth grade. From then on, the world changed on the outside while she stayed inside.

.

It was her time to shine. She was proud. Of all she went through, she finally made it. She will be the first in her family to graduate.

She Wept

She wept to her mother, but she didn't want to listen. She wept to her father, but he did things the same as her mother. She wept to God, but she got a feeling that he had more important things to worry about than her.

"Why won't anyone listen to me? It feels like I am put on this earth to be by myself forever."

The clock is ticking. She can't stop it. She grows more and more concerned that no one is listening to her. She fights for a way to let herself out. She can't stand it any more. She wants to be heard.

"I feel very sorry for their loss. I know how much that they loved their daughter. It must be hard for them. She was their only daughter."

"It's all their fault, they should have seen it coming and put a stop to it. If it was my daughter, I would've known it if she was having thoughts about killing herself."

And her mom wept, but no one heard it. Her father wept, but no one wanted to hear it. God wept, but he had no one to weep to.

.

She loved him. She loved him even more than life itself. He was always there to listen to her. She was grateful to God everyday for sending him to her. She was happy.

All That She Knew

Four years have passed by. She tries to remember, out of the four years, which memory was the best? But all the memories got caught up in time, in a place that was non existent. All that she has left are the lessons she has learned and the feelings attached to them.

"Out of my high school experience, I've grown so much as an individual. I lost my friends, but then I gained new ones. Sometimes during school it was hard because I didn't have any idea who I was or what I wanted to be. It hurt to see some of my friends who changed not for the better but for the worse. And for a little while I was spinning the wrong way myself. I still don't know where I am headed, but I am ready for anything that is coming my way."

She was right. She was ready for anything. The memories she had from school sadly fade away. But the lessons learned stay as footprints forever imprinted in her heart.

.

She turned eight years old today. She had a long sun dress on. She was glad it was her birthday. She was so happy that she ran outside to her backyard. She put her arms out as far as they could go. She started to spin. Slowly at first, but as she continued to spin, she started to go faster and faster until she couldn't remember.

Dear Michelle (pretending games),

You wear a cross that's turned
the wrong way out.
You wear your heart on a necklace.
Do you think that they will leave you?

So many times you played
the image of the mother.
You protect your family first,
instead of your self.

You are an expert in role playing,
of keeping the peace. You are so
consumed, you don't know
what you are here to hear.

But what are you supposed to do?
You are a woman, and in being a
woman comes certain responsibilities.
You can't help it.

Aya, my friend.
You put up a silent fight.
That is what's killing you.
Do you want the whole

world not to hear you?
You need to speak even if it's just a whisper.
You just might change the world.

I cannot tell you where you are at.
I never saw it myself.
But what are you keeping inside,
that can't see out?

I hear a tune though,
it's all that I can hear and feel.
It's so loud I can hear it
going through my skin.

"And everyone here's to blame.
Yeah, everyone here
gets caught up in the
pleasure of the pain."

So why are you always slammed
down when you're trying to get
back up? You keep your self
there because you love that kind of pleasure.

But keep your self up
until you find some other
type of love or feelings.
Cause I know you're trying hard.

We'll see each other again.
I know we will.
Because I am a part of you,
as you are a part of me.

your friend,
        Michelle

Estakio Beltran: In Every Dark Room

Letter Poem To Self
To MY self:

What's up, little man? How
you been? Listen, I know
times are hard for you right
now but you got to keep
going. Keep fighting those
battles. I know it's hard. I
can feel your pain. I am
with you. I see your
dreams, those horrible
dreams you get at night.
Fight!
Move on. Speak to free
yourself. Don't lose your
voice. Stay alive or I will
never come to be. Scream
and be the voice of the
people. Manifest your glory
so that your very soul may
be seen from even a long
distance. Then there will be
no question. Everyone will
know it's you. No more
need for lies, for bureaucracy,
or conformity. Just you,
yourself, and me.

Malinche Poem
Malinche

Maldita Mujer—
Those who curse you—
Your meaning is evil
yet your roots
are clean.
You're a disgrace.
You are the
black bee
and a spitting image
of me.
We have fought
similar battles—
Our scars are
living trophies
of our strengths
and the selfish need
to survive.
Then I scream out
loud,
I am a Malinche!
I am a whore
from which a new race
shall be born—
A race that will
grow to hate me.

From the manuscript:

Death of A Mailman

I'm going to write, write the stories of the voices that speak to me.
The whispers in my ears, y el sonido del viento punzando sobre mis
tambores. I am going to write so that people don't forget me.
I'm gonna leave no doubt of my existence...

Estakio Beltran~ May 27.01

[Whispers] "Pus que no saben."

"No. ¿Qué paso?"

"Lo mataron. Lo mataron... ¡Fue asesinado a sangre fría!"

"¿Pero who would do such a thing?"

"Quien sabe, amaneció muerto."

"Nadie sabe..."

"Pero, era tan simpático."

"Pobrecito, el cartero always brought us good news."

"¿Ahora quien va a tomar su lugar?"

"Siéntate! Don't be jumping around back there. Mijo you're gonna get us pulled over. Now sit down!"

"Why do we have to go?"

Tito gazed back at his old house, at the yard he used to play in, and at the neighbors he always said hi to on his way home from school. He pressed his face hard against the back window of the old "Chevel," harder and harder the farther and farther they got. From the outside, his nose was so flat that his nostrils made him look like a pig. The air exhaling from his lungs clouded his sight until he could see no more.

"Why Mom, why do we go?"

What do I do now?

"Mom, you have an ulcer... Do you know what that means?"

"Ay m'ijo, pues that I can't have anymore chile."

"Ay mom, you crack me up!"

Estaba Viva la Noche

He couldn't sleep. Simplemente Tito se revolcaba in the sabanas de la cama. Turn after turn after turn. His stomach was twisting into infinite knots that tied into balls. His feet were cold, so cold they made him shiver, yet covered with sweat. Un sudor tan frió.

Finally the sun rose. As the morning greeted Tito, his body was beginning to get covered with rain. A soft light rain was descending from the stormy sky. He closed his eyes and listened to the sound of the rain beating on the roof of the house, getting louder and louder, until the rain gathered on his forehead and poured into the saltiness of his tears. *And no one, not even the rain, knew how he felt.* Un aire de tristeza le llega a Tito. A low whistle came out of him, and knocked him on his knees. Then uneasiness overcame him, a fright so big it brought the cold sweats with it. Tito began to feel como si la tierra se abría y se lo tragaba en ése instante. But the earth did not devour him in one gulp. Instead it sucked on him slowly, starting with his feet. They were soaked into hot mud. Puddles of water, like tears of the gazing eye, are little mouths open to the infierno.

María Juega

Juega María, juega con tus muñecas the elote. Acaríalas con tus manos de seda. Por tu nombre eres Madre.

"Yo jugaba con muñecas de elote. Las bestia con basura y les hablaba. En mi niñez tan corta, me la pasaba en la cocina."

Después de haberse levantado temprano para cocinar para los hombres, después de haber hecho el café y sentar el pan dulce al centro de la mesa, Maria amasaba la masa con sus manos pequeñas. El agua tibia estaba recién traída del poso. Cargaba una jarra de barro. Una canterota y su vestido blanco.

Bajó al poso después de haber entendido the whistles calling to her at night. She knew what they meant, as she knew many new things now. When she got there he was squatting down on a rock. His eyes looked up to hers and out of his purple lips came out, "Mi morena, we have to go. Our parents will never agree with us." And they fled, after a quick kiss, together holding hands as if the darkness and loneliness of the well had married them. Their only witnesses were the water in the bucket thrown to the side of the well, half empty.

Y el café se quemó, esperando esa agua que nunca llegó.

Sun.

At the end of the day it is as if the water is calling you. First your eyes, it invites them in with a stream of lights. A shine so splendid, they squint, overwhelmed by brightness.

He Had To Get Out

It was a beautiful day and he hadn't been outside of these walls in what seemed to be years. The clock in the living room ticked after tick after tick. It was the only thing moving everything else suspended. The wasting of water followed each tick. Drop by drop falling into the emptiness of the kitchen sink. The squeak of his shoes pacing up and down the halls, created a song. He looked at the pictures on the wall. All of them were strangers. People he didn't know, but who reminded him of someone. The glass frame protecting one of the pictures reflected something he did recognize, the look in his own eyes. A loud noise coming from the outside made him turn his head. He put the picture face down on the floor. Soon they would be here.

In Every Dark Room There's A Secret

¡No pus no entro!
It's dark in there.
What do you know about darkness?
Nothing happens in the dark!
Now come and go into the dark, away from all this.
Escape the light and join us.
No—I can't...

Contesten

And the phone rang and rang and rang. It rang ten times in that lonely room. Tito could hear the silence of the empty room as it rang and rang and rang. The call went unanswered. Mama didn't pick up the phone. Maybe she's too busy to talk right now. Or maybe she's sick and is at the hospital? Tito calls the hospital to find out. The phone doesn't ring as much here. It is picked up by a fake voice after the second ring. In-between the words of this noise, Tito could still hear the loneliness of this place. He pictured the offices with piles of paper work gathered on top of the desk. Each with a secret. Not all have their names on them.

Te quedaste como un perro en la calle, aullando de dolor. Las puertas cerradas. I don't want to forget you, mom. Dejas parte de tu corazón. Como té quiero. No llores por mi que talvez no merezco tus lagrimas. No llores que los vientos soplan mas duros.

"No te quiero perder Dios sabrá cuando no veros."

"Si madre, solo Dios sabrá."

As she once fed me and what she ate filled me.

I, too, shall eat for her, at every meal.

I shall eat something in her name.

Mamasita.

I Am a Man Walking on Glass

Pressing my footsteps
Gently
Against the sharp edges
To pave the way
For many more
To follow,
I am
An *abrecaminos*.

Interview

Es Como un Infierno
(Interview of a Farm Worker)

"Me levanto temprano para evitar el sol." But no matter how early I come, the sun always surprises me. I see the empty asparagus boxes running away from me when I have a full hand. At twelve we try to rest, but it only gets hotter and hotter. We figure that if we hurry we might get done picking before the earth melts, and our bodies cremate into asparagus soup. "Después de la una, ya perdiste." At that time the earth is boiling hot, the sun is still beating on you and your water is all gone, but el pinché espárrago is popping out of the ground faster than you can pick it. "Que bien los gringos no comen yerba, fíjese."

"Es muy difícil este trabajo." Debes en cuando toman un descansito. Se sientan al fin del curco, voltean las cajas bacías de espárrago y las usan como sillas. Sacan su "lonche" de bolsas plásticas de Safeway. When they pull out their tacos to eat, I can see the cold tortilla se parte de estar seca y fría. The water they drink is hot, coming from the water jugs sitting on the boiling earth.

"You really never know when a day is over. You don't really know when to call it quits. The heat of the day keeps the asparagus growing and no matter what pace you work, you never leave a bare field. Even the first row you picked before the sun came is now ready to be picked again."

"No si le digo que es un infierno."

"Es un cuento de nunca acabar."

Como a las cuatro se suben al coche, todos cubiertos en polvo. Sus manos manchadas de verde y un olor fuerte. The day is not over yet. Now the women go home to prepare supper, and the men will stop by the store to pick up some cold beer and come back. They will go home before the sun sets. Eat dinner and fall dead on the floor. And the night will pass too fast for them. Before they know it, the sound of an alarm clock crying out desperately will awaken them. When they open their eyes and look at one another, nothing changes. They are all still covered in dust and they still have green hands. It's not like in the movies where the murderer wakes up with stained hands and can't remember what happened. The farm workers know what happened. Their sore bodies are living reminders of yesterday, today and tomorrow.

"Sometimes, de pura muina y coraje uno se pone a chillar, ya que le queda hacer."

"Mire que como niños lloramos. Pero a ver que se puede hacer. Nada. Y si le digo muchacho, es como un infierno."

The Treasure Gatherers

If I close my eyes from the yawning preacher

I am taken back to the days of the campo,
crystals decorating the vineyards.
Asparagus tips kissed by the dew of the morning
scatter like pearls
at the bottom of a dead brown sea.

The campesino is a treasure gatherer.

Waking early they see
the rising of the biggest pearl,
stripes of orange wedging through a black sky.

The eyes of the campesino take in the fields,
backs stiffened by the straps of their picking bags.
Soldiers of an orange captain
harvest the crystals left by the light.

They will work hard.
The sun will give them jewels of their own.
Diamonds dripping from the side of their eyes,
perlas de sudor,
which they wipe on worn handkerchiefs
and hide in back pockets.

Liberación

¡Ayúdame, Señor,
regalame luz y
fuerza para vivir!

Libérame Señor
pon en mí
de nuevo una sonrisa.
Haz que
las tempestades en mi vida
cesen,
y que nazca en mí

un nuevo Sol.

Para que me acompañe
durante mis noches tristes

es que mi vida es un bloque de hielo

Derríteme con tu presencia, o Señor
hasta que mi cuerpo,
Como agua hirviendo,
se transforme en vapor

Part III

Macchu Picchu

Las Alturas de Nuestras Vidas
A Collaborative Poem of a Sacred Journey

"But I've never said something that I want to say now, about my family. My brother, who filled out the applications for my parents when they were going to be legal, could have put my name on the paper because I was under 18 years old. He didn't because that was going to cost 100 dollars more."

María Rosa Barriga

The Path to Macchu Picchu

Eloisa Gonzalez

A year ago, I set out on one of the most important journeys that has crossed my life. I had taken the path to the peak of Macchu Picchu—Machu Picchu had become my sacred sanctuary. It was the peak of Macchu Picchu where I discovered myself. Underneath the stones of my sacred land, I discovered the purity and fractures of my life.

Step by step, I continued going up the path to Macchu Picchu. I was eager to find myself. As I looked back, my anger had converted into energy. No longer did it hold me back. It pushed me forward. I carried ambition, spirituality, and love. Those were the things I needed to survive. Those were the tools I used to resurrect my voice from its death. I had maintained it silent for many years. No longer would it be contained. My voice would finally breathe its words.

In my journey, each word I wrote and spoke was a rigid rock I climbed. Stories of my life were inscribed in each rock. Each story had penetrated into my mind, keeping the past alive. Understanding the past helped me understand my journey as well as my reason for existence. I know that I needed to finish the journey in order to begin.

I watched the others struggle with each step, but I could see their ambition on their faces. They were eager to make it. The only tools of defense and protection were the voices, pens, and the past. That's what kept us going. As we moved towards the top, we were anxious to arrive, even though we knew we never would arrive. It was a journey without an end; it was only the beginning.

The journey of Macchu Picchu is in the journey of poetry writing. It is the journey in which we discover our true meanings and our fears through words. Through poems we learn about our past and present. The poems help us unleash the flame for the future and *abrir los caminos, open the ways.* The journey will always remain in our heads and our hearts. Like Antonia Caro mentions in her poem " I Have Climbed to Macchu Picchu. I know that I will keep this experience with me forever."

Macchu Picchu is more than just a journey. It's an identity. It becomes part of who we are. As Marco Gutiérrez calls Macchu Picchu, it's "the place of change." Macchu Picchu has become the place where one takes a new life form built from the old. Like a butterfly that breaks free from its cocoon. The butterfly removes itself from its comfort zone, and moves freely into the world. Reaching the top of Macchu Picchu releases us freely into the world.

Sometime in our lives, we must have come across someone who reached the top of Macchu Picchu. Our ancestors have reached Macchu Picchu's peak. Anyone who has opened the ways has reached Macchu Picchu. They have set our present and our future by altering our past.

My mother, Eloisa Gonzalez, and my father, Lorenzo Gonzalez, have been my abrecaminos, the ones who have opened the way. When my parents crossed el rio to enter the United States, they burst through the mountain of Macchu Picchu. They changed our future with one hope they carried out into reality. They lit the fire in my life.

When my parents crossed the border into los Estados Unidos, they opened the doors to my path to Macchu Picchu. They might have not noticed, but they were preparing me for the changes life had to offer. With the history of pain, love, and effort, I acquired ambition for my journey to Macchu Picchu. Our historia was like no other. It was my purpose to continue up the mountain.

Many of the abrecaminos who are currently climbing Macchu Picchu are discovering their flames and their historias. They are finding the love and ambition that will help them continue up the mountain. Through their poems they are revealing their historias and their truths. They are opening other caminos.

This has been a most exciting and challenging year. I have been able to tell my stories and assist others in telling theirs. I also have been able to work as a co-editor for two sections of *Seeking Light in Each Dark Room/Buscando Luz en Cada Cuarto Oscuro.* I helped in selecting the Macchu Picchu poems and in selecting the Letter Poems to the Latin American Women. We made our selections based on two criteria: we tried to select the best writing and we tried to tell one collaborative story within the many. As I read through the poems, it makes my heart skip in new ways. My soul has awakened once again. The poems are a challenge: may they make strong readers; may they take readers to new places inside themselves.

Las Alturas de Nuestras Vidas
A Collaborative Poem of a Journey
with Pablo Neruda as Our Guide

Part One

"I put my brow amid the deep waves."
—Pablo Neruda

It is 12:34 p.m., Saturday morning
and I am still here in my bed.

As I lie here,
I think about most things in my life.

Why do I have to be the one
who does things around the house?

Cooking, cleaning—looking after siblings,
I feel tired and worn out.

I could pass out.
I don't want to be here.

Why can't I have what I want?
A question to ask you, "Can I keep you?"

You seem so far away.
The reach of a giant,

wouldn't be able to touch you.
My best friend won't give me the time of day.

I can't stand living here in my house.
I don't like the haters around me.

Why do people always have something to say
when they don't even know you ?

—Monica Pola

"Noches desdichadas hasta la ultima harina."
—*Pablo Neruda*

The life is an illusion.
La vida es solamente ilusión, llena de esperanzas.

Ho a caso tu no tienes la ilusión
siempre de alcanzar tus sueños,
siempre alcanzar los que quieres, si
es posible romper barreras en tu camino hacerlo.

I always remember a mi mama
diciendonos con su cara de angel, por favor mijas,
you guys always
have to start by giving your hand
to another person.

Whatever you don't want for you
don't wish it to another person.

I think that is really true, it is the
best thing you can do, if you
want respect for your self you
need to have respect for others.

I have this in me each morning.

Yo creo que todos debemos poner
de nuestra parte empezando por
admitir cuando nos equivocamos
en cosas, nadie es perfecto en este mundo.

So that our own opinions can be bigger—
y haci enseñar a los demás a
admitir sus equivocaciones con
nuestro ejemplo.

—María Rosa Barriga

It is my last day in "La Cuestita."
I don't feel happy.
But I don't want to go to the U.S.
And I don't like to go by airplane.

I want more days to stay here with
my only friend that I have.
I know that we have to go because
in the U.S. we have opportunities.
My friend and I are so sad.

Even our thoughts are sad. She and I
are thinking about a better life.
When I was going to the airport
from Guadalajara,
I saw my friend "Lupe" too sad.

When she was going with her
sister to the school, she told me
goodbye. When I saw the last house
of my town, I said, "One day I will
be returning because I am going to
another country and looking for other
friends that I never had."

—Maribel Padilla

With the Victory in Your Hand

*"The ominous adversity of each day
was like a black glass from which they drank."*
—Pablo Neruda

Fighting against the angel
there is a monster in the waters.
It kills souls.
It steps on the flowers of hope.
It destroys the light of the waters.
It fought against their strengths
and killed them.

51

Its words were fireballs
falling on their hearts.

The meanness of its soul
devoured their dreams.
The souls followed down.
One by one,
they formed a line.
Their dead bodies were there
and the smell of death rose up to heaven.
It smelled in the heights
when their bones were burned.

—Cristal Manjarréz

"Iba entre las calles y la atmosfera, llegando y despidiendo."
—Pablo Neruda

I am 12 years old.
My father left me.
Where is he?
Why did he go?
I feel lost and alone.

Some one found me.
I don't know him.
Did love find me beneath my sadness?
Did I find love inside my sadness?
I don't know.
I feel lost and alone.

From house to house I look for myself
and the years have passed, people and places change.
My father has changed.
I don't know him.
Do I need him?
Do I need love?
I am 17 years old, lost and alone.

—Tatiana Whizar

Part Two

"No tuve sitio donde descansar la mano."
—*Pablo Neruda*

Today is Sunday. There are
many things that I can do,
like go to the fair or go dancing.

But I just want
to think about you.

Yesterday I kissed you, like
I hadn't kissed you before.
Today is Sunday, but my mind
wants to stay on Saturday.
Yesterday I kissed you and
I can't forget about it.

My heart starts to hit
my chest, every time that

I close my eyes. My mind
is tired. I am not tired.

I want to see you. I want to
feel you. I want to kiss you.

—Gastón Pérez

*...hijos de un otoño rabioso
que hiciera temblar el miserable arból de las razas asustadas*
—*Pablo Neruda*

Where were you when I needed
you? When I needed to talk?
When I was vying for your time?
I needed you to help me learn
about life. To give me words of
encouragement every time I did well.
You're my dad, but at times it felt as

though I didn't even know you.
Now that my freshman year is here
you actually start acting as if you
care. Upset over my progress report.

It just puzzles me because you never
spent much time with me before.
Yet in those crucial times in my life
I always wanted to seek your advice
and you weren't there. You were out
drinking your problems away not
aware that your youngest son
needed you. It happened often
when I was growing up. I needed
you, yet you always let me down. I
always looked up to you. You were
my hero but you never taught me
much. It was so hard knowing that
my role model never had time for me.
You just completely shut me out of
your life. Now that I'm older you
want to get involved in my life as if
you were there with me all along.
Why now after so many years?
Your words have no value to me
anymore. I respect you as a man
but it is hard to ignore your
absence from my life. You left me
out on my own. Left me to learn
as I went along. I'm not that little
kid anymore. Once, you were the one
I wanted to be like. You did a good
job in helping raise my older brothers.
I guess you were too busy to be in
my life. Now that I'm older you
want to pretend like you were
always there. Giving me useless
advice. Why do you even bother,
anyway? Just go back to whatever
you were doing and let me live my
life and make my own decisions.

I don't need you. There's nothing
you can do anymore. I learned things
on my own without you and I don't
need you there telling me what to do.

—Oscar Rosales

"Tearing away at the heart right up to the grave?"
—Pablo Neruda

I want to know
why hate is around everything.
How did this four letter word
become so powerful?

Tell me how did this word
come about?
This word can hurt
so many people,

when people say they
hate you.
They usually say that word
out of anger.

Most people don't really mean it.
Others can mean it and that word can hurt like no other.
That word can really hurt your
self-esteem.

I want to know
what people are thinking when
they let this four letter word
roll off their tongue.

Tell me
why anyone would want to
tell someone they
hate them.

I want to know
who came up with this word,
and what were they thinking
when they did?

Tell me
why anyone would want to
use such a strong word
to hurt another?

—Monica Pola

"Mighty death invited me many times."
—Pablo Neruda

To see what death means—

But why me? I was too small
to know what it truly meant.

But why me, to lose
someone so special?

It was not her time. Not yet, not yet.

She wanted me to be happy.
She wanted the best for me

and I'm sad to say that I
will never see her, nor touch her.

She would always open doors
when everybody shut the doors on me.

—Eleazar Herrera

Part Three

"Todos desfallecieron esperando su muerte diaria."
—*Pablo Neruda*

"Not one death but many deaths came to each"

I'm glad this was all a dream, not being noticed not being heard. I stand in
silence
outside my house waiting for someone to open the door. I knock on the door,

again and again. No one opens the door. I look through the window and my
family is
there. I tap on the glass window and no one looks. I tap harder and louder and
no one

looks, everyone looks at the TV and in there the news—the news had my
picture, a picture
of me, I could not believe that the picture on TV was me,
my face was all

bloody and my body was on the spilled milk that was all over the floor, then the
news said
that I had been killed at the Mini Market down the street when a guy

was trying to rob the store. But it turns out that my picture wasn't the only one,
but
the person that was robbing the store turned out to be my cousin. He died, too,
he was

shot by the owner, but the owner missed and then the second shot hit him. I
cried
outside the window, and I didn't know whether I cried for me or if I cried for
my

family waiting for me to come home with a gallon of milk. I think as I cried,
Why must death
come to me, why must death take not one but two in my family?

—Martha Gamboa

"Todos desfalecieron esperando su muerte."
—*Pablo Neruda*

"Peace," one word, but the
most important right now.
"Taliban," one religion, but
the most polemic in this
moment. Death, a lot of dead.

What's happening with the world?
What's happening with
this world that God gives us?

Rich people getting richer,
poor people getting poor.
Today I saw the news, but
I saw them with my hurt, too.
I was afraid, I wanted to cry.
I do not know what
was inside me.

—Gastón Pérez

*todos desfallecieron esperando su muerte, su
corta muerte diaria*
—*Pablo Neruda*

I'm trapped within my own mind.
Trapped in a world I didn't create
for myself, but have grown accustomed
to. I'm treated like a common thief
and no one wants to hear what I have
to say. They just figure that I'm just
another fucking *spic* here to
contribute to the downfall of society.
Not only do I get this at school but
also at home. I got in trouble once
again and my dad gives yet another
lecture as the stream of profanity spews
from his mouth. Even he doesn't believe
in me anymore. I don't even care anymore.

Why should I? It's not like anybody
will listen to me. I don't even know how
to get away or where to even start.
Every time I get something good going,
it always fails and blows up in my face.
I just can't win. I sit in my room as I
think of eroded dreams, trying to figure
out what to do. Here I am now, six years
later, thinking about a past that seems so
distant. I was so afraid of what awaited me.
I wasn't aware that I was capable of
maturing so much. I have faced my fears
and my doubts and have battled to move
on and do something with my life. I now
know what it will take to survive. No
longer awaiting death at my door, I move
on. There is still a lot I must do and my
time is just starting. Death tried intimidating
but I no longer fear it. If it wants me, it's
going to have to fight. I'm not going
to be an easy win.

—Oscar Rosales

Part Four

*"entonces fui por calle y calle y rio y rio, y ciudad y ciudad y
cama y cama, y atravesó el desierto mi máscara salobre."*
—*Pablo Neruda*

"No era possible tu visita sin altos y enterrados patrimonies de lagrimas."

It was a normal day.
Dad had left a week ago.
He said "I have a job to do, it won't take long"

I was so attached to my father.
It had been just one week

and I missed him so much.

Adriana, my oldest sister, came into the room.
Luciana, another sister, and I were talking.
She told us that dad wasn't coming back.
That he was in jail.

At first I would write to him every day.
And as the years passed,
the days became weeks,
the weeks became months,
the months became seasons,
until I stopped writing.
I forgot about him.

All the memories of who he was,
of what we had, faded away through the years.
I tried so hard to remember him.

Suddenly, without knowing, I killed him.
Death is not always physical.
You can kill someone by forgetting them.
You can become death.
I forgot about my father.
He has died inside of me.

But now as I look back
knowing that I survived such loss,
I have learned so much.
Every night that I cried,

every moment that I felt alone
made me the strong and independent young woman
that I am today

—Tatiana Whizar

My mother was very happy
with her five children and her mother.
She always had her eyes full of light,

and very bright. She was always laughing
and she never had her face sad
until December 1st in 1996. She
lost her mother who was one
of the people that she loved.

Until this day, her eyes are full of
light and her face full of nostalgia,
sobrevivieron. This day was the worst
of all her life, porque a pasar that
she had her father and her children.
She never would be the same person
without her mother.

Because she said that the life
is not life if you don't have your
seres queridos living with you pero
no se resigna, to lose one of the
people that she loves a lot y para
ella lo que dice, "que fue lo mas triste
fue darle la despedida y nunca volverla a ver."

—Maribel Padilla

...entonces fui por calle y calle y rio y rio, y ciudad y ciudad, y cama y cama, y atraves el desierto
mi mascara salobre
—Pablo Neruda

To many it seems like a
normal Friday. It is late
September as autumn makes
its presence felt with its cool winds.
It feels as though I'm always moving,
never really finding a place I can
call home. Moving once
again, this time from Cowiche to Yakima.
I'm tired of relocating, of
wandering aimlessly. I've
never lived in a place for
more than four years at a time.
Now I have to leave behind the

only place I felt at home.

On the move once again.
It's been like that my whole life.
First from Guadalajara in Mexico to Los Angeles.
From LA to Yakima, back to LA, and then
back to Yakima again. After that,
it was to East Valley and then
finally to Cowiche.
Now I have to move back
to Yakima and finish out my
High School years at either
Ike or Davis.

But why now?
I don't want to leave.
This is the year I make State.
The first wrestler at the 215 lb. weight
class to ever make it to State
tournament for Highland High School.
I don't want to leave my friends,
my teammates, and my school. It
is the start of my junior year and it
feels as though I am abandoning a
project that is yet to be completed. I
was supposed to take over as Captain
this year. I just can't leave. There are
people who depend on me and expect
me to lead them in this sport, as well as
in football. They fought along side me
and were there after every crushing
defeat as well every great victory.
Now I have to leave them all behind.
I don't have the heart to tell them yet.
I just greet them in the hallway,
without telling them what is going
on as I go turn in all the textbooks
in my locker.

—Oscar Rosales

Part Five

If I think about all my wounds, no way I
can describe it in my life time. It all started here at Davis High my freshman year,

January 28, 1999. First death took my only grandma I knew, in a car
accident: Raquel Zarate. And then my neighbor, Jose Acosta, who was shot and

killed. Then my mom's cousin who was close to our family, shot to death—
there
were so many holes in his body I didn't know where to start. Then my

grandma's sister died of a heart attack in Mexico. Cada mes de ese año lo
destesto cuando I remember de todas las personas que pertenecenn en mi vida.

Todas a que ya's caras me ayudaron a salir de mis problemas, todas las
personas que amaban. Este año, el año de mis quince, era el año lleno de

puras memorias de tragedias. Why must they go month by month? Marcela,
Sofia Salamanca, mis amigas, mis amigas, porque ellas, ¿Porque? I don't know.

Why do you take so many loving people around me? I don't know why, but I
want to
know! Yo quiero saber mis amigos, Juanito, y Javier, también, y mi primo, Jorge.

But why so many deaths? Why must death take so many lives?

—Martha Gamboa

Part Six

"High citadel of terraced stones."
—Pablo Neruda

I'm on my way to school,
a new journey awaits me.
I have my notebook and
a black pen; my mind
has been cleared to a new

set of information.
They said it was high,
a mountain that can almost touch

the sky. Big monuments and
rooms made of stone that
purify. I believe that
when I descend from that
place called "Macchu Picchu"
my attitude and way at living
is going to have a 360 degree
change. I'm going to become
more mature and my poems are
going to be written at a
mature level.

—Marco Gutiérrez

"Luchando por la union."

Me encuentro en las alturas
de Macchu Picchu, porque
aquí descansaron los pies
del hombre y haci quiero
descansar yo, junto a ti
Macchu Picchu. Vengo aquí
para luchar en contra
de la diferencias con
palabras bonitas y dando
ejemplo como este ahi
que hacer cual abeja que
en la colmena, frabrica
par a todo dulces panales,
a que hacer como el agua
queba serena brindando
al mundo entero frescos
ravdales, ahi que imitar
al viento que siembrea flores,
los mismo en las montañas
que el la llanuras, ahi que hacer

como los granos que estan
reunidos en una sola mazorca.
Esto quiere decir que siempre
ahi que estar unidos pobres
y ricos buenos y malos y
que no importe el lugar de
horijen para que
nos rechasen mejor
ahi que vivir la vida
sembrando amores con
la vista y el alma
siempre en altura.

—Rosalinda Campos

Part Seven

"Una permanencia de piedra y planar."
—Pablo Neruda

Carta al Tae Kwon Do

I remember when I met you,
I was mad.
Tae kwon do isn't what I wanted.
I wanted to be a gymnast.

It didn't take much time to like you.
In just weeks, I could not let go of you.
Every day I would learn something new.
You became the reason for me not to give up.

When I lost my father, you gave me one:
Jose Martin Lopez Rosales, my "sabonim."

When I had troubles you made them go away.
When I was lost I would always find myself inside of you.

You gave me true friendship

and a sneak of what love is.

When everyone doubted in my victory I was scared.
I gave you my heart, you gave me victory, true happiness and so much more.

I had won that national.
I was part of the team that was going to represent Mexico
in the world championships.

Everything you gave me was positive.
The victories,
the defeats.
In victories I felt talented.
In defeats, I would know my errors.

You took me away from my family, friends and school.
But that made me stronger.
I learned to be independent.
Thank you.

—Tatiana Whizar

"Today the empty air no longer weeps,
no longer knows your feet of
clay, has now forgotten your
pitchers that filtered the sky."
                    —Pablo Neruda

Virgencita de Guadalupe gracias,
muchas gracias por hacer me sentir
como si as retirado la muerte
de mi camino.
Como si un día me agarraste
y me voltiaste de ese camino malo
a un camino bueno. Un camino
donde hay puro amor
paz, libertad, no existe el
dolor y los pecados inperdonables.
¿Porque? porque tu eres

como una madre, una madre
con la que puedo hablar y confiar
que le puedo contar mis problemas

y no me trata como si fuera
una cualquiera. Gracias
virgencita por esa bosesita
linda en las noches y a todo
momento disiendome que hacer
y que no hacer. Madre mia yo
reconosco que yo andaba por
el camino malo y feo, donde
hay mucho dolor, adicción, y pecados
grandes, donde uno camina sobre
espinas y ni haci nos transformamos.
No queremos agachar la cabeza

por el maldito orgullo. Pero gracias
a ti, madre yo, ya voy por el camino
bueno y perdida no estoy. Yo sé
que no soy perfecta y nunca lo
seré pero trataré de ser buena y
ayudar a los demás con las abilida-
des que tu hijo me regalo. Yo sé
que cuando lea esta carta en el
podium de nuestra clase, tu y tu hijo me
estaran escuchando. God I want
to tell you that I am very thankful
to you for sharing your mom with me.
Thank you for all the abilities that
I have, for giving me life.
De nuevo gracias, por esta vida que
me as prestado, por que yo se que
es prestada y te prometo que no
te vas a arepentir.

Amen (asi sea)

—Erika Cruz

*"Aquí los pies del hombre
descansaron de noche junto
a los pies del aguila en los*

alturas guarida, carniceras
y en la aurora."

Estaba yo en el mero fondo
y tu me extendiste tus brazos
para subir contigo.

Escale tus piedras, y traté de subir
pero algo siempre se entrevenia,
y yo volvía a caer,

Eres tan alta que quisiera pronto
estar arriba y
mirar para abajo todo lo
que deje para llegar a ti.

Mi meta era llegar a ti
y al fin lo logre a

escapar a llegar a ti—
A ti Machu Picchu.

—Jessica Padilla

Part Eight

"I've tried to swim in the most expansive lives,
in the most free-flowing estuaries."
—Pablo Neruda

Glass full of dreams.
Their lives were pure,
as a clean glass.
They lived in holiness.
Fighting to live,
they hid behind the narrow walls.
Trying to survive,
they shaded their hearts.
When they were being sacrificed
they died with courage,
holding the victory in their hands.

—Cristal Manjarréz

"Come to my very heart."

Watching my mom cry without stop.
She's drowning in tears.
She tries to swim out but can't.
She fights with all her will.
She is swimming towards
the other side of the river.
She wants to get to the other side.
She wants to give her children
a life with more opportunities.
Not caring if she dies, thinking about her
children. She is a brave person,
full of life and love. She is one of a kind.
She deserves to live happy and with no more pain.
She has suffered enough; it is time to give her
happiness.

—Laura Mendoza

"Me encuentro cruzando un Rio."

En toda mi vida nunca
habia cruzado rios, o un
mundo differente, pero
nunca me imagine cruzar
este grande y profundo rio,
este rio es como un sendero
sin rumbo.

Cuando era pequeña yo
soñaba contener a mi
familia junta y feliz pero
una desgracia me llevo a
perder a mi padre en
tonces fue cuando me
dio por saber de la vida.

Porque cuando hay un

gran amor se pierde
porque habiento tantos
sueños llegan el aire
y lo destruye tal vez
no me explique pero
yo me entiendo.

En esta etapa aprendí
a sufrir por no tener
un padre, por no tener
amor o suspiro de mi padre.

Por eso es que yo estoy
cruzando un gran rio
sin fin que yo aun día
cruzaré estoy en medio
de este rio.

Y por eso estoy aquí en la
clase de literatura tal vez
mis palabras no lo dijan todo
pero ha hoy me encuentro
en un mundo nuevo para mi
he aprendido a ser otra, a
ser como quiero ser,
soy como soy.

Es un mundo que yo
he realizado con sacrificios
y amargos momentos pero
al fin de este sendero
se que mis seres queridos
se sitiran orgullosos de mi.

—Rosalinda Campos

Ya estoy cansada de estar nadando en el rio de otros,

Ya voy a nadar en mi rio empezar una nueva
vida empezar aquí en esta clase que me

ha cambiado empezar aquí con mis
nuevos amigo y amigas. De este día en
adelante yo ya empezé una nueva vida.

El día que someone that I
know, family or not, have died, I grow

a new life everytime stronger y más fuerte,
and in my vida wanting to become what

they could have accomplished,
and me wanting to live my nueva vida para

que ellos ya que estan en el cielo puedan
estar felices por mi que pude hacer y

acabar lo que ellos no pudieron porque
dejaron la muerte que se los llevaran .

Why must they leave and why must I live
to keep their dreams alive? I see myself in their position

Why don't I give up on my life? Is it me that keeps
me alive, or is it my family that pushes me to
my potential, while all those close to me die and
leave me behind in this struggle of everyday life?

I thank you. I have learned and made up for the mistakes.
I see my homies, homegirls, family and friends leaving me with this struggle.

Yeah, this struggle, the stuggle of
everyday life
that is now to me well worth it.

—Martha Gamboa

"What language do you bring to the ear..."

You are like no other person
I have ever known.

Your words and thoughts
inspire me deeply

and influence me
to take a large step in life.

Your voice is deep and strong,
but sweet and warm

at the same time.
Your smile is strong

so I forget all my
problems that I carry.

Your hugs are tender,
I feel safe in your arms.

I've learned that life is too short
and I need to swallow my pride.

Now, I have opened
my eyes, and see life.

Life is mystical and
beautiful at the same time.

You have helped me
love the invisible beauty of life.

Crossing the deep, rushing
Columbia River was an eye opener.

Deep in the river,
my life stood before me.

I could see my life rushing
underneath me,

joined with the small
waves of the river.

Now, every time I look at your
blue eyes,

I see my life deep inside.
Your eyes draw me

and stun me numb.
The glow makes me weak

and makes me think
of the love that exists.

Our love is strong.
We've been through lots.

Jealous and selfish people
have tried to tear us apart,

but we managed to
pull through
with our heads up,
and find our way together again.

People who don't have dreams
and want us to go down

with them,
just block our way.

Day by day,
we learn to kick them out

of our way
and continue

with the waves
down the river.

—Eloisa Gonzalez

Part Nine

Wrestling evaporated water.
Viento maligno del infierno.
Tree vision, frontera de fuego.
Carnviorous C.D., familia de manzanas.
Music permeating from cement sneakers.
Pesas disparnando nubes.
Precipitous taco hurricane.
El hermano de la pared.
Exceptionally insane enchiladas.
Derritida luz de plata.
Racist potato chips, acero inocente.
Impoverished pizza, cascada de almas.
Perplexed autumn, computadora delirante.
Walking sky scraper, cuadro rocoso.
Ominous football, identidad de oro.
Hilarious sky on ground.
Sueños de montaña fuerte.
Stereo of vision, páginas de vida.
Deafening silence, refresco sediente.
Dark sunlight, oscuridad brillante.
Talking timepiece, casa sin muros.
Flying office building, pantalones electricos.
Bottomless backpack, tarea de los dioses.
Forest of ancestry, raza del sol.
Clouds of immigrant, furia del retrato.
Field of nightmares, escombros de la memoria.

—Oscar Rosales

"Sideral eagle, vineyard of mist, lost bastion, blind scimitar."
—Pablo Neruda

Slow pulse vision dreams,
whirling passionate Red Fish drawing into my life.

Dream vision stumbling, walking woman.
Secrets of the undiscovered world.

Lights and more lights. Furious love and joy.
Opening eyes, seeing the real world.

Righteous passion. Love with me
gold crystal puppy

Chain of events change our world
by our change of luck.

—Uziel Estrada

Part Ten

When I started to write this poem,
I was at the library sitting in front of a computer.
I decided to think about something,
I didn't know what.

Oh man, poetry came first to
my mind, and some questions followed it.
Who am I now?
I didn't like poetry.
Does that mean that I am on
Macchu Picchu?
Who am I now?

—Gastón Pérez

Slave's Tears

I see a man freed from a past of unrevealed
questions. And an answer to a never-ending question.
I do not see what the answer is,
but I can see that he feels free.
He is trying to communicate
how the slaves lived here.
Neruda is imagining how the
slaves lived. He is saying,
I see a body, a thousand bodies
with the rain and night. Neruda was
watching the city's houses.
They were not covered, and in the
night when the time was rainy,
their ceiling was the cold.

—Antonia Caro

I want to know what I will be doing
not right now but in ten years. I want to
know if I will become an engineer like I'm
planning. I want to know if I will become

a bad example for society or a good role model
to follow. What will the man inside
me be doing or destroying? I want to
know what hides beneath these years.

Tell me how I will end up my life.
Tell me if the man inside me chooses
the right decisions and follows the
right paths for a decent life. Tell me.

—Marco Gutiérrez

"Stone upon stone, and man, where was he?"

I want to know why when I was little
I didn't have everything I wanted.

I want to know why I never played sports.
I want to know why God brought me to earth.
I want to know why I feel lucky these days.

Tell me why I didn't have everything when
I was little. Was it because my parents couldn't afford it?

Tell me why I never played sports. Was it
because I was afraid of getting hurt?

Tell me why God brought me to earth to live.
Is it because he has something prepared for me here?

Tell me why I feel lucky today. Is
it probably because I have my mother beside me?

—Uziel Estrada

Part Eleven

New World

"Let me forget today this joy, which is greater than the sea."
—Pablo Neruda

I see that these poems of Pablo Neruda
bring life upon ourselves. I've been opening
doors to my life, every word and sentence.

It truly has its details. *I rise up to*

be born with me means to me to
get going, move on, don't stay the same.

*Spot where you were yesterday. See a world
of differences.* This means, Juan Cortapiedras,
Juan Comefrio, Juan Peizdescalzos. It means

people who worked on Macchu Picchu,
worked their lives to see that mountain top.
They struggled until their lives changed.

—Uziel Estrada

*"Kiss the secret stones with me.
The torrential silver of the Urubamba."*

Come now, rejoice.
We are free from fear.
We owned the land.
The waters of the river were separated
and we crossed them.
Let us rise.
Let us sing a new song,
a song of freedom and victory.
The stones of the wall drank your tears.
They held your tired hands,
and cried with you.
But now they celebrate your victory.

—Cristal Manjarréz

La mirada temerosa—

*The hand over the hypotenuse of rough
blood and sackcloth. . .*
                    —Pablo Neruda

Under the glance, all that I can see is
a strong person loving natural things.

78

The Bible is his torment,
remote from the real world.

Friendly with all the people,
maybe they'll make good.

The bad word deteriorates his soul,
catches on the time.

Wants to have everything, but doesn't
stick-up the winds.

Suspicious of everybody and everything.

—Natividad Méndez

Part Twelve

I Have Climbed to Macchu Picchu.

Now I know that I have
been to Macchu Picchu without having
been there. I have learned
from these poems. I didn't know
how to express my feelings by
writing a poem. It has changed
my life completely. I have climbed
to the top of Macchu Picchu and I
have rested beside the eagle's feet.
I have felt the slave's pain. I saw
the City of Stone built with the
slave's tears. I have seen this
sacred place. I know that I
will keep this experience with
me forever. And one of his images
I liked most—
  Rise up to be born with me,
My brother.

—Antonia Caro

Mom Is the Best Gift in Life

"Acudid a mis venas y a mi boca."
—*Pablo Neruda*

Dad and mom are nice to me.
I can't say that they are
perfect. But they try their
best, to give us the best life. They
don't do it with *gifts artificiales*, they
give us things more importantes,
como, apoyo, consejos, fuerzas
para luchar en el futuro.
Nos han enseñado a luchar por lo que
queremos. Yo y mis hermanas tenemos
que trabajar y estudiar at the same time.
Pero eso nos hace tener más fuerza
y apreciando las cosas
Por el esfuerzo que nos
han costado y haci poder
subir esa montaña tan
grande de Macchu Picchu y
entonces dar las gracias
a todos por su ayuda y apoyo,
to my mom, dad, sisters, Bodeen,
Salatino, Cole, Garcia. Thanks everyone.

Pero las especiales
gracias a Dios por
todo lo que me ha dado
y por estas personas tan
lindas que me han apoyado.

Con la ayuda de todos
ellos siento el viento en
la cima de Macchu Picchu
que mueve mi cabello de un
lado a otro, es maravilloso
aunque apenas empezó la lucha.

—María Rosa Barriga

Part IV

Letter Poems to Women Seeking Light

A veces hay la noche,
pero la luz es fiel y vuelve siempre

Rosario Castellanos

Sometimes there is night,
but the light is faithful and always returns

El resplandor de ser

In each symbol, this many more of me

From one image we make twelve.
From another image we make nine more.

This is just the beginning. Before we are done we will have over fifty, and then we will lose count and it won't matter.

We are young women and young men. We are making images of women in Latin American society. We are taking from the images given to us in history, real historical women, with complex histories, multiple images and stories, reading about them, studying them. We write to them and about them, talking to them and with each other, discovering them in ourselves and in our lives. And we are finding new ways for women to be. We are finding new ways to be with women.

This is liberating work for all of us. It is the work of liberation. It is done through poetry, *floricanto*, poetry being the genre of liberation, poetry being the vehicle strong enough to support our explorations, flower and song, poetry liberating and breaking open the history, poetry liberating and breaking open the writers.

Malinche and Guadalupe. Two women, both mothers, present at the birth of history in the New World. *La Raza Cosmica.* 1519 and 1531. Malinche opens the doors to the Aztec kingdom for Cortés. Juan Diego tries to explain his vision at the hill of Tepeyac to the Catholic bishop. History and myth. The first two images of women arrive at the beginning.

Good woman, bad woman. Written into the history, at the beginning.

I don't believe in good woman/bad woman and neither do the writers.

Inés Hernandez Avila initiates me into the story. Singling me out as one of the only men in a small group of people, she asks me, "And Jim, what is the word for *macho* in your culture?" Without a word to name the behavior, how does one break open the stereotype?

Inés Hernandez Avila, poet and professor at the University of California, interprets the images of women, breaking them open for me. This work is done, as Inés says elsewhere, "one bird at a time." Birds are symbols of the soul, male and female.

Malinche breaks open to reveal many images. She is: abrecaminos, one who opens the way—pathbreaker, ex-slave, multi-cultural, multi-lingual, *correveidile* (go-between)—even with its roots in gossip, a critical image, mother, daughter, lover. Sexual and political, a power-broker. Beauty and envy of many; legend and myth. For starters.

Guadalupe is sacred history, a miracle story. But she belongs to secular history too, and her goodness comes at a cost. An essay by Andre Guerrero on Chicano Theology, shows her to open and reveal an image of faith, an image of hope, an image of liberator, and an image battling against *machismo*.

I tell the story of Inés teaching me when I introduce Malinche. Introducing her, I give them the stories written by the Uruguayan writer Eduardo Galeano from *Memoria del Fuego/Memory of Fire*.

What a legacy to explore. What riches we've been given. What other culture/civilization gives its women real names of real women entering into history at the beginning, in cosmic time? From two we make twenty. From two we count until we lose count. Until it doesn't matter. Until we come to us. In our complexity. In our complexities.

We look instead for the archetypal images in each of us. Deep, universal images existing in each of us. Images true to our experiences of who we are. Images we can claim and use. Multiple images. Many ways to be. And many ways to explore them.

And it's a story not lost on the young men. When the women are abrecaminos, so are the men. We are always looking at images of men and women in our reading and our writing, in our ways of talking and listening with one another. This is what we were doing when we began with our study of Pablo Neruda. First we read the love poems. And we wrote our own. Then we went with Neruda up the mountain of Macchu Picchu.

Young men are interested in words that captivate the heart of the beloved. A paradigm shift occurs in the passage to adulthood. Men learn to look at themselves and women with new eyes, from new perspectives. The maturing man in the poet changes Neruda's point of view entirely.

Young men learn to listen. Listening to the women, listening to themselves, opens radical new possibilities. They become listeners in the world. Deep listening changes everything. Listening is a way of loving, a way of being. When we listen to each other, we understand. We don't covet.

Now we're not talking men and women. We're talking about ourselves. *Seres humanos.* Each other. But we're still looking at images of women in Latin America.

From two we go to three. To Sor Juana. Sor Juana Inés de la Cruz. 1651. Poet. Theologian. The woman who wanted to learn so badly she disguised herself as a man, doing everything necessary to live within the mask in order to become her truth. Sor Juana, the woman's face on the Mexican peso. What other nation has a story to match Sor Juana's? From Sor Juana we find poet, theologian, essayist, scholar, liberator, orphan, luchadora (fighter), nun, student. Read Sor Juana. Read Octavio Paz on Sor Juana.

This morning I'm still dizzy from listening to the abrecaminos' reading of their letter poems to Sor Juana. Oswaldo Plasencia writes, "You hide your truth in order to speak another truth." Showing me his poem before the reading, Gastón Pérez asks me if he can use a word in a certain way. He shows me the line, imploring Sor Juana to "Infect me with your courage."

Sor Juana writes, "...porque se digo que fui/celebrada por milagro/ de discreción/ me desmiente..."—in Margaret Sayers Peden's translation, "...if I say that I was known/ and celebrated for my discretion,/ I prove the very opposite..." Lines jump off the page again this morning, and the poem, "Fragment of Doña Leonor's Monologue/ Written From a Noble Woman's House" implodes in me. Lines break open. "I must record each incident." Break us open: "...but if silent, none will know the truth of me." And "To tell you I was born with beauty will be forgiven." We have been reading the poem for a week. The oldest Spanish breaks across time: "...that though the living causes pain,/ the telling creates peace of mind."

The list of images grows. We begin to see more in ourselves.

These three historical, mythological images of women break open to become the many. And we study them, in history, as writers and poets, still needing contemporary images, models and archetypes of our time.

Writers interview their mothers and other Latinas. They explore and name their mothers' places of birth. They ask questions. *What were your dreams, Mother?* They track down their mothers' stories, paralleling and following similar times from studies of Sor Juana. They try to make connections. Connections between their mothers and Sor Juana. Connections between their mothers and themselves. They try to understand. They try to understand as writers.

Another way to be. *Otra manera de ser.*

We read the works of three contemporary women: the Mexican feminist, Rosario Castellanos, the Chicana feminist Gloria Anzaldúa, and from Guatemala, the Nobel Prize winner, Rigoberta Menchú.

From Rosario Castellanos we discover the image, "otra manera de ser," another way to be. And threshold, *umbral.* A poster over the entrance to our writing room alerts us, if our eyes are open, that we are at the threshold, being offered other worlds, other ways to perception. The *abrecaminos* repeat Rosario's way of knowing, writing what she knows, until it becomes theirs, a mantra and a discovery. An uncovering.

Rigoberta Menchú connects the writers to place or intimacy. She reaches places inside they didn't know they knew. The Chicana *abrecaminos* Martha Gamboa writes, "You want to end machismo/but you have to speak first with//the mothers, because the mothers / begin the change with their children." Roberto Méndez, writing from the point of view of a *Mexicano*, but already from here, and writing in English, says, "Indian people that sometimes don't//speak Spanish and they don't have/voz ni voto.../someone that represents them ni/ quien hable por ellos and help them." Finally, another primarily *voz Mexicana*, Antonia Caro finishes her poem: "You knew that those intellectuals/were more ignorant than you, the Indian."

There are greater differences within the culture than between cultures.

It always startles me when I remember first hearing this. I always nod my head. We don't have to agree. We only have to listen. We come from many worlds. We speak multiple truths. I try to understand myself. I try to understand you.

No one creates more sparks, or stranger alliances than Gloria Anzaldúa. Clear the throat. Aclarar la garganta. Freedom. The strongest Guadalupanas align themselves with Anzaldúa. "Phrase by phrase, sentence by sentence," Claudia Guzman writes, "...she is the only woman out of all the women...that I relate to." Marco Gutiérrez asks, "Gloria, how come you are/so hard and rude on me?" And even in disagreement, Antonia Caro locates the binding connection: "you are a woman of courage/valor. And nobody will/ put *candades* in our mouths, because/ women have to express what she feels and thinks." No padlocks for Anzaldúa, or Caro.

We read the women, we write poems to them, all the time making our list of images, archetypes, ways of being found in the women, and found in each of us. We are trying to understand, to make new sense, to make literature.

Many others. *Literatura es un mundo Latina*. Stories. Poems. Autobiography. *Testimonio*. Drama.

Ourselves. Images of us. That's the primary work. That's the exploration in these poems.

Jim Bodeen
December, 2001—March 2002

Letter Poems to Women Seeking Light:

Latinas Who Opened the First Doors in Our Histories

Letters to Malinche

The Woman, the Mary, the Poem, Voice Universal, Flowers That Smell So Good They Kill, the Perfect Plan to Malinche

Hey Malinche, my name is Abraham. I am
one of your many sons. When I found this out
I was shocked, so I looked for you until
I found you. You are the good, the bad,

the ugly, the beautiful, and the smart one.
All together you are the Eve of Mexican culture.
And you are a part of all women in

the world, forever. You betrayed me, us,
the Aztecs to build a different world.
I thank you
because you give me two women
to choose from. Although sometimes

I don't get that choice. You do. Thanks.
I forgive you, you are an eye opener
and a tongue

to and for women, you are free
from all, you are above

all women.
Even the other one.

—Abraham Mancilla

Dear Malinche,

I'm sitting in class,
thinking about myself
thinking about you.
I'm seeing and hearing these people argue.
About where they're from and what they believe to be true.
Little do they know, they're ignorant, and so am I.

But I feel what I was taught is the truth.
I don't know nothing else, I don't want to know otherwise.
Tell me your story, but you aren't changing my mind.

La Llorona and you, are you the person?
I don't think you are,
but the idea is in my head.
I've heard stories about La Llorona
but never about you
until now.
You're a lot easier to believe
because of your background.
I think La Llorona was made up
like Santa Claus, just so we would listen.
Never cross paths with La Llorona.

—Ricardo Torres

¿Sera Verdad?

Having this little time to study about a
woman who was called Malinche, the love of
Cortés, mother, daughter sold by her own mother.

I don't know much about your life and
your journey with Los Españoles during la
conquista de Mexico. But here in this class,
we found some things that identify you
like a woman who made a sacrifice for her life.
I believe that those things

you did were because no tenías opción. But
in Mexican culture you are la traidora,
la mala mujer, who helped Los Españoles to
conquer Mexico. Mother of Cortes's son to whom you were

given por los señores de Yucatan. You
were sombra, vieja, consejera, go-between,
through the conquest of Mexico. Hija de
tu madre la quien te regalo, pero tu
la podistes perdonar por eso.
Después de todo,
tu tuvistes tiempo to avenge yourself.
The debt is paid. You weren't a mala mujer.
Tu sacrificastes tu vida para continuar
viviendo cabalgando beside him.

Fuiste respetado por todos aquelles que
te humillaron cuando no eras nada. Now your black
eyes were enough para colgar a cualquier que no te guste.
Mother, hija, amante, guia, interpretete, consejera
go between.
Traicionada por tu madre, por tu
propia gente que te regalo a Cortés
por eso. Tu también eres una traidora
que traiconó a su gente por sobrevivir.
Tener la vida o perderla
es mejor sacrificar a unos cuantos
traidores que morir por culpa de aquellos
que te traicionaron.

Now you Malinche are someone in our
culture. I know because I am a Mexicano
que también—who also—will do the same things
to sobrevivir y no morir embano por alguién,
or alungos, que no sirven para nada bueno.

—German Ruíz

"Entangled Beliefs, But Free Spirits."

Malinche, tu fuiste vendida
como si fueras un animal
sin importarles tu sufrimiento
tu suplicos, y tus lagrimas.

Fuiste maltratada y jusgada
sin antes poder hablar.
Pero aún, you knew how to forgive
all those lenguas venenosas that attacked you.

Eres buena
even if they remember you as a traidora
porque tu corazón
siempre a sido bueno.

Asi como la vida te tratoó
fuerte y injustamente dolor tras dolor
te a recompensado

Dandote una vida mejor
siendo tu como la reina "the queen"
al lado de un hombre maravilloso
quien te saco' de tu maldito poso

I'm in a world similar to yours
pero no estoy pasando por lo que pasastes.
I see a lot of hypocrites,
mucha violencia, celos, odio, y egoistas.
Pero, que importa, hablemos de ti.

I heard you were a whore
pero se que no es cierto,
because you were given,
you never gave yourself—
like Gloria Trevi, quien también
fue jusgada and ever since,
she's been given a bad reputation.

Let them talk
porque con sus hijos
ellos veran a que se le llama whore
because what you most hate
es lo que tendras en tu casa.

Yo pienso que tu fuiste una gran mujer
you forgave without asking anything in return—
y no todos sabemos perdonar.
You were, y siempre seras,
una abrecaminos

—Rosa Robles

Mujer Traidora

I am here miles and miles away writing about
you Malinche, from right here where I am, in the north.
There's not much difference between there and here
for us humans beings. I hear people comment some
bad stuff about you because you are a *traidora*. But
I am right here to tell you something: If you decide
to leave Cortés, it's your business, I cannot change your
thoughts. Feel good if you decide that would change
your life. In life we know plenty of stuff and things that
change us, like when you want to change something because
you either like it or you're tired of it, change your mind
and turn to another direction and get what you been
working for and start progressing. I'm sure every human
being in this world knows it. That's why I say it.
But Malinche that doesn't change your beauty and fineness
as a woman. I think you're a strong woman with guts.
Life is tough for many people, but I see myself
differently than others. When it comes to a problem,
I try as fast as I can to get it over with because
I don't want to stick to it at one point. I feel I want to die.
Malinche everybody in life makes mistakes, but we really
learn from them. In case we see each other's faces one

day, I would love to talk more about these conversations.

—Uziel Estrada

.

Letters To Guadalupe

Guadalupe: Mother, Symbol of Faith, of Identity, as Hope, A Symbol Against Machismo—and a Liberator

La Virgen de Guadalupe has always existed
in my life. She is present at all times and
I know she's open, ready to hear my prayers and cries.
I have never seen La Virgen, except on

drawings on our walls, and I know my
parents carry images of her. I don't think
anyone has really seen her after she
appeared to Juan Diego December 9, 1531.
Sometimes I ask myself if she really does exist?
Was this all made up into legend
or myth? Does this symbol or image
mean anything, or was it drawn by
someone according to their imagination?
It's like not knowing if heaven or hell
really exist, or if there really is a god.
It comes from inside, it's something
you strongly believe in.

La Virgen is God's messenger, that's why
we know God does exist.
To me *La Virgen* symbolizes faith. It's a
mystery in us that drives us to believe
in something we cherish and hold but
do not see. We trust our parents and
our church that taught us to believe.
So trusting something or someone is
included in understanding faith.
We trust that we are not being deceived.

La Virgen has come into my life and
showed me the importance of being
human and the love that God has for us.
La Virgen is my guiding light, and to all
Mexicans, who believe in her. She is one of us.
She is one of our oppressed;
in that sense you find alliance in her. She
brings hope to our people, that there is
a better way. Guadalupe does not abandon
or forget the poor. The symbol is there,
demonstrating justice for oppressed Chicanos.
Without oppression, hope couldn't exist,
because there wouldn't be anything to
hope for.
I've wondered what I would be if I
didn't believe en *La Virgen*, in God, in faith,
or even hope. I came to the conclusion
that I just wouldn't be.

—Claudia Guzmán

.

Dear Virgin,

Where are you when we need you most?
Are you there right beside us or do you
leave us in our times of hardships to grow
stronger on our own?
      I believe in you, therefore you are with
me when I most need you. You are there
when I question my religion and I don't
know what to believe.
      You are the mother of all Mexicans. Mother
of all mothers. Your love is unconditional like
my mother's. We sin everyday and your love
still stays strong.

You don't have to come and appear in front
of me for me to believe in you. I behave with you.
I know you're here, somewhere.

I think everything happens for a reason.
I believe you're those reasons. You're looking over us,
all of us.

You, along with my mother, have kept me out
of a lot of trouble. I think you were there to help
my mother raise me and all my other brothers
and sisters.

I think you are there to point us in the
right direction, but in the end it's our decisions
that place us where we are.

—Ricardo Torres

.

Danos Nuestro Pan De Cada Día.

Hoy recuerdo
a misa

de pequeña.

Eres amada por muchos.
Te dicen la Virgen de Guadalupe.

I remember
resando a ti
con mi madre,
cada noche.

Resan a ti
y a todos los santos.

Since the day you appeared to Juan Diego,
others have claimed to have seen you.
Pero, ¿sera verdad?

It wouldn't make any difference to me now.

Ahora, creo algo diferente.

Creo que eres la madre de Jesus,
Esposa de Jose.
Pero más que eso, no.

—Clementina Abúndiz

.

Virgen, Mensaje de Paz

I do not know if you remember me
Virgen morena. Virgen Divina I am
she who only in her times of need
comes *to implorar tu misericordia.*
Soy aquel who for the temptations
of this sinful world your loving message
ha ignorado, mensaje de paz y amor.
For that Virgin I am she, on my knees.
Virgin, glory to she who in
her dreams, your manto has even
touched and in her prayers your
sweet voice at her ear arrived.
Bendito the man that your light
has accepted.
There are no words to show love
of believing in faith in you *Virgen
Morena.* Endless numbers of people
keep dragging signs to show you
their honor.
*Virgen Morena que con sus
manos sembro rosas bellas
y puso en el cielo millones
de esrellas yo se que con
celo nos cubre tu manto.
Madre de los Mexicanos
orgullo y encanto.
Reina de Mexico y Emperatris*

de America hay una sola
palabra que te describe
        Amor.
Abnegada, Madre, Orgullo
Y Refugio de los Mexicanos.

    —Antonia Caro

.

En el Cielo una Hermosa Mañana

Is it you?
Are you the symbol that represents all Mexicans?
Even those who don't believe in you?
Do you represent a part of me?
Yes, all Mexicans have Guadalupe in their hearts.
It is something we are born with.
It is something we identify with.
It is our symbol. A beautiful symbol.
I remember when I was little
I represented you.
I passed through my neighborhood
thinking I was Guadalupe,
La madre del niño Jesus hijo de Dios.
I felt so special.
I felt blessed.
I felt you, you were in me
y fui Guadalupe.
Todas las noches le rezaba a mi virgencita
que todo saliera bien.
Asi es, tenía una imagen, un simbolo
en el cual encontraba paz y seguridad.
We need an image, a symbol,
something that we can see.
You, I can't just believe in something.
There is always an image that represents your *creencias,*
even when they don't give you one, you imagine it.
The image is what makes the *creencias* stronger.

97

Who cares if the image is misused.
You did not misuse it.
Let it turn into a political image,
a "best seller,"
don't think you did it.
No pienses que el comprar una estampilla
contribuyes en convertir tu creencia
en un "best seller."
You're buying it because of your creencia
not because it's nice and everyone has it,
or because it makes you feel more Mexican—
you buy it because when you ask your virgencita
"cuidame, tengo miedo, cuidame"
and you turn and look at the image and say
"no me dejes solo, te necesito, cuidame virgencita"
you can really feel her presence
by looking at her, by having her image in your hands,
en tus manos.
Cuando tienes algo en tus manos
es much más fuerte que tenerlo en tu cabeza
So take that image, use it wisely
ponla en tus manos
que ahi es donde pertenece.

—Tatiana Whizar

.

Letters to Sor Juana

Abriendome La Puerta

En los tiempos de antes
las mujeres
han sido tratados
como basura
y no realmente
tomadas en cuento.

Tu Sor Juana
desafortunadamente
viviste en esos tiempos.

The high-class priests
were scared,
scared of us
becoming inteligentes
and taking over.
That is why they forbid
women de tu tiempo
to study
and become someone.
Solamente los hombres
sin verguenzas
pudieron estudiar.

Even though this was the law
tu la quebraste
No te importo que te pudieran
haber matado.

You broke the law.
You broke the silence
that we women
were hiding behind.

Tu abriste
una de las puertas necesitadas
para hoy—you poder,
estudiar y seguir adelante.
Gracias,

—Clementina Abúndiz

P.S. Sino fuera por ti:
¿Donde estariamos hoy?

·Target of All Eyes, Admired, Center of Attention,

Fighter, Genius, Writer, Poet, Playwright

Dear Sor Juana,

    I would like to thank you on behalf of all women in the world. I, too, am born of noble blood, God's blood. I'm glad that I got the opportunity to know you from what you left behind. Hope and prosperity for women is what you left behind. You combined Malinche and Guadalupe to become what you are. If it wasn't for you I wouldn't have my Godly, nice, and respectful ways, as well as my mean and cruel ways. You dreamed of an education, regardless of the sacrifice and risk it took. I wouldn't be able to go to school and learn, and for that I thank you. I believe that "we" the women are the light, not the men. They are the pain that lives within us all. For some women, their light shines so bright, illuminating everything, lighting their path. For others, it is easily put out or dimmed by those around them. My mother is like you, is you, Sor Juana. She is a dreamer and fighter, stopping at nothing until achieving her goal, overcoming the vast pain caused by men in her life. Yet they are made for us women. They're supposed to be our soul mates. Well thanks to strong women like you and women like my mother, we are finding out that women don't need men in their lives for anything. Needing and wanting are two different things. "All my wretchedness may find that though the living causes pain the telling creates peace of mind."

—Daisy Hernandez

Dedicated Sor Juana

Sor Juana, I never heard of you until today.
From what I hear, you were a dedicated person.
You changed your appearance to study.
I don't know if I could ever do that.

You were like a chameleon,
changing your appearance

so they would not discover you,
always hiding from the truth.
Was it to get to the truth? I don't know.
I guess education meant a lot to you.
Me, I don't care. I just do what I have to do,
just enough to get by.
I never take any risks.
I stay away.
I don't want to be discovered.
I guess I'm like a chameleon, too.

—Oswaldo Plascencia

.

La Mujer que Enseño el Camino, que Tuvo Ganas, que Cambio la Vida del Ser Humano Por Medio de Poesía y de Angustias

Quien ira a decir que el tiempo
cambiaria el curso del viento.

Sor Juana, since you were little, you
used to play with swords and

dressed like a boy. You had your
own reasons. A symbol of ganas,
faith and hope is what we
humans see in you. You are a

role model for women that want
to learn how to live their lives
Juana you don't know how much
your effort against machismo has

changed the life of women, especially
those women, que han sido maltratadas
por hombres, ellos no tiene la conciencia

tranquila, ellos no saben lo que han

echo al pegarle a una mejor or al
no dejurla estudiar. Your ideas and
different point of view about life
not only helped women to move on

and to liberate themselves. Your ideas also
helped the men to understand that women
are as important as the men, and that
women have their own dreams
to experience. In our society
your image and your life were

judged because one time you dressed
like a man y por que un día
tu quisiste estudiar, pero esto
sin embargo le dio la libertad a
muchas mujeres.

—Antonio Ruíz

.

"Women of Strengths: Fruitless Mind of Dreams"

Here, alone in my room, I'm reading and thinking
about differences, about making a good letter poem
to you, Sor Juana Inez de la Cruz. As I read about
you, I find really good interest, you talking
about dreams and also how the images help you
explore them. This to me seems like you go into
a place where you choose your favorite dream you've
been wanting to dream. In one point of my life
I've always wanted to dream me and my family going
on vacation to Mexico, but it was difficult. I thought
about it all day and night, and perhaps I'd dream
it at night and it would happen. I dreamed it, that was
luck. In the dream it made me feel good, as I wanted,
I got a lot of worries away from my body and

felt light. You know, Sor Juana, I am strong
with dreams, because everybody like me dreams, and sometimes
discussing our dreams with other people makes us more
intelligent. Nobody should ever leave or forget their
best dreams, because if we let go all of our dreams,
they permanently are going to be like frozen barrels,
which will be scared and never give us good
thoughts about living good.
Sor Juana next time we meet, I will enjoy
exploring the world of dreams. So we can be stronger
and face them closely every time we meet with them.

— Uziel Estrada

Against the Grain

I'm ignorant. The most ignorant person I know
There is so much to learn.
So little time?
I think not.

18 years old.
How bad you wanted an education.
Most of us take it for granted.
We feel willing to hand it over at any price.

It's only an education, after all.
I wish I wanted one as bad as you did,
but I have to be motivated,
day in and out.

I have heart
but I really don't know how to use it.
Tengo ganas,
but I rally don't know to use *ganas* either.

Even writing this letter,

I feel like I'm not putting much into it.

I procrastinate too much.
I need to re-focus.
I'm going with the flow
instead of against the grain.

—Ricardo Torres

.

Holding On

You came to my knowledge
in a perfect moment.
The way you never gave up on your dreams
gave me strength to hold on to mine.

Women around the globe
are able to identify with you,
luchadoras, poetas, escritoras,
soñadoras, teologas, genios
and chainbreakers,
they look up to you and find strength.

When I read about you I felt stupid
me sentí como una idiota
because the chains that held you down
cannot compare to mine.
Yours were so tight and thick
not letting you breathe
and still you managed to break free.
Mine...mine let me breathe and they're thin, too,
but everyday they become thicker and thicker.

Yesterday I gave up.
I decided to live shackled down.
I let go of the key,
the same key you used to break your chains
which is our dreams.
Yesterday I believed that my dream
was impossible to fulfill.
Today I read about you and your struggle to fulfill your dream.

Not only were they against you,
they also said words than can destroy a person.
They pushed you down too many times
and you stood up in such an incredible way
that they could not say anything but had to accept it .
All that I read about you
made me realize how weak I am.
They pushed me down one time,
they said one word,
and killed my dreams.
One word and I let them go.

Let me tell you, Sor Juana,
now that I have a little glimpse
of what you were,and who you were,
you have not only made me proud to be Mexican
but you have given me strength
to hold on tight to my dreams.

I like comparing myself to others,
but it's important with whom I compare.
I can compare myself with a person
that has everything given to them in their hand
and say...I have struggled...
But I compare myself to you
and realize I don't know what struggle really is.
Everything is in my hands.
 I am the reason my dream was gone, not them.
No solo me diste fuerzas
pero me hiciste dar cuenta que nadie puede quitarte tus sueños más
que tu. Gracias.

—Tatiana Whizar

Letters to Rosario Castellanos

La Soledad de una Mujer

Rosario no sé mucho de ti
pero tus versos me conmueven.
Me hacen ver el mundo en que

tu vivías. Soledad, olvido, huallas
borradas. Aún así comprendo.
Eres una mujer por todas las

Mujeres. Voz por cuales no tienen.
In you I see someone strong,
timid, and with a big voz.

You wrote only what you knew,
what you saw, and felt. Aquí
como tu dices que de tu

sueños naciste. That same dream
made you go where you are.
Aún a si te admiro.

—Beatriz Rivera

.

In My Agony

Rosario Castellanos
grew up tired of
her agony, but she
did not give up
even though she
could not forget her pain
    She created love, and
did not have anyone

to give it to.
The world cries of pain

and Rosario cries for the world.
La soledad la acompaña
cada día cuando está triste
entre la oscuridad.
Between the water
she finds the *huello,* footprint
on the road she walks every day
but she takes the wrong
way, because she was dreaming
that God was dreaming her
but God asked her
Y tu de donde has salido

de mi sueño en acido
y de mi sueño me esostenido.

—Pedro Campos

.

"I can only talk about what I know."
Rosario Castellanos

Suicide—
not the answer.
The words that you write
make sense to me
and they're engraved in my mind forever.

Solitude,
is this all you knew?
All that you wanted to know,
shut off from the rest of the world,
is this why you write?

Forgotten memories.
Footprints nowhere to be found.
I haven't seen the world yet,
but I'm headed there,

and not alone.

Not in chains,
but a load on my shoulders,
plenty of unanswered questions.
We kill what we love?
Then I must hate myself, according to you.

.

I don't understand this.
What is forgotten hurts no one else
but ourselves—
affects people around us.
Someday I'll know, too.

When I'm gone, who will care?
Who will protect my family from the cold?
Are we all victims in life?
Life, like an unfinished book
No one will gather up the unfinished pages

Hope, are you no more than stone?

Electrocuted by a lamp, stepping out of the shower in Israel,

it came as shock to all of Mexico,
Israel, Europe, the United States,
Central America and Chile.
All suffered a loss

I know now
Suicide is not the answer.
It's all clear to me,
but I still have questions,
and I'm still looking for answers.

Hope, are you no more than stone?

—Ricardo Torres

La Vida Entre La Soledad.

No, no quiero consuelo ni olvido, ni esperanza. Quiero valor para permanecer.
—Rosario Castellanos

Rosario you are strong like the
true poets, and very intelligent like
some. But I understand that you
grew up in isolation and in your poem
when you said, "I was born from
my dream. I am my own child and
my dreams sustain me." You said these
hard words, maybe because your
mother didn't support your dreams,
but you had success in your goals
and dreams without help. Por que
solo el verte hecho poeta te
mantiene es tu alimento el expresar
tus sufrimientos y triunfos a los
demas. Tú tratas de decir que
como de tus sueños nació el ser
poeta y cualquiera puede realizar su
sueño sin interferncia de nadie. Rosario
yo y todos los que estamos aquí siempre
pasamos por etapas donde
tenemos que luchar para
lograr nuestros objetivos. Por ejemplo,
yo lucho ante proponerme el estar
aquí enfrente de mis compañeros y expresarles
mis intereses, sufrimientos y luchas les
digo parte de mi vida. Rosario, thank you
for teaching us your effort and for
giving us the advice to follow our dreams
and I admire you.

—Maribel Padilla

.

El Aprender De Tus Palabras

Rosario Castellanos
Damos la vida sólo a lo que odiamos

Dear Rosario: La humanidad está
cambiando cada día. Escribiendo para
los Indios de las Alturas de Chiapas y
Oaxaca, consuelo de los que sufren.

Find me a beautiful river to wash
my days porque ahora escribo
esto, estoy aprendiendo tu vida,
tus ideas, tus sentimientos, que un día
tu escribiste. Fuiste util para
quien te necesitaba.
Tu me has enseñado another
way of being free and human.
¿Por qué ahora no hay personas como
tú? ¿Por qué?
Someday I will know porque.
Mother India.
Vivirás eternamente en mí.

Rosario Castellanos
el derecho a existir.

—Bertha Campos

.

Loud Silence

Dear Rosario:

    Your poems caught
me, when I most needed it. Tus poemas
alimentan mi alma, con sabiduria and
something else that I just cannot explain.
    Your poems are el
alimento que satisface mi hambre,
    nuestra hambre, la
rabia y fortalesa que nos mantiene en

pie, día tras día.
You loved Native Americans como hermanos
y hermanas. You were their perro
guardian that protected them from
discrimination and poverty. At any
           time you looked back
for a reason or excuse to quit helping
           your brothers. You
were like raindrops. No more
dust in the wind, now wind carries
your love and your poems. Rosario,
you said "I can only talk about what
           I know" and you
never stopped talking because you knew
           everything and more.
Tu eras una maestra que enseña con
           su escritura without
teaching a class. Your death is a
mystery, a puzzle to form, un trabalenguas
que desifrar. I sometimes feel that I
don't belong here, that my first language
           in some way is
losing power inside me. The first language
           can no longer hold
me to it. I need your writing. I need
           you here, para
renacer, to heal my soul once again.

—Marco Gutiérrez

.

La Mujer Que Intento Ser De Otra Manera

I am in my bedroom. This
morning is a cold morning. Las
hojas empiezan a caer de los arboles; the
winter is coming. I am thinking and writing
a letter poem to you, Rosario Castellanos.

Right now in this world there are many
people who need help from others. La gente
que tiene más tiene el derecho de ayudar a los
que no tienen, pero no es asi. Especially the Indian people that
sometimes don't have the support from

the government and they live abandonados
en la lejania de los cerros. But you,
Rosario, te almiro por haber ayudado ha
esta gente. You tried to change the world
in other different ways. Also you changed

the world around you. Porque quisiste
ser diferente de los otras poetas Rosario?
That's my question. But I don't care
que me puedas decir about my question.
Also I think that with your

poems you can change los
pensamientos de la gente. If
the people want to change the world
where they live, they have to change *ellos mismos,*
then try to change the world where they live.

—Roberto Méndez

.

"La Esponja Exprimida"

As I wash the dishes
I focus on the sponge
y veo como absorbe el jabón
y se exprime en los trastes.

You come to my mind Rosario,
porque tú eres como ella.
You absorb every movement
para depués convertirlo en tu arte
y cuando desenredas tu conocimiento

se lo pasas a las personas que te rodean.

You are intellect,
sabes lo que quieres y lo que pretendes.
You make us readers arrive where you are at.
You defend your people in your poems,
you tell them porque para el día de mañana.
Tu sabes que tus sacrificios,
valdran la pena "quiero valor para permanecer."

Te escribo este poema en presente y en futuro
porque tu para mi, todavia estas aquí
y seguiras estando aquí.

My world is privileged—
priviligiado por tener la oportunidad
de leer tus poemas
que son el fruto que tu nos as pasado.

te puedo decir que me has dejado en blanco,
o sea sorprendida
eres una gran escritora
y dejame repetirte,
que eres como una esponja exprimidora.

—Rosa Robles

.

La Mujer de Lenguaje de Trabalenguas

Bienvenida Rosario "La Soñadora poeta
de las nubes." Traté de seguir tus huellas.
En el bullismo cortuito de ir y venir de los días
del Siglo 20. En mis sueños soñé
que caminaba y buscaba la paz del silencio.
¿Qué se puede encontrar huyendo de las
arideces y desengaños del mundo?
Como la madre India buscando consuelo.
Ignorando que el mundo todavía es hermoso.
Que el universo marcha como debiera.

Tratando de estar el nudo de los vislumbres,
repentinos, abandonado, en las tinieblas,

Anunciando la verdad serena y plácida,
the serene and placid truth.
Encontrando el camino de la libertad.
Finding a way of liberation, aprendiendo
del silencio, mirando el mundo, oliendo
la naturaleza, platicando, con el viento,
siguiendo las huellas de los años.

Buscando respuestas del existir sin
encontrarlas. Tratando de acatar
el consejo de los años de otro modo
de ser libre. Algún día lo sabré.

Recuerdos, preguntas, sin respuestas.
Buscando puertas de escape para
ser feliz.

La vida está llena de engaños, y
arideces. Esfuérzate por ser feliz.
No olvides, tienes derecho a existir.
Cualquiera que sean tus ideas,
no eres menos que las plantas
y estrellas. Eres una creatura del universo.
Que tienes tu historia

horizontes del ayer y hoy y siempre.
The world seeks another way to see.
El mundo busca otra manera de ver.

—María Caro

Letters to Rigoberta Menchú

The First Xena, Warrior Protector of the People

You were not a princess
but you were destined to rule.
No en la manera de gobernar

pero si en tu forma de pensar.
You were powerful como un dragón
with your sword's power.
You scared intruders
not in battles, pero con verdades.

Tus palabras son fuertes
porque la verdad duele
como si te atraviesa una flecha en el corazón.

Tu fuiste la primer Xena, Rigoberta,
because like a warrior,
tu defendías a tu gente,
not with the sword, pero con tu voz
porque tu voz, es la voz, de mil voces.

—Rosa Robles

.

Thank You, Rigoberta Mechú!

A light of possibility
gives me power to go against my
own odds.

I see with your eyes it is possible
to make it in your world.
In a little time I will
travel a path

A path I have not ventured
into the skin of Mexico's
being.

I tell you this because I'm scared to
let others know...
"I am leaving for Mexico."
You don't give me power to face them yet,
especially my parents.

But you give me an idea of
what I face.

I'm not sure how people may react
to me leaving

or which emotional doors I'm
going to open

but from you—
your insight on your culture.

It gives me hope
hope to change my future,

my family's future
and my children's future.

So when I do get older
I can say, "I took that chance,"
and, " I am proud!"

—Yoshikovasha Segura

.

Breaking Through

Rigoberta Menchú

You are a strong
and powerful woman.

You are like lightning
You impact as you strike.

You create change as you speak.
You are an abrecaminos.
You want to end machismo

but you have to speak to start with

the mothers, because the mothers
begin the change with their children.

—Martha Gamboa

Amor a Tu Pueblo

Rigoberta mujer obrera,
la mujer campesina, la
mujer ladina pobre y mujer
indijena, que luchaste
por un mejor futuro para
tu gente de Guatemala
al miro tu fuerza de voluntad
con la que renunciaste
al matrimonio y a tu
maternidad por amor a
tu pueblo que dijiste
que no te importaba una
bonita casa si no tu
pueblo que vivía en
condiciones de horror
y te de si diste mejor
a luchar y gracias a
tu lucha ganaste el
premio novel de la paz
y todo por amor a tu pueblo.

—Rosalinda Campos

Letter to Rigoberta Menchú
La Mujer Que Encontró Un Camino

Your country suffers,
I can hear it cry.

You must suffer
but I can't hear you cry.

You are strong
and wipe the tears off your face and country.

You learned the language
of those who hurt your country, the government,

so that you not only fight with sticks and stones
but with a voice, so that you'll be heard.

You lead many women and men that look up to you.
You are an image that is followed
and you teach them how to fight,
how to have a voice.

Dejaste la oportunidad de ser madre
algo tan importante para toda mujer,
pero el pueblo es tu hijo.
Luchas por el como una madre lucha por su hijo.

Eres una abrecaminos para toda,s mujeres,
para las comunidades indigenas
para el pueblo de Guatemala,
para todos, eres mi abrecaminos.

—Tatiana Whizar

.

Strong Woman With Great Independence, Different Views, Standing Strong, Holding Firm, Never Giving Up, No Matter How Different, Statements or Opinions Said Without Remorse, "There Will Be A Time When Things Will Be Different"

In this world, education and independence
are within our reach. Yet to so many it
remains unattainable. The people work
so hard. Why no children for you? A hard

decision like that forever without laughter or happiness that a child brings. Education is important. "Porque si no aprenden, no avancan." Teaching others to make better choices. Yet so many remain ignorant or maybe it is just pride. Those who work hard have their child's future in mind. "Porque la semilla que quedara sera la que va aprovechar después el producto de ese trabajo." Education. Essential for all. You. Not held down by men, held back only by what you allow yourself to be held from. What made you come and reach these conclusions? You know your future. Faith and time are on your side. *Porque yo se que todo llega a su tiempo y cuando se hace con calm a es cuando las cosas marchan bien.*

—Daisy Hernandez

Espejo Indigena

Untiring warrior that Guatemala
saw born and growing.
You Indian indigena of courage most
affectionate of the most deep
of the land.

You who had to learn the language
of the colonizer to give values
to the rights of the indigenous
people of Latin America.

You who made the echo of
your voice of liberation should be
heard through out the skies.

Rigoberta Menchú, enterprising woman
who exalted your culture and fought
for the rights that had to be.

Indian illiterate, that even the
intellectual people admire. You have
from me, my respect and admiration.

You who were given the privilege
from God for the reality of being
Indian of brown skin tainted by the sun.
That at the same time is embarrassed for
once being for reasons of
discrimination of some white foolish
people that denied the rights.

In my point of view, your culture
has my admiration and respect.
Not a reason of embarrassment. Being
Indian is proud because Indians
in nature have all, rich cultures
and wisdom, and a language, unique
because they understand nature and animals—

the phenomenon of nature.
They don't need the books and
the help of teachers.

You, Indigenous Indian, that do
not count with the advance of technology,
can make all with your
hands and your imagination.
You that don't have material fortunes, nor
riches nor commodities.
But you have something with
more value, the felicity that any
intellectuals wish they had.

You that live in the mountains
far from the cities and its problems

and worries of daily life,
you that fight for the rights
of the human being.

—María Caro

.

La Mujer Que Lucha Por Los Derechos De Otros

Rigoberta, I am here sitting on
a bench in a park. I am looking
at a soccer field y me estoy
inspirando escribiendo a letter
poem to you, Rigoberta Menchú.

You know, Rigoberta, that in this
world many people don't have the
same rights. There are people que
tiene más que otros, especialmente
Indian people that sometimes don't

speak Spanish and they don't have
voz ni voto. Those people don't have
someone that represents them ni
quien hable por ellos and who helps them,
telling them that they have the same

rights que otra gente que no sufre,
y que tiene más que ellos. Te admiro
because you were one of them that
decided to help them, pero tu te tuviste que
superar para lograr ayudarlos—you did that

because all those people era tu pueblo.
You had learned how to speak Spanish,
and hablar por los derechos de tu
gente y vigilar que their rights fueran
respetados como gente y no violados.

—Roberto Méndez

.

A Woman Full of Anger

*"We have kept our identity
hidden because we have resisted."*
                            —*Rigoberta Menchú*

Mujer luchadora, who has
luchado to preserve her customs and
ideas.
    Has luchado for the Indian rights.
You have made your voice to be heard.

    You who don't need to hide your
rostro behind a mask of noble feelings
and a heart of love.
    You gave up your own happiness
to give it to your town, your Raza, without
thinking of yourself, only of them.
    A woman full of anger who does
not need expensive shoes nor to straighten
the hair for more beauty, because
that is not important for you. You always
say that one has to shine like the one
you are because your apparel is not
important, only the person.
    You who use your apron as
part of your identity to be respected.
    Mujer emprendedora who understood
the language of the plants. You spoke
with naturalness and you could
guess the designios.
    You were treated as an ignorant
person, without them knowing that
that ignorant Indian was full of
knowledge that she did not need
books to acquire knowledge.
    You knew that those intellectuals
were more ignorant than you, the Indian.

—Antonia Caro

Mujer de las Montañas

The eyes of humanity are
looking to one woman, who is respected
for what she has done, and for her
knowledge about rights for women,
particularly for Native American Women.

Rigoberta, I want to ask you, what does
it feel to win the Premio Nobel de la
Paz? And then be called a liar
by American writers?
They said that you made up your stories
and they were not your own experiences.

Now I can tell why. Our teacher
told us the truth and the reasons
American writers talked bad things
about your book.
I want to tell you that you
are a person to admire. You wrote
your feelings, and the feelings of others
on a piece of paper,
and those feelings penetrated our

hearts while we were reading them. You are
a woman to follow, because with your
wisdom you will lead us to the concord
of a new world full of peace and fairness.
You are the esperanza
for our Native American people who
suffer and live in a world lacking
justice and full of prejudice.

—Antonio Ruíz

Rigoberta Menchú

Rigoberta,
your passion
for your people's justice,
and anger of not being heard
is the best kind of characteristic
that someone could have.

I loved your story
and feel that I
should learn more
about you.

I'm looking forward
to learning about more women
with the same courage
as you and your mother.

Your decision about sacrificing
your happiness
and your chance
of starting

your own family
es de admirarse.

No creo que muchas
personas quisieran
y hicieran algo por su gente
and the generations
to come, porque piensan
que algun día vendra la justicia sola.
sin la lucha de ellos y de sus familias.

Without voice there is no justice.

But I myself
don't think that I wouldn't
get married or not start a family
of my own for justice of my people

or my justice.
I would try to have
a better life by living
and not forgetting the injustice.

Possibly going back
to help in some way.

This is why
you are a brave woman
who generations will look up to.

—Blanca Flores

.

Letters to Gloria Anzaldúa

La Mujer Alacrana

Tus manos son como una araña
son venenosas y atrapadoras,
like the spider, you trap and get rid of what you dislike.

Your mouth strikes and kills like a snake
when it comes to defend itself.
But it also throws fire
y deja cicatrices de tu hocico rebelde.

Your eyes are like a mirror
que refleja el infierno
de tus viejas tradiciones.

You are a tornado.
You mix old traditions
and crush them like sand.

Tu no eres muñica de nadie,
que le dan cuerda cuando quieren

because you are not a copy,
you are original.

Tu voz extremece la tierra
como un temblor.
Se roba las palabras
como el respiro se rota el oxigeno.

—Rosa Robles

.

A Rebel Woman

A rebel woman que nunca
te callaste, en ti está la rebeldia.
Your rebellion cost you too much.
You felt inutal, estúpida, e impotente.
Fuistes una mujer hocicona, que
nunca te dejastes de nadie, y
contestabas para atras. Eso es
lo que te hizó especial.
You left your tierra, tu gente to
find yourself, but tu no dices si te
pudistes encontrar a tí misma.
In the nights in your bed atormentada
por el silencio que te gritaba y te
reclamaba porque la vida te hizo
asi "Rebelde." Tu mente correcta
no se defendía o no respondería
quien seria tan estupido para
soportar tu rebeldia.
No por ser rebelde te ganarás
respeto. But nobody can judge
another because that's the way
you are and nobody can change another.
Dijiste que eramos una raza
Vencida. But I think we are not.
We are luchadores. As the same you are.
Porque si estamos aquí

es luchar salir adelante—
it is to struggle and fight to get ahead.
You are a woman full of
courage, valor. And nobody will
put candados over our mouths, because
women have to express what we
feel and think.

—Antonia Caro

Wild Woman

Gloria how come you are
so hard and rude on me?
Is there any bad experience
that you personally had

with a man? Or you just heard
that men were bad and evil?
How come you include all men
into your wrong concept?

I personally don't like when
somebody talks in plural, when
it includes myself, like for example
when my mother regaña a mi hermano,

then she starts to talk in plural, referring
to me, and I always say, "Ay, I didn't
do it, porque tan bien me incluye a mi."
I think that you overload

your anger on to men. *Damn it, you
are killing us.* You consider us as a
wild animal, a disgusting *cerdo*, a
living thing with no feelings and

that cannot have the capacity
to love and respect a woman.

Gloria, let me ask you something,
How were you born? Did you just

appear like nothing on the ground?
Of course not. A man gave you life.
I think I know why you left, having
nothing, so you could find yourself. Not

because you were lazy. You wouldn't
take any responsibility, you were too
much of a rebelde. Indomitable. Your image
of marriage is that women are

sirvientes de los hombres, but I
think that in a marriage a man
and woman divide the responsibilities
of the house. That's why they form

a couple. I personally think that
women need men, as well as men
need women, because I think that
there is not a person that would

like to live the best years of their
lives alone, die alone, having a
boring life. I think that your
bad idea towards men, kills a man's

good intentions towards women,
because just like you think
that all men are bad, you cause
men to think bad about women.

I just want to tell you
that all men are not bad.
You just got to find the right
one. I also want to admit that

your rebeldia te impulso a sobre
salir. Your writing, it's so

powerful the blind can see it,
y un sordo escucharlo. You

uncovered the truth with such
violence and wildness that the
highest level of conceptions are
knocked down. Tu fuiste, hocicona

repelona, chismosa, malcriada,
for the good of women. Gloria
please change. I feel black
and white about you.

—Marco Gutiérrez

A Rebel Girl in the Way

Gloria, I agree but at the same time,
I disagree, with your terms about women.

I can't say you are
thinking in the wrong way,
because all of us,
have a different thoughts.

But I'm going to be clear
with you. Sometimes

women need to be alone,
because we never are going
to understand our feelings.

I think that all of us
have a time when we don't
like to hear our parents y
mucho menos las personas
que nos rodean.

But sometimes I would
like to break the rules of
my house, my religion,

but we need to be strong,
and open our eyes
for the coming future
because we never know
what's going to happen.

We have a voice,
we have a culture, but it's
not wrong to learn cultures.

Sometimes it's O.K. to
go out from reality,
but holding our rebel
thoughts we can fight
for ourselves with
the people who want

to take us out of the
game of life and from our roads.
Be how you are, because
nobody is going to change
your thoughts.

—Paloma Pérez

Strong Woman

Lady Gloria Anzaldúa I don't know
much of you because I never
had a class like this
one where we get
the chance of knowing our own
culture and knowing
our people who made
history in Mexico
and every other state. So
that's why we are
proud of you Gloria

Anzaldúa, and also for what
you did, live your own
traditions.
But why Gloria?
Why did you have to do
such a thing like
that you left your mom
as if you didn't care
about her?

—Octavio Saucedo

Being the Way

Understanding Gloria Anzaldúa is understanding her words, and understanding her words is understanding where you come from. As I go reading phrase by phrase, sentence by sentence, I realize that she is the woman out of all the women we've studied, I relate the most to.

As well as Gloria, I don't find the strength to leave the source of my family to move away for college. But as she said, "I had to leave home so I could find myself, find my own nature buried under the personality that has been imposed on me." I know once I leave my house, my room, my neighborhood, and everything, it will never be the same as before. Gloria Anzuldúa did it and became an independent woman, not caring what others thought, but by doing as she thought was right.

Culture is something to be taught and to be passed on by generation to generation. Culture forms our beliefs. It only dies when someone stops believing in it, or sees it another way, as Gloria did. For example, men being in power, men having the last word, and all women doing as they ask. A man's job is to put food on the table and maintain a family. If a man didn't work, or couldn't work, he was not a real man. As for a woman, if she rebels, she is a *mala mujer.* If a woman doesn't renounce herself in favor of the male, she is selfish. If a woman remains a virgin until she marries, she is a good woman. A woman could only turn to three things: *to the church as a nun, to the streets as a prostitute, or to the home as a mother.*

131

It's things like this that Mexican parents bring and try to pass on to their children. It's ignorance that clouds their minds. Now, fortunately, women have a fourth choice. The choice of leaving home, not necessarily to marry, but to look for an education. This way we show men that we are capable of doing something other than laying down and having kids. Women don't have to depend on men. We also could be successful. We may never be equal in strength, but we are in knowledge.

Gloria talks about blending with people as *mestiza*. The future depends on the mixture of many cultures interacting together, getting along with each other. It's a way we perceive reality, the way we see ourselves. Ignorance splits people and creates prejudice. We have to break it down and finally realize the problem between the white race and the colored, between males and females. It all lies in ourselves, our cultures, our languages, and our thoughts.

I'm glad Gloria came along and did wrong in everyone's eyes, not realizing that she was breaking the chains for the generations to come, for us.

—Claudia Guzmán

.

Rebelde

Mi estimada Gloria lo que se acerca de ti es muy
poco, pero lo que se es suficiente para darme
cuenta lo que ha sido de tu vida para analizarte
como persona dices que eres rebelde como

los mexicanos no sé exactamente lo que
quieres decir con esa palabras. Dices que te
costó muy caro tu rebeldía también me dejas
con las mismas a oscuras lo que si entiendo

es cuando dices haz esto y haz lo otro
sin considerar tus deseos, porque todos somos
humanos y tenemos el derecho de escuchar las
ideas de cada persona como humanos que somos.

Pero déjame decirte que no tengo nada que
admirarte aunque tenías unas cuantas ideas
buenas en tu mente pero eso no es suficiente
para que yo te admire tus frases las escucho

todos los días de cualquier persona que me
encuentro por allí por lo tanto no puedo admirarte
porque si te admiro tengo que admirar a todo
el mundo y no se puede admirar a todo el mundo.

Solamente se pueden admirar a ciertas personas
que deveras han luchado por algo y lo logran
esas son las personas que yo admiro así es
mi querida Gloria solamente quiero darte

algunos de los nombres de las mujeres que
se an ganado mi almiración y no sólo la mía
sino del mundo entero, ellas son mi madre
desde luego, la Virgen de Guadalupe, Rigoberta Menchú

Sor Juana, la Malinche, Rosario Castellanos.
Estas seis mujeres son las que yo admiro
realmente en el sentido profesional pero en el
sentido emocional admiro a todas las mujeres.

De algunas de las seis mujeres que mencioné
no sabía nada cuando empecé a estudiarlas
pero conforme iba descubriendo cosas acerca
de ellas las admiraba más y más.

—Natividad Méndez

.

"Voces Perdidas del Ayer y Hoy"

Mesclas de diferentes razas
que dan fruto a una nueva
generación,reblede y necia

raza mestiza chicana.

Gloria Anzaldúa la Mujer
de la mala vida tu mujer
maleducada que no supiste ser
una dama por tu agresibidad
y ironia antelos demas.

Tu que te ocultaste detras
de tu disfras de indiferensia
que lo usabas para protegerte

Mujer sorda cerrrada a la
realidad que no sabes entender
ni valorar ni escuchar como pides
imposibles que te escuchen
y te entiendad si no te
haceptas a ti misma ni sabes escuchar.

No jusges y no seras jusgada
no trates de cambiar el mundo
ni el destino porque el mundo
y el destino somos cada uno
cada ser humano que es unico
que forma su propia historia.

Tu que dices que eres de una
raza diferente que quieres
formar tu propia cultura
para tu raza.

No te entiendo al igual
que atodos los piensan
que son diferentes los
blancos, los negros, y los
de piel morena.

Todos somos seres humanos
iguales debajo de la piel.
Nuestra sangre es del mismo color.

Nacemos igual y morimos igual.
Todos las personas somos iguales
aunque nos diferensian el color,
sexo, religion, y costumbres
pero sentimos soñamos no
lo olvides se tu mismo.

—María Caro

Finding Ourselves: Reality!

Blanca Flores

One of the most interesting Latinas that I know is my Aunt Juana Flores. She's interesting to me because she was the first in my family from my dad's side to get a good job. She wasn't satisfied with being a dental assistant. She wanted more. She wanted to advance in that field. So she told the dentist that she worked with and he told her where she could go to classes that she had to pay for to get her license to be a certified RDA.

I'm not sure to what level she got because for all the responsibility she had she would get paid more, so she moved to another office. She knows what her work is worth. She decided not to work at all for a few years to take care of her daughters. She took them and picked them up from school, tended her house, and was able to cook a good meal for my uncle every day. I admire her attitude so much. I need to be like her in the way that she says what's on her mind at all times. She also gives me advice but she doesn't sound like she's demanding or imposing. She sounds like she's just giving me some of her knowledge.

All of the women that we read about are important because they all opened doors, made a way where there is no way, for *La Raza*. This means a great deal to me.

But the one woman that I can relate to most is Gloria Anzaldúa. She, like myself, had a problem with speaking out her mind, but the difference is that she has found her way of letting out her thoughts, and I still need to work on it. But she also has more in common with me than just that. I, too, find myself having to move to feel better about life. My surroundings have a lot to do a lot with my attitude. So did Gloria's. She had to leave her valley to find herself. I have to go back to my valley to find myself. Gloria and I have a very special need in common—we both need our space to think things through. I need to be alone to concentrate, and she had to learn new languages and beliefs to find herself. I have already found myself in that sense.

The first woman that is important to me is my mom, Adelaida Méndez. She's important to me because part of my identity —*viene de mi mamá. Mi carácter y terques viene de mi mamá.* I have got her attitude when I'm mad. Since she knows that and knows that I like my space—

she respects that—and leaves me alone when I'm mad. She also lets me make my own decisions because she doesn't want to be with me like she was with her mom—Angelina Sánchez. To my mom it is very important that we can trust each other and communicate well at all times. She is easy to talk to and she's very *comprensiva*. I respected — and still do respect—her decisions. She won't argue or deny me from doing things that are good in making me independent and that could help me as an adult. My mom—since I was 8 years old —that I remember—has always given all my sisters and me advice. She never thought that we were too young for knowing about life and about what was happening around us. She has always told us with tears in her eyes, about what she's gone through. *Maybe I cry more than all of my family because they don't cry enough.* So when I do, I can't stop.

Another woman that we studied was Rosario Castellanos. She's a very controversial woman. Her poems—I couldn't understand them— took me two times to read. I may never understand all but I got the idea. *Una mujer fuerte que se dedicó a ser la voz de los indios.* She wrote a poem called "Muro de Lamentaciones" that I like the most, and feel that is her strongest. She has courage. She shows it by saying, "In my genealogy there is only one word: solitude." She says just what she feels; I admire her for that. But I did find a similarity, which is that we can only write about what we know. I found myself to be an advocate like her. She writes about Indians and I write about Mexicans.

My power is my *sencillez*. I'll never be *celoza* of what other people have. I won't envy what I can't afford that others have. I will live happy with what I have as long as I know that I did try at least to get a good education after high school. I also find myself to be a caring person, even to people I've seen but never spoken to. One time, the first time that I've gone to a funeral, I cried more then the lady's relatives. So I went into the hall. But I don't know how to explain my crying. All I know is that I couldn't stop from crying, even in the hallway. My mom made me go. That was the only time she imposed something on me that I didn't want to do.

The women's struggles teach us how we can overcome our struggles like they did. I learned that there is only a struggle because we let it be a struggle, instead of taking care of it or dealing with it. I've learned that my voice has to be heard—that everyone's voice has to be heard. I can do that with what I have, which is my interest in writing. There is no need to be shy, quiet or keep anything to yourself. (Myself) *No hay peor lucha que la que no se hace.*

I've learned many things about myself. Like I can't stay shy and quiet forever if I want to succeed in life. I need to speak my mind. (Get mad if it's necessary.) Also that it's not always what your *costumbres* are that makes the right way for individuals to live.

As a woman, I see and notice things that my boyfriend doesn't. Like on the phone he'll call me and sometimes he sounds sad but he tells me "really, no there's nothing that's bothering me or that's worrying me," when in reality he can't communicate his personal/ inner feelings right. So he doesn't try. But I know that something is bothering him. He prefers to talk about what I feel than to let me know what's going on with him. I think that we both learn from each other. If I have a concern he'll help me come down and point out things to clear my head. This is one thing that I like about our relationship. (We can help each other because we understand each other.)

As a woman, I'm also caring to everyone and their feelings. I care a lot about everyone I know and what they're going through. I find myself wanting to know people. I know more than what I see. I'm able to read into conversations. I'm also very understanding and easy to talk to.

One Of Each

Marco Gutiérrez

Each woman tries to be herself. Some women are talkative, polite, mean, *chismosas*, responsible and scholars. I've been around many women, and by the way they act I can tell how they really are with men. Some girls think that they are so pretty that they would not talk to you, but if they see you in a nice car, and the wallet loaded with money that you have been saving for week, they just come to you and in some hours they paralyze you by their beauty. And then you ask them out and then next week they don't even remember you. I personally like to be close with girls because they look fragile, beautiful. It takes the sweet part of my art, my way of talking changes, now I'm more polite.

The most interesting woman that I know is my grandmother; her name is Genoveva Espinoza. She is a *luchadora*. Since I was two, she took care of me, and then my brothers. She was always the mother that wasn't there for us. She never felt inferior of working like a young woman. I see myself in her as always wanting the best for myself and for the family. She made my brothers into good students and human beings. She told us many times to study hard so we could be someone in the future.

Gloria Anzaldúa is the most important woman that I studied, because *ella no se comforma con poquito*. She wants the best for the woman. She didn't care about the price of equality, she just did it. She lets it be known to myself that if I am not comfortable with what I have, there is no reason to be strict with it. Go for the best. Show no mercy to conquer what is best for myself. She teaches me that being weak and waiting for the others to let you do what you want to do is wrong. If you just go for it, even if you hurt someone, it might be for the best. If it hurts someone, it could mean you were right and did the right thing.

The second best woman that I like is Sor Juana, because she is the opposite of Gloria Anzaldúa. Sor Juana didn't hate men; she became one of us, so she could have an education. It's like if you can't beat the enemy, become one of them. That's what Sor Juana did, but she did it for *necesidad* because she was hungry for success and truth.

Sor Juana and Gloria are so different, but they still reflect themselves in a mirror in some ways. They both wrote what they felt in their hearts, which is what amazes us today and forever. They reflect on us their strength, their passion of what is unreachable and injustice in the world. Now, in some ways, they set goals in our minds.

It seems like Sor Juana and Gloria had trouble with men. Their struggles during life are similar to mine because I had to struggle to find myself in a new community. I had to struggle in school trying to find myself so that at one time I felt that I did not fit there, but thanks to Sor Juana and Gloria I opened up my space, my path, and I put away the obstacles that held me from getting there. Today I am an *abrecaminos*.

After exploring myself and the different women, I learned that too much is never enough, and that the tallest mountain can still be reached. I'm more focused and mature about what I really want in life. I learned that men and women have equal power and opportunities.

So what? So what if I ever thought bad about women? I am not perfect. Nobody is perfect. We all commit mistakes and learn from them. So what if I said that Gloria Anzaldúa was a bad role model for society and that she put down all women in America because of her hate towards men.

So what if I got tired of reading about women? It was maybe because in their writing they let me know how life is for women. They also put on my face their struggles and hardships that I did not care about at a certain point. I thought they had a perfect life, but after reading their stories, I changed my view towards women. Thanks *mujeres*, you just filled me an with understanding and consideration.

Never Spotless

Rosa Robles

When a woman breaks the traditions of her town, her image becomes stained. That is why a lot of women never succeed. I see myself in Gloria Anzaldúa because she is one these women. Her hunger for a new way of life, her fight for her freedom, and her desire to unwrap herself from her old traditions, have made her image a *mala mujer,* but we must see that it is *only* an image, not truth itself.

Gloria Anzaldúa, since birth, already carried her veins full of hot blood. She knew that what she thought was not wrong. With her rebellious way and her poisonous mouth, she was considered *una perdida.* But truly she was showing her people and other women that she was not going to be like them, a man's slave tortured by old customs. She wanted to succeed; she wanted to have a life, not be an old traditional housewife. I like Gloria's personality, because even though her people gave her their back, that did not hold her down or make her change. She was a strong woman who never took a step backwards.

Gloria has helped me discover that I am not what others say I am. *Una perdida, rebelde y hocicona,* but a strong intelligent woman. Before I had read about her, I felt like I had the image of a *mala mujer,* but now I have realized that I was 100% wrong. No one has the right to judge other women, or me. I have discovered that in order to become something and succeed, I first have to let go of the chains that hold me down, chains which are my old traditions.

The family that I come from, has these old customs where women are not free, but like slaves to the men. But I have not, and will not, adopt these traditions. It is not in my blood. My father is a macho man. Whatever he says is what has to be done. I disagree with this because he is taking control of the women in the house as he wants to. All my life I have dreamed of being the first in my entire family to graduate from college. But my parents are so traditional that they put me down. They say a woman's job is to be home with her husband. I disagree. They do not even let me go to dances or have a boyfriend, because to them I will burn myself, meaning that people will talk about me and create a bad image about me. I do not mind if I am not allowed to date or go to the dances because I am not interested in them at this point of my life, but Gloria has passed me the strength and knowledge to fight back and ignore the people that throw rocks at me. How are we women ever going to be important if the people around us do not miss an opportunity to put us down? I do not care a bit what people say about me as long as I am happy with myself. I can be a *rebelda, hocicona, malcriada,* but I can also be free.

Gloria Anzaldúa has filled my mind with good images about her and myself. If she survived through the fire people threw at her, I know I can, too. She has influenced me for the good and the better.

Another important woman that I have learned about, and see a part of an image in me is Malinche. This is one of the greatest women I have read about. She was sold, and then given to a Spaniard, who was Cortés. I do not see how people can refer to her as a *mala mujer.* No one cared about her suffering, or what she went through. How can they say she was a *traidora* when it was her people who treated her like she was an object? *They were the mala mujeres, not* Malinche. I admire her for her strength and her great heart. She forgave her people, including her mother. To me, Malinche was a good woman. She was not a prostitute, nor a traitor, nor a bad woman.

In the way that I compare myself to Malinche is that on my father's side, the family created an image of me as a *traidora, loca*, and somehow related to a prostitute, which is not at all truth. *Do not throw rocks when your house is made of glass.* Two of my uncles and one of my aunts said that I lied to my parents all the time, and that I had had many boyfriends and saw them without my parents' consent. They also added to that, saying, *who knows what I had done with them*, and that they were surprised that I was not pregnant yet. When this got to my ears, I was very angry and so I went to ask them if what I had heard was true. Of course, they denied everything, but then came the day when I heard it myself from their mouths. They did not know I was there but since that day, I no longer have gone to visit them. But I have, and will continue, to demonstrate to them that it is not true, never has been, and never will be. No matter what they say or do, I will succeed. Deep inside me, I know that I am a good woman, but like Malinche, I forgive them for their calumnies because I know that they were the bad persons.

I thank God for these struggles that I have had in my life, because he might have sent them to me to make me stronger and to encourage other women as well. Life is not about listening and doing what other people tell you to, but about exploring life yourself and learning from it. No one else in your life knows what is right or wrong for you, because you are the one who is living your life. Your future is in your hands.

I have learned how to stand firm and speak my thoughts out and let others know what I think in the way of *So what?* and *¿y que?* If I am going in the wrong way, who cares? If I believe it's the right way, I will continue to go that way. I might be a woman, but let me tell you, as a woman I have the same power as a man. I am strong and intelligent. I have the *ganas,* and let me say that I am, and will always be, myself—a good woman, even if others create bad images of me.

Part V

Interviews with Our Mothers and Fathers

My grandma chose some of my uncles and aunts to go and live in
the ciudad so that they could keep going to school.
Unfortunately my mother was not one. Out of four of them
only Uncle Ramon took advantage. He is now a history teacher
at a high school in Morelia, Mexico.

Cesar Farias

Eloisa Gonzalez de Ruano proudly holds the image of her mother, Macaira Molina, and her father, Réyes Ruano, in her hands and in her face. My mother is a product of my grandparents' lives, which began August 4, 1957, in San Isidro, Jalisco. Her father, Réyes, was born on December 27, 1922 in El Durasnito, Jalisco. Eloisa's mother was born on March 11, 1933 in San Isidro, Jalisco.

Eloisa lived through the cycle of hard labor and sweat on the several farms she and her family migrated to. She was born with the wings of an angel that allowed her to soar free from farm to farm. Eloisa also soared past las fronteras. Her energy and passion led her to a different and exciting life. She learned to live in the American culture. She is learning to understand the American culture and the language. Through Eloisa's ability to learn, she has taught her children to experience the privilege of education.

Recently my mother and I were in the living room discussing my future plans of going to college. Curiously, I asked my mother whether or not she'd enjoy studying and would consider attending college sometime. A spark lit in her eye and with a joyous smile, she replied, "yes."

I didn't understand at first why a woman like her, who only attended school until the fourth grade, would appreciate education. Then it hit me. My mother is a smart woman with many inspiring gifts. She is an abrecaminos. She was born to bang down the doors and open her ways. My mother had seen what education had done to me. It made me a fighter. It made my mother a fighter.

Currently my mother is studying English with the hopes of becoming fluent in the language. After acquiring the English language, she is going to get her GED. With the GED, she plans to enroll in college and explore career possibilities. She has taught us all, it's never too late to pursue our dreams if they still burn inside us.

Lorenzo Gonzalez holds the picture of his parents, Anselmo and Guadalupe Gonzalez, admirably. Through the cycle of life, Lorenzo has become his own man. Determined as he is, Lorenzo has pursued a first year of English education. My father will no longer accept humiliation. He is set on acquiring the American language.

Lorenzo was born to Anselmo Gonzalez and Guadelupe Perez on July 7, 1951 in El Organo, Jalisco. Lorenzo lived a difficult life raising his family because his father wasn't always there. Through all the hardships, Lorenzo found the ability to love his mother, Guadalupe Perez, and his father, Anselmo Gonzalez.

Abuelita Lupe saw the light of life on August 31, 1931 in El Organo, Jalisco. Anselmo took his breath of life on April 21, 1928 in Yahualica, Jalisco. They raised their 13 children in the humble town of Yahualica, Mexico. In Yahualica, Lorenzo had to be a man at the age of five. Deprived of education, he did the only thing that was left, work.

An Original Story

Eloisa Gonzalez

My mother's name is Eloisa Gonzalez Ruano. She was born August 4, 1957 in a very small town called San Isidro, which is located in Jalisco, México. She was born into a very poor, loving family with very strict guidelines.

At the age of four, my mother lived an extremely poor life. She and her family and would go days without eating. They also barely had clothes. My mother's clothes were sometimes made out of costales, or sacks, that her mother sewn together. As a child my mother would play with dolls made out of rags. The doll's hair was made out of corn hair and her other toys were made out of barro.

At age seven my mother was able to go to school along with her 6 siblings during that time. During those years, it was a harsh time for my mother. The rich kids would humiliate her and her siblings because of their economic situation. My mother kept her head up and continued to go to school as long as she could, which was up to fourth grade. She would reuse paper as often as she could. She would also use small pieces of pencils to write with and would sharpen them with razor blades.

At age 7, my mother's dreams were to have things she was limited on such as toys, candy, clothes, and food. Her needs were transferred into desires. My mother still loved her life and enjoyed every breath of it. She had desires for her future. At the age of seven, my mother wanted to continue to study to become a teacher. She wanted to be able to help her parents and be able to travel.

At 15, my mother got married, and at age 16 she had a child. At that point she decide to go to the United States. My mother mentioned that her life had changed economic wise, but she had a rough time improving her economic structure. As she moved to the U.S., my father, mother, and sister lived in a cardboard box. My mother and father worked in the fields. My mother realized life was rough and new responsibilities had developed. My mother's dreams had changed. She wanted a home to live in and a job so she could provide for her kids. She didn't want her kids to suffer as she did.

My mother's life took a rocky spin at the age of 30. She had gotten extremely ill. She was close to death. My mother had a serious heart and lung condition that was incurable, but only treatable. All she dreamed about now was to get better in order to provide for her kids.

At 40, her life had taken a big change. Three of her children had married. Loneliness had started to fill her life. My mother wasn't able to work anymore because of her illness, and one of her daughters had a nervous breakdown. She was forced to move to a new state, Washington, away from her family. It was hard to readjust.

Finally, at the age of 42, her life had taken a better step. Two tumors were discovered, one in her eye and the other in her stomach. Both were removed in time. Her daughter had recovered and more children were added to the family, two grandsons.

Now her dreams are that her youngest child, me, graduates and continues to receive a higher education. She's done everything she can to support me. She's a dreamer and an accomplisher. She's put faith in front of reality.

Otro Imagen de La Vida

A year has gone by since the last time I interviewed my mother. Yet, there is much more that I haven't been able to discover. A lot of my questions remained unanswered until recently. A second interview was done. It was necessary in order to keep our family story alive.

In November 1973, an eight and a half-month pregnant sixteen-year-old woman and her twenty-two-year-old husband set out to the United States, the land of dreams. The pregnant woman and her husband were my mother, Eloisa Gonzalez Ruano, and my father, Lorenzo Gonzalez Pérez. My mother and father were leaving their homeland in search of a better life for their soon-to-arrive baby. They had hopes and dreams in their eyes. They believed that over the miles of land and past the river, a miracle life would be born.

The journey first started when mis padres left their small, humble town of Yahucalica, located in Jalisco, México. They were heading to Tijuana, México, on a camillon. It was a rough time for my mother and father. The ride was too rough for my pregnant mother. There was no money for food or clothing. All the money they had would be needed to pay for the transportation.

Fear raced through their heads. What would happen if they were to be caught? What would become of their soon-to-arrive child? The hope of arriving in the United States is what kept them on the camillon. A hope for a wonderful life for their child is what kept them sane. La tristeza de la separación de la familia les empezó a hervir. For once in their life, they were independent and alone.

When they arrived in Tijuana, they continued their journey towards the border. My mother would be the first to intend to pass the border by foot. Without my father, she took her steps forward, praying deep inside. She was rejected and sent back. My rigorous mother tried and tried again, even though fear was stuck in her throat. She was sent back three times, with my father waiting on the Mexican side. My father would wait until my mother could cross before he took his steps.

The stress built and the fear embellished. *Mi madre* got sick and came close to delivering her baby on the border pass. The thought of her baby being born in the United States kept her strong. She would wait and deliver the baby in the States.

Fortunately, an in-law's cousin arrived in Tijuana. She placed my mother in her car and covered her inflated stomach with a large blanket. As they crossed the Tijuana border, my mother pretended to be asleep. Her innocent, baby face led the border officials to believe that my mother was a young child of the driver. Arriving near San Clemente, California, a second deception was in place. Once again, the innocent and asleep child led the officials to believe she was the driver's child. The cousin's objective in passing my mother through the borders was successful.

Finally, my mother had successfully arrived in the United States. She was housed with an in-law's large distant family; she felt depressed and alone. She feared for my father, who stayed behind to make sure she would make it across safely. It took a week before my father arrived in Torrance, California, where my mother was situated. My father had passed through the border with help from a *coyote*. My father was first dropped off in Englewood, California, near Long Beach, where he stayed with his uncles. Later, he met my mother in Torrance.

After one month in Torrance, the baby was born. She would be marked in our family history as Maria, named after the Virgin Maria. During her arrival, there was no one to help. It was Christmas Eve, and everyone was too drunk to help. My mother received a ride to the hospital from an in-law's wife, but an ambulance returned the complete family home. In the hospital, my mother was afraid la migra would take them and their baby. They were afraid of the future. Reality had come into play.

In Torrance, my father was working as a gardener, trying to provide a decent living for his family. The income was too low, so my parents were forced to leave Torrance and move to Stockton, California. My father left two weeks earlier to find jobs for both of them. Later, my mother followed. In Stockton, they worked in the cherry fields and earned low-wages. Their income would only provide for food, but no money for shelter. So my father built a house out of a cardboard box and placed it in an area in the field. There, my mother, father, and the 5-month baby would sleep.

Soon, my parents left Stockton and headed to Linden, California, to work in the peach and pear fields. The owners provided food and clothing for the baby and shelter for the whole family. Finally, their baby was receiving appropriate nutrition. In Linden, my mother would work with the baby strapped to her back or resting on the ground. Their life was finally getting better.

Nine months later after residing in Linden, my mother became pregnant again. The neighbors warned my mother about the health services. They filled my mother with hollow lies. They told her she would not receive medical attention for her pregnancy because of her illegal status. So my mother fled back to Mexico, while my father stayed for four months before he returned to Mexico.

In México, mi madre saved the money my father sent her during his four month period in Linden. They had money to invite their second child, María Isabel, into a comfortable world. Isabel would be set upon a world of dreams and pain. My parents were revealed to such a world, past the miles of land and over the river.

By Eloisa Gonzalez
Independent English Study
January 2002

152

It's just me and my mom, María Saucedo in the photograph. Well, there are just three pictures on the wall. In one picture I am holding my Mom. In the second one, I am still hugging my mom, and on the third one my Mom is pointing to the frame of pictures that I am holding. In the picture, it's me holding my family in the picture. My mom and my dad and my sister Olivia and Esmeralda and Lionel and Gustavo and Ubaldo. My dad's name is Leonel Ricardo. My mom and my dad got married when they were 18. They were from a rancho. They were born in a little town called Aquila, Michoacán. The photo that I am holding was taken ten years ago. What I can see in the photo with me and my mom is that mom was telling about our family. One time my brother fell down from the horse. To me it was really funny because he got dirt in his face. That was in Michoacán. My mom had fifteen kids, and two kids died. We are going to make a book with these photos about our *raíces* and traditions. Every one of us in this class is working to make a good book. My mom right now is 56 years old and my dad is 54 years old. The first time that my parents came to the U.S. they were around 40 years old, or maybe less and they only stayed four or five years and then they went back and stayed there like ten years. They decided to come back and here we are. Probably what my parents want us to keep for them are their traditions, like for example, the girl shouldn't have sex until the marriage, and keep the same religion no matter what.

About a Woman's Life

Octavio Saucedo

I asked my mother how old she was when she got married, and she told me that she was 18 years old. Then I also asked her how old my dad was, and she told me that he was 17 years old. My mom had fourteen kids, three girls and eleven boys. I asked her if there is anything that she still wants, and she said, "Nothing, because I really have everything."

I asked her in what year she was born, and she told me that she was born in 1944. I asked her when was the first time that she came over here to the United States, and that was in 1981. She came here for two years and they went back to Mexico in 1983.

I asked how many boyfriends she had, and she told me that she only had seven boyfriends and that she was born in Aquila, Michoacán.

I also asked her what she did for fun, and she told me that she didn't really do a lot, because her mom and dad were hard people and she couldn't do much, or go places with friends. She could only go to dances with her brothers and they had to be back in time.

These are our parents. Their names are Antonio Caro and María Isabel Caro. This picture was taken on February 21 of 1999 at Ayotitlan, when my oldest sister got married at Ayotitlan, Jalisco, in front of the church. My sister and I did the interview by phone and letters because my parents are in Mexico. We are using this picture because it is the only one we have. My older sister took the others we had, and she is living in Cocula, Jalisco, Mexico.

"Because The Good in All of You Is Mine"

Antonia Caro

The story of a great woman, a journey, *hecha historia. Mamita* how could I describe the love that I feel, *si no hay* words to describe it.

My mother María Isabel Caro was born in Colima. She is the fourth of five children. Her mom's name is Serafi Sanchez, and her father's name is Alejandro Sanchez. They lived in Colima until she was eight years old, where she studied *"Corte y Confección.* Then they moved to Jalisco. When she was 28 years old, she married my father, Antonio Caro. She has five children. My mother still lives in Villegas, Jalisco. I came to Yakima in 1998. This interview was conducted over the telephone between Yakima and Villegas.

"I was born on November Fifth 1946 in Colima, Colima. I lived there until I was eight years old. My childhood was one of my happier life times. When I was eight I used to be nosy and curious. I always wanted to do all the things that my mother and my grandma were doing. They are the persons that I most admired because since I was a child they gave me advice and they also gave me *manazos* when I did the things that they told me not to do. I remember that I was a *niña barbera* because when I wanted things like candies I used to do *cariñitos* to my mother or my grandma *"para que me los dieran."* My grandma influenced me and has played a very important role in my life. I know that I passed the greatest moments at her side. I know that they have tried to inculcate the best values and customs, those values I have inculcated to my children."

My mother has always been a very patient and loving person always wanting the best for her children.

"She is much like my grandma, the one I admire for the delicious way she cooks and because she was the only one I knew. It was important to have known my other grandparents but I thank God for knowing and enjoying my grandma, Jesús. I remember when I went with her to the shop of *Las Martha's* where she would give me pieces of fabric to make dresses for my dolls and also so my grandma would make my dresses *plizados*. I remember also that I wanted to be a fashion designer when I would grow up, like her.

"When I was eight years old we moved to live in Guadalajara, Jalisco. It was a radical change to which I had to adapt. My school *Leon Avicario*, I liked much the same, like the city, but what I liked most was riding with my parents through the city and they would buy me *trastesitos de barro* to make food like my mom. But through the passing of time the moment to leave the *trastecitos de barro* and the *muñecas* had arrived. I wasn't a child any more. I converted to a young lady.

"Now I had to change the dolls and the *trastecitos* for books. Now I had to act and think different. At the age of 15 I returned to study *Corte y Confección* in Colima with my grandma. Here I lived the happy moments of my youth, the adventures with my partners from school, with my friends from the *colonia*, the *fiestas de la feria de la villa, y las tardeadas de los Domingos. En esa epoca todo era muy sano,* it was very healthy, and I had a lot of fun. My dream to study *Corte y Confección* had been accomplished. I was a fashion designer. When I turned 20, I returned to Guadalajara. I began to work at the house of *Casa de Modas Lupita*. There I worked for eight years. Soon I met your father Antonio Caro, the one I soon got married to at the age of 28 because I considered it an appropriate age to form a family, and also because I wanted to enjoy my youth, my parents, and my friends. I treated a lot of people like good *amigos*, but none of them interested me. We were not compatible. I wanted to get married with a person that would share my likes and ideas.

"My new life as a woman and a homemaker began. I left the house of style to dedicate myself to my husband and to my home. My new life gave birth to five children, four daughters and one son. I had a beautiful life and I was very happy after my children were born. A completely radical change came. My husband had decided for us to move to a ranch in Jalisco "Villegas." It was very difficult to be used to, even though I counted on the comforts. I was very happy with my five children and my husband, I didn't need anything else. But I wanted another type of life for my children. My son could learn a lot from the *campo*, but not my daughters. They had all grown up and I had to think on a future because I wanted the best for you that you study a career. Also, your father agreed with me. Like your father, I counted on permission of the U.S to obtain residence status. We got citizenship so all of you could study whatever you wanted to, in Mexico or in the U.S. The first time we entered California to get to know some places, and your father didn't like it there to live, and we returned to Mexico."

On August 3, 1999, we all came to Yakima where Antonia and my sisters María and Luz and I had to live and study. Now our parents only come to visit for three months every year, from August to November and then they return to Mexico.

"It's something very difficult to leave them alone because I would love for us to always be together like the family we are. Now is the day that everyone chooses a direction and forms their own family, this is the law of life, but I know it's for your own good and future. Because the good in all of you is mine. Now everyone will make their own destiny."

"Mi Gran Madre"

María y Antonia Caro

¿Qué hay detrás de una gran mujer buena y humilde? Es una gran jornada hecha historia. Mi dulce Madre, no hay palabras para describirla y decirle como la quiero y amo Mamita mía.

Mi gran Madre María es Isabel Sánchez, hija de Alejandro Sánchez y Serafí De Haro originarios de Colima, Colima. Ella nació en Colima, Colima y vivió también en Jalisco. Estudió Corte y Confección. Se casó con mí Padre Antonio Caro. Es la cuarta de cinco hijos y tiene cinco hijos.

La historia de una gran mujer empieza el 4 de noviembre de 1946 en Colima, Colima, donde fue su lugar de origen y vivió su niñez hasta los ocho años de edad. Mi Madre María Isabel describe su niñez como una de las más felices etapa. Ella recuerda que era una niña muy metiche y preguntona, siempre queriendo hacer lo que hacía su Madre Serafí De Haro y su Abuela materna Jesús Ramírez.

Estas dos mujeres fueron ejemplos a seguir para ella. Su Madre es ejemplo de una mujer paciente, comprensiva, amorosa que siempre le daba consejos y le inculcaba buenos modales y costumbres. Siempre quería lo mejor para sus hijos y también siempre ha sido admirada por hacer ricas comidas.

Mi madre describe a su abuela como un gran personaje en su vida y uno de los seres que más quiere, ya que fue la única abuela que conoció. Lamenta no haber conocido a sus antepasados, sus otros abuelos. Pero le da las gracias a Dios por haber conocido a su abuela Jesús Ramírez.

Recuerda los grandes momentos vividos de su niñez al lado de su abuela en el taller de costuras de las Martha's donde su abuela trabajaba. Ella la acompañaba algunas veces para que las dueñas del taller le dieran unos pedazos de tela para hacerle ropita a sus muñecas y su abuela le hiciera vestidos plisados. Ella admiraba a su abuela y le encantaba como le hacía sus vestidos. Y quería ser costurera cuando fuera grande.

Cuando tenía ocho años de edad sus padres se mudaron a vivir a Guadalajara, Jalisco. Para ella fue un cambio total de vida al cual pronto se adaptó. Su Escuela Leona Avicario le gustaba mucho al igual que la ciudad. Lo que más le gustaba era pasear con sus papás por la ciudad y que le compraran trastesitos de barro para hacer comida como su mamá. El momento de dejar las muñecas y los trastesitos de barro había llegado. La niña se convertía en mujer.

Las muñecas y trastesitos se cambiaban por libros de importancia. Cambió los juegos tontos por pensamientos de niña grande. A la edad de 15 años regresó a estudiar "Corte y Confección" a Colima con su abuela. Fueron los tiempos más felices que vivió en su juventud debido a las aventuras con sus compañeras de la escuela, las tardes de paseos con sus amigas de la colonia, las fiestas de la feria de la Villa y las tardeadas de los domingos. Y por fin su sueño de ser costurera, se le había hecho realidad. Era una modista.

Regresó a Guadalajara a la edad de 20 años y comenzó a trabajar en "La Casa de Modas Lupita" donde trabajó por 8 años. Conoció a mi papá Antonio. Con él pronto se comprometió y se casó el día de su cumpleaños, a los 28 años de edad.

Su nueva vida de señora de hogar comenzó. Dejó la casa de modas para dedicarse a su hogar. Su nueva vida dio fruto a 5 hijos, 4 mujeres y un varón. Su matrimonio era hermoso y todo marchaba muy bien. Pero después de que nacieron todos sus hijos hubo otro cambio de vida. Dejó la ciudad para irse a vivir al lado de su marido en un nuevo hogar en su rancho en Villegas, Jalisco. Le fue difícil adaptarse aunque contaba con todas las comodidades. Pero era muy feliz con su marido y sus 5 hijos. Todo era hermoso pero quería otra forma de vida para sus hijos. Su hijo podía aprender mucho del campo pero sus hijas no. Sus hijos ya eran grandes y era necesario pensar en su futuro. Ella creía que era mejor que todos estudiaran una carrera profesional.

Su marido pensaba igual. El contaba con permiso de residente de los EE.UU. y decidió arreglarles a su esposa y a sus hijos la residencia para que sus hijos estudiaran donde quisieran en México o en los EE.UU. El 17 de noviembre de 1998, toda la familia obtuvo el permiso de residencia de Los EE.UU. Visitamos algunas partes de California y a mi hermano y hermana mayor no les gustó California y nos tuvimos que regresar a México. El 3 de agosto de 1999, mis padres decidieron venir a Los EE.UU. a Yakima donde mis hermanas Antonia y Luz María y yo, María, tendríamos que quedarnos a estudiar. Ese año Luz no resistió estar separada de nuestros papás y se tuvo que regresar a México y por lo tanto Antonia y yo nos quedamos solas a vivir con una familia quien era amigos de mi padre. A pesar de que nos trataron muy bien, existía un vacío en mí que no podía llenar con nada. Me faltaba el amor de mi familia. Por lo tanto el 3 de marzo del 2000 mi hermano llegó a Yakima para quedarse con nosotras Antonia,

Luz quien había regresado y yo María, a apoyarnos hasta que terminemos de estudiar. Él nos apoya económicamente y le tenemos un gran respeto como nuestro segundo padre. Es un amor, a pesar de que es muy joven. Esta es una de las grandes enseñanzas que nuestros padres nos han inculcado, el apoyarnos y el estar unidos. Por eso, mis padres se quedan sin preocuparse en México y solamente nos visitan cada año por tres meses de agosto a noviembre y después regresan a México.

Es muy difícil que algunos vivan en México y otros en los EE.UU. porque nos queremos mucho. Pero mis padres piensan que los hijos no van a vivir con sus padres por toda la vida y además es por nuestro bien que estudiemos. Nos fue muy difícil soportar y superar este sufrimiento de vivir distanciados pero es la ley de la vida. Los hijos crecen y deben formar su propia vida. En la vida, no es toda felicidad o sufrimiento.

The people in the pictures are my mom, Delfina Sánchez and myself, Bertha Gutiérrez. In one of the pictures we sat on our sofa while the pictures were taken. The second we took next to our wall, with my mom holding a drawing of my grandpa. This drawing was actually a photo of my grandma and grandpa. But since my grandpa died when my mom was only 17, she wanted to have something of him. She loves that drawing. My mom is 39 with 5 children. My grandpa was in the picture. I guess my grandpa and my mom had a very good relationship. So when my grandpa died, she was heartbroken. That's why she made big mistakes in her life. My grandpa's name was Celestino Sánchez. He was born in Mexico, and was the 5th of 8 children. He loved his kids very much.

Mother's Hidden Secrets

Bertha Gutiérrez

On November 12,1964 a bright light shone and a beautiful baby girl was born. Catalina and Celestino Sánchez had their daughter who they named Delfina Sánchez. She was the fourth of eight children. For some reason she became Celestino's favorite daughter. But that love wasn't going to last for a long time.

At the age of four, Delfina goes with her older sisters to leave their father's lunch about two miles from their home where he worked out in his fields.

By that time, my grandpa was well respected. Because of that my aunts didn't get married so young. They got married when they were 20 or so. Back in those days that age was considered old. Back then girls were getting married as young as 12-13 years of age.

At a young age, my mom started to learn how to cook. She was lucky because her three younger brothers had to help out in the fields. My mom got to stay home. From what I was told my grandma was the main household. What she said had to be done. My mom told me that my grandma said that a well-educated lady could take care of her family at a very young age. One story my mom told me about is when she was 9 or 10. My grandma was trying to show her how to turn over the tortilla, and she couldn't, so my grandma grabbed her hand and placed it on the hot stove. That supposedly was to show my mom a lesson, kind of like a punishment. My grandma was the one who would spank all of the kids. I think that's why my mom liked my grandpa more. Because he always defended them. But all of this changed when my grandpa died.

At the age of 16, my grandpa was killed by a drunk driver. Because of this my mom's life changed for the worse. Since there was no father in the picture, guys started to look at my mom. Unluckily my mom fell in love at the age of 17, and from this relationship she had her first daughter. Because of this, my grandma was furious. She didn't want that grandchild or my mom. As a matter of fact she kicked her out of her house, and told my mom to go out and work to support herself and her kid. My mom didn't know what to do. My mom was a single mother. The guy left my mom after he heard he was going to be beaten up, possibly killed, by my grandma's brother because he had disrespected her family. So my mom was alone.

Because of this, my mom decided to give her baby away. But instead, my uncle told my mom to give him the baby, and he would take care of her. My mom, with no other choice, accepted. Then she left to the U.S. to make money to support herself and send money to her daughter. In 1982 my mom fell in love with Nereo Gutiérrez. They got married and in 1983 I was born. After me, they had two other daughters and a son.

Although my mom has gone through a lot of pain, through the death of her father, and having to give up her daughter because her mom didn't accept her, to the loss of her husband, she has managed. She has a great job and her kids are in school. One of them is going to make her happy because she will be the first girl to graduate from high school. That is me. Everything is pretty much going her way.

I want to thank my mom for everything she has done for me. I thank God for giving me a mom like her. Even through the hard times, she's been there. And I also want to thank my teacher for this assignment. Because of this interview, I found out things I didn't know about her. It made me realize that my mom has had it hard. But now it's up to us to help her out. So thank you.

My mom grew up in a middle class family. Even like this though, she didn't get a lot of education. As a child she was told lots of stories. Some of these stories she's told me. For example, she's told me that in her town there was a lady that got killed by her husband because he was jealous. So through the years when men would go to the river next to her home they would always see a beautiful lady with long black hair in a dress. But when they would try to talk to her she would disappear.

These kinds of stories get me nervous and make me think, *why we don't have things like that here?* It's weird when I hear my mom talk about things like that.

This is a picture of me and my mom, Jobita Torres. The picture was taken in my dining room. We took a bunch of pictures, with me, my Dad, Jose, and Mom. You will never catch me and my father this close unless we're posing for a picture. Me and my mother are close. We don't talk about everything but we do talk about the important things in life. She is always stressing about me furthering my education after high school. The dining room is where we get together and get our grub on. The family has never been completely together at the dining room table, it's too small and there are too many of us. There are eight of us. Five boys and three girls. Two older brothers and three older sisters, other than myself. I was the sixth to be born. Though most of my older siblings have gone their own way and made their own families, they still almost always come around. My three older sisters all live in Yakima and have children of their own. My oldest brother also lives in Yakima and has a family of his own.

In The Palm of Her Hands

Ricardo Torres

My mother, Jobita Hernandez, was born on July 23rd 1954, in El Platanal, Michoacán. She was raised in Guadalajara, Jalisco.

During this interview I thought a lot about myself. I thought about my mom and my family. I thought about what it would have been like had my parents not moved here, to the "land of opportunity," the United States.

As a little girl, my mom always had what she needed and received everything she wanted. My mom was the only girl and the youngest of three children. Her brothers were away and always working. She spent a lot of time with my grandma, Feliza Ochoa. She used to play with dolls and run around outside. My mother's childhood was easy.

My mom's brother lived away from home in a *rancho* called *El Capulín*, in Michoacán. There, at the age of ten, she met my father, José Torres. My dad didn't have much as a little kid. He was poor. But all that didn't matter to my mom. She would go back and forth from her home to the *rancho*. She would watch my dad race horses. Over the years she and my father grew close.

My dad's mom did not approve of my mom. She said that he would not be able to buy her all the things *a las que ella estaba acostumbrada*. My mom's parents didn't approve of my father, either. They didn't like the fact that my mom was young and involved with a guy.

But regardless of what both sides thought, in 1970 my dad asked for my mom's hand in marriage. My mom was 16 years old and my father was 19 years old. On February 12th 1970 at 1:00 p.m., my mom and dad were married.

Their first child was born in 1971. 1973 was the first year my dad came to the United States. My dad would go back and forth over the years. He would stay in the United States and go back every year to visit my mom and my brothers and sisters. My dad would send her money and write her letters when he wasn't with her and was working in the United States.

I did not know those letters existed up until about four years ago. I would have never thought there was a side to my father like this. In the letters he never forgot to mention us or the children that were born up to that point. In the letters he told my mom how much he loved her, and how he wanted her to move to the United States.

My uncle would tell my mom how dangerous it would be to attempt to come to the United States. But my mom didn't listen. She wanted to be with my dad. In 1985, after I was born, my mom came to the United States. She carried me in her arms. Though the immigration caught us the first time, we made it through the next morning at about 7:00 a.m. We stopped in California and that same day we made it to Washington.

We lived in the small town of Toppenish from 1985. My mom would have two more kids there. In 1991 we moved to Yakima, Washington.

I asked my mom:

How did you picture the United States before you came? "Nobody told me anything about the United States. Your father was the only one. He would tell me how much he wanted us to move with him. Your dad would always say how much we would benefit if we moved down here."

What do you like most about the United States? "I like the opportunities you and your brothers and sisters have. They're more than we ever had in Mexico. There are a lot more opportunities for Mexicans here."

What would you do different or change if you could go back? "I wouldn't change anything. The only thing I regret is not coming with your father the first time he asked in 1973."

My mom and my dad have been married for 31 years. My mom says, *Son muchos años pero poquito tiempo*. "They are many years, but very little time." My dad didn't think my mom would marry him because he was poor. *Mi ama dice que "eso no importaba"*. It wasn't important to her.

My brothers and I have put my mom through a lot. And now that I look back on it, I feel bad. I have never apologized to my mom. But writing this has brought me closer to her. I'm also one step closer to apologizing to her. I don't know what I would do without her. My mom is me. I see her attributes in me. The good ones and the bad ones. She's been my mom and dad, in a sense. I have never and probably never will be close to my father. She makes up for that, though. She's good at it, too. I think it's my mom's Mexican roots that make her so strong. She has never broken down. My mom carried me across the border in her arms and she has been carrying me ever since. Thanks to her, we're here now chasing our dreams.

On Sunday February 10th the pictures of Blanca Flores (me), with my mother, Adelaida Méndez, were taken. In none of these pictures can you see who is in the house. So I'll let you know that my mom's boyfriend, Joe Linger, was within a few steps watching a football game. Also my sisters, Yesenia and Maria, were sitting down watching, thinking that I should stop laughing. In half of these pictures we are in the living room and in the other half in the yard. In the pictures that were taken in the living room you can see a hallway that leads to the other rooms and bathroom. In some we are standing and in others just sitting on the carpet floor. In the pictures in the back yard you can see the brick fence, and behind the fence are my mom's Ford Runner and their Chrysler Van. You can't see my car behind the Ford Runner. In one picture my mother and I were talking about what the pictures were for. So I was telling her to remember. I said, "It's for a book that will be made with the questions that I asked you when I made it into a story of your life." She smiled, because the picture of us both will be beside her story for people to see our faces.

Mi Mama Buena, Comprensiva, Cariñosa, y Con Carácter

Blanca Flores

What my mom remembers of her childhood is that she was very a light-skinned little girl, who at the age of four, would play with a girl to jump from a *pretil*, a railing, and when they lived *en un altito*, on a hill, and she already had to help to *acariar agua*. One day my mom's little friend fell and hit herself on the face, and it was funny to my mom. She started laughing and soon they were both laughing, but they kept on jumping until after her friend stopped crying. Then my mom fell after she jumped and hit herself in the same spot. From that moment she decided that she would never have fun at other people's expense. Another thing that she remembers, is one night when she went to the bathroom, and a black *alacran* bit her and she felt *entumida*. She yelled and her mom saw the *alacran* and *abuelita* took it off of my mom because she couldn't see it.

My mother's story begins in Santa María, Michoacán, where she was born April 6, 1966. She was born to Angelina Sánches and Jesus Méndez. They were poor and lived in a little house. Her mother would work to help get money for the house and food. My grandma worked cutting limes, chile, tobacco and mangos, while accompanied by the sons of her oldest boys. My grandma had 8 children; 3 girls and 5 boys. She felt that they were poor because my grandpa didn't like to work other people's lands, only on his own.

The day came when my grandma *enfadada* of the life that she was living, left to the U.S. She *dejó* her husband and 8 children. She left her husband and children. Like there was no woman to clean. My mother, at 12 years old, and being the oldest girl, had to cook, clean, wash, and carry water to the house from a well with her other two sisters. My grandma's leaving was enough for my grandpa, and he took all the kids from school so they could help around the house, or on the land. *Girls in the house and boys outside.* My mom remembers getting hit by my grandpa because she wouldn't clean or do something at the house like she was supposed to, and she would go with her friends. She hated cooking (which she still doesn't like too much), and especially she hated not being able to attend school.

My grandma *regresó* to Mexico when my mom was 14 years old and took 7 of her kids to the United States, leaving the oldest boy Juan, with his father. My mom didn't want to leave. She said, *"Porque tenía un novio llamado Abel Cárdenas."* He wanted to marry her but my grandpa found out that she was planning on leaving with him because she didn't want to leave to the U.S. One of my mom's cousins told on her. So she started back home and left him. When she got home, she remembers my grandpa pulling her in by her long hair and dragging her into the house. The good thing is that my mom is so lovely that even though she loved that guy, she still says that she wouldn't have wanted things to be different because she has us girls.

While my grandma was gone my mom started to feel anger towards her mother for leaving them with her dad. To this day I still feel like there's a feeling of resentment by mom towards her mom because they get angry at each other very easily. My grandma would write to my mom and send her money but my grandpa never gave it to her. She later found out about this.

They left to the United States and lived in Canoga Park, California where my grandma put them all in school and worked at a restaurant. At the age of 16 my mom met a girl named Juana Flores and they became best friends. My mom would visit Juana at her house and met Juana's family. Since my mom still had an issue with my grandma, she would spend a lot of time at her friend Juana's house. She met Juana's brother, Salvador. They started dating and when they had 3 months together my mother left to Salvador's house to live with him. She later had a baby girl at the age of 17. Her friend Juana (who is my favorite aunt) told her to name her baby Blanca Estela.

Now at age 35 she has gone through a lot and has accomplished many things. For example, she became a legal resident and got a mortgage to buy a house. She also took her father from his house in Michoacán to try to save him from cancer (which she did with God's help) and made him a legal resident. He now is able to work and save money every year to go back to his home in Mexico to fix it up, and especially this helps him to get away from the cold that he doesn't like. Since my mother disapproves of her parents' disciplinary ways, she doesn't hit or pinch us. She said she hated her mother pinching her.

When I was 15 years old my mom and dad got divorced. She left my dad when I was 9 years old, taking me along with my 3 sisters. I remember spending holidays, or half of the holidays, and every weekend, with my dad and my family from his side. When I was 12 years old we moved to Washington and every summer after that year, 1995, my sisters and I would go visit my family and dad in California. We still do this. In 1998 she had my little sister Natalie Esmeralda Salinas from her second marriage. She is now divorcing from this marriage. But she has worked hard to support and raise us by working two jobs. She is finally settled down and happier than ever (which she deserves), living with her boyfriend Joe, in Moxee. She rents her house in Yakima. As of January 6, 2002, my sister Erica made her a first time grandma with a beautiful little girl named Joana Marisa Mendoza.

My mother and I have a great relationship. She trusts me and respects my decisions as I do hers. She always has us in mind when deciding. She makes us feel useful by asking our opinions, even if she has already made up her mind. I can always tell her the bad side to things if there is one, but she makes the final decision. We even have a joint account and I pay her bills and deposit her money and keep track of her money. She knows that I'd never take a dollar without asking. I don't know if every parent or child apologizes to each other after yelling at the other or getting upset at the other without probable cause. But that is one of the things that my mother and I always do, which is really good because this way we feel better later.

I think it is weird when I hear classmates saying that they better get to the mail before their parents because of their grades. My mother has never insisted on me getting good grades or even showing her my report card. *She knows what to expect from me without getting proof.* This is why I believe that I do good in school, because I do not have pressure to do good. It just comes naturally. The funny thing is that I'd like for her to ask me for my report card. She knows me so well that she doesn't need a report card to tell her about my accomplishments.

The two women in the picture are Daisy and Maria Hernandez. This picture was taken on February 22, 2002. This mother and daughter, as you see in the picture, have a very close and wonderful relationship. When the picture was taken, Maria had just arrived home from work at Memorial Hospital, and Daisy had just gotten home from school. This is one of the few times, between their busy schedules, that they especially look forward to. Maria and Daisy know the importance of spending time together as mother and daughter, and as friends as well. Maria encourages Daisy to be an abrecaminos and help out others in any way that she can. Daisy believes that her mother has been very helpful in teaching her the best. To Daisy, Maria is a true example of an abrecaminos.

La Estrella de mi Vida, La Primera Abrecaminos

Daisy Hernandez

Red lights stopping traffic. People on their way to work or school. On September 6, 1958, that light turned green for the first time at 10:30 a.m., giving way to the new life born that day. In Juchitlan, Jalisco, the always-on-the-go, Maria Consuelo Arroyo, was born.

Jesus Arroyo and Isabel Renteria married. The greatest example of love shone through them. Anyone could see how in love they were, and how perfect they were for each other. Their gentle and tender ways blessed the lives of those around them.

By the time of Maria's birth, Isabel and Jesus already had seven children, four boys and three girls. After her, Isabel had five more children, three girls and two boys. Sadly, her eleventh child, Castulo, died at six months. This left in order of birth: Chila, Chuy, Quiro, Alfredo, Esperanza, Atanacio, Estela, Maria, Adriana, Graciela, Reymundo, and Irma.

Maria's grandparents, Castulo and Emiliana, had a house next door to the family in San Ignacio. However, Maria never got the chance to meet Castulo since he died before she was born. Regardless, Maria enjoyed watching her own mother. She admired the way she was able to display the affection she had for Emiliana. It was the everyday little things that Isabel would do for Emiliana, such as bringing her flowers or a pop from the store. As insignificant as the item seemed to others, it was always given with love. This is a quality of her mother that Maria tried to give back to Isabel and Emiliana.

Now for having such a big family, Isabel did a good job of keeping them in order. Jesus also did his best. Every Sunday without fail was picnic Sunday. Her parents took ALL the kids to parks. And never was it the same ones. Jesus always found a new and different one. The family would spend all day swimming, eating, playing, and talking. Maria always looked forward to Sundays. This is one of her greatest childhood memories.

As a teenager, Maria was good at getting in at least a little trouble. Now the kids knew that if they asked their mom for permission to do something and it was denied, then it was useless to ask their father.

As a child, Maria wondered often why she couldn't do what her friends were allowed to do. But in her later years, Maria grew to appreciate her mother for looking out for her in that sense.

Maria was never denied the opportunity to talk to boys. Since she and her sisters were tomboys, boys just didn't really factor into her life much other than as companions, or friends.

All the kids were assigned chores, which they had to complete every day without fail. Maria was in charge of ironing. She detested very much having to iron tee shirts. So being the mischievous child that she was, Maria used to tear the shirts and stick them under the mattress. When the time came to iron again, there would be one less shirt to struggle with.

This little act of sin was nothing compared to the trouble she and Adriana gave to her mom one day. Isabel sent Maria to run an errand. Instead, Maria stopped at a neighborhood birthday party with her sister. Somehow her mom found out and she showed up. The girls raced home and hid under the bed. They knew not to hide but they couldn't help it this time. Adriana could not help laughing at Isabel, pregnant I might add, on her knees using a broom to try and scare them out. That incident taught them both a thing or two.

When Maria was sixteen, she moved to Guadalajara with her Aunt Eustolia and Uncle Miguel. He parents stayed in San Ignacio. Eustolia was her father's only sister. She wouldn't change moving for anything. Maria admired her aunt. Eustolia stressed the importance of education and the pursuit of a better life. Maria enjoyed the time she spent with them. She loved running errands with her uncle who spent all day talking to her.

At the age of seventeen and a half, Maria's life made a drastic turning point. Not only was she going to leave the city, but also the country. She had the choice of moving to Pasco, WA. or staying in San Ignacio. As much as she disliked the idea, Maria, Estela, and Adriana, started their journey into America with the company of their father. She felt very bad for leaving her mother behind, knowing how hard it would be without her, especially at that age.

Maria, her sisters, and her father, were brought across the border. The fear factor was not very high since at the time, the girls did not realize the danger. Looking back, they have all come to appreciate the woman who got them across safely.

When they arrived in Pasco, the girls had a choice of staying home or going to the fields. They, of course, chose the fields to try and raise enough money to bring to their mom and the rest of their siblings.

In the time that they were there, Jesus would allow them to go to the movies, visit with friends, and get out. Anything that would help them miss their mom a little less, not forget, but just soothe the aching caused by their separation. It took one year before they were able to bring the rest of the family. But Maria and her sisters were never happier than at the sight of their mother and siblings.

At the age of eighteen, Maria met Jose Hernandez. Little did she know that he would be the man she would marry. At the time,

Jose came to see her sister. Over the course of four months he started liking Maria. Finally he told her he liked her. Maria was uneasy about this since he did start out with the intent to win over her sister.

Jose eventually won her over. Maria worked nights about five miles from where Jose lived. Yet he would walk in the middle of the cold winter nights just to take her flowers or candy or maybe talk for a little while. This quality about him reminded her of her grandma and mother. She thought that their relationship would be a short-time thing, yet they haven't parted since.

Jose and Maria always talked of marriage and living together. Because of some circumstances, Maria was forced to run away. A little after this time, she got married. When asked if she would change anything, Maria would have liked to leave her house to get married.

Regardless of everything, Jose made Maria very happy. He made her feel complete, filling that missing void. She loved his humor and thoughtfulness. Jose would steal flowers from the neighbor's garden to give to Maria when he returned from work. They had little money, yet they made do. They would have enough for movies, but not enough for snacks. They would improvise and bring their own plastic containers full of food.

After two months of marriage, Maria discovered she was pregnant, but unfortunately she miscarried. Feelings of sadness and despair followed her for a long time. The sun came out for her again on the morning of September 15, 1981 when her oldest daughter, Claudia Elizabeth was born. Maria could not have been happier. When it came time to name her daughter, Maria remembered a big beautiful-eyed childhood friend she had. Never in her wildest dreams did she ever think her daughter would also have the same eyes.

Maria loves the qualities Claudia has. Always thinking of others before herself, feeling so secure about the things she does. Setting a goal for herself regardless of how unattainable it may seem and not quitting until it is achieved. She has the independence of her great grandmother, grand mother, and mother.

On April 30, 1984, spring showers helped a flower bloom. Maria gave life to Daisy that night. Maria has memories of Daisy smiling all the time. This caused laughter since she would smile and would show only gums since her teeth hadn't grown in yet. Daisy is a reminder of Maria's mother Isabel, and Grandmother Emiliana, with her thoughtfulness and compassion and need to protect others before herself, even though she is going crazy inside. She also looks like her mom, and in the mental way is much like her with her willingness to try anything, *well almost anything.*

The few times Maria got the chance to take her daughters to her mother, Isabel expressed her pride. She stated that Maria had the most beautifully educated and well-mannered children.

Sadly in 1986, Jesus called Maria to tell her that Isabel was extremely ill. Maria left her two daughters in Jose's care and traveled to Mexico from Pasco as soon as was possible.

On a rainy dark day, Isabel Renteria Arroyo was laid to rest. Sad and hurt, Maria could not help feeling a little pride as she looked around and saw all the people in attendance at the funeral. Her aunt, however, couldn't handle it and passed out.

Despite the tragedy, Maria and her family grew closer together. They helped each other out in so many ways. Jose also helped by trying to get her mind off the subject of her mother's death.

A few years passed and Maria gave birth to her last child. A boy named Jose was born on March 5, 1989 in Yakima, WA. He was a tiny baby boy but he learned fast. His little legs had him walking at ten months. His qualities of stubbornness are very much like his father's.

In her thirties, Maria moved to a new world. Montgomery, Alabama was a place like no other. She had to overcome the obstacle of learning to communicate in English. Tornadoes and severe rainstorms later, the family returned to Yakima once again.

At thirty-nine Maria had the scare of her life when she discovered a lump on one of her breasts. Tests and tears later it proved to be nothing. But Maria never appreciated every moment of every day more than after that experience. At forty years of age, Maria hurt her back at work. This resulted in depression, feelings of despair and helplessness. In the three years following, Maria had two surgeries to help correct the problem from which she is still recovering.

With forty-three years of experience and success, Maria has remained very humble. She has raised three children who have overcome many obstacles in their time. She has learned many new skills that most don't care to learn. Always looking for ways to improve herself, Maria is a great example of a self-made woman.

She is a woman of greatness, who should have nothing go wrong in her life. When others would have thrown in the towel, Maria would have raised the bar higher. She sees the silver lining in every cloud. She is the good in everything, meanwhile bringing out the kind-hearted in everybody. She illuminates her surroundings with her virtuous ways.

Any regrets Maria has are related to her education. She has a great desire to finish getting her GED. She is always encouraging her children to go to college, regardless of what is required financially to get them there. Knowing her longing to finish, her children and husband encourage her to go to school. She went back and started taking classes to help get her GED.

Time and time again, Maria tries her hardest to better herself and her family. She is a wonderful woman to be admired, with a vast knowledge of life. She is breaking the chains. *Abriendo caminos donde no hay entrada.*

On this day I sit proud of what I've become. As I look to my left and then to my right, I see I have the best parents ever, realizing that without them, I wouldn't be much. I stand proud of my mother who is so strong, yet so sensitive. She stands high as the head of the household. My father, on the other hand, stays home and watches over the kids. This is something different, yet unique, about *mi familia*. My father's attitude and heart seems hard like a stone. He looks tough, like nothing has ever knocked him down. I know deep inside there is a weakness to be discovered. My mom's emotions seem to show through as a very emotional person. They say they love you unconditionally. They say they will always be there through thick and thin, and sure enough, they are. They offer the most love, and even give up their own life for you, yet they are the ones we hurt the most.

Soñando con Los Ojos Abiertos
(Dreaming with Eyes Wide Open)

Claudia Guzmán

On June 15, 1950 in Guadalajara, Jalisco, a child with the given name of Victoria Gutiérrez was born to Maria and Aurelio Gutiérrez. She was meant to be the first daughter, therefore she stood on the highest step as head of her siblings yet to come.

As a child she played house with dolls made out of the old

remains of corncobs. She never attended school because her parents didn't have enough money, plus her father always said, *La escuela no es para las mujeres. Las mujeres son a más de casa y nada más, atienden a sus hijos y a su marido. School isn't for women. Women are for the house and taking care of the children.*

At the early age of ten she had to help her mother with chores around the house, making breakfast, lunch and dinner, while her mother was busy caring for her younger children.

As she became older and grew into adolescence, lots of responsibilities came into place. When she turned 14 she had to go out and get a job. What her parents made was not enough to support the family. She cleaned and cooked at rich ladies' houses. She didn't make much but it put food on the table. Victoria worked with real nice and loving ladies. As the housekeeper, she had to go out and buy groceries. Victoria did not know how to read or write or even count. The ladies actually became her teachers. For now Victoria could count, read and write. She was very fortunate for this to come her way.

As a teenager Victoria was very shy and frightened to do a lot of things. She always respected her elders and did as she was told. She got along great with her parents. Her parents thought she was a blessing to the family. She helped them out a lot. They couldn't ask for more than what she had given them. Victoria suffered a lot as a teenager. She said they were her hardest years. Her life was not easy. This is not how she would have wanted to live but she really didn't have a choice. You can't pick out your family, just like you can't pick out your kids. *It's blessed by God, as it's God's will.*

Along the way she had her good times as goes a roller coaster. When she turned 18 through 19 she started partying and going out a lot. By the age of 20 she realized that she could no longer be afraid to do new things, to be alone, and to stand up for herself.

On 1974, at the age of 24, Victoria crossed the border for the first time with a *coyote* from Tijuana to California and finally to Oregon, her destination. There she worked for a lady in a nursery home. It was just her luck that same year they sent out a report to where she was living and immigration came and took her back to Mexico.

In 1975, the following year, she crossed the border once again with a *coyote,* and returned to Oregon. After a year or so, in 1976 she met a man who she worked with and fell in love and married him in Vancouver, WA. After three years or so, Victoria divorced without an explanation. Even though now she was legal, she returned to Guadalajara because she was not happy.

On June 22, 1979 she married a man whom she had known since they were kids, when they only lived a block apart. Who would have ever known her love was right in front of her? When she got married, something inside of her told her he was the right man. He was someone to live with the rest of her life and grow old with.

That same year they packed all their belongings and returned to the U.S., full of hopes and dreams, to live a better life. She planned to work hard to make money for herself and to send to her family in Mexico. Her dream was of returning to Mexico someday, not rich, but with something to live off of. Leaving her house and her family was the hardest thing, but thinking of a better life brought tears of happiness and sadness all at once. It was a scary feeling, thinking of not returning, and wondering if she would ever see her parents again.

Year after year passed without seeing her family, just communicating through the telephone and letters filled with money for them. Within 12 years, Victoria had 5 children whom she adores, 2 sons and 3 daughters. They bring happiness and a reason to live and keep her going forward, with whatever surprises life brings her way.

Now, at age 51, having lived half her life in the U.S., all she ever wanted was realized with the exception of returning back to her land. Seeing her family once or twice a year is not enough. Somehow this place keeps her grounded. *Staying forever in Mexico is a mission impossible.* Here is where she belongs and all her tough years are finally over. Now she has her own family to raise and take care of.

Victoria is very happy, she has fulfilled everything she has set her mind to, and even gone beyond. She's not mad for not returning, but grateful that she opened many doors. This place had made her what she is now and given her everything she's got with great effort.

When asked what her new dreams were, she answered, to see all her children in college and follow their dreams wherever they take them.

March 22, 2002

My Aunt Martha is with me in this photo. Her name is Martha Sánchez Martínez. When my teacher came to my house he asked about my mother, but I told him the real history about my mother. He didn't know. So the day he took the photographs he knew everything. Then he was talking with my cousins and my sister. When he started to take the photographs we tried to smile, but it was impossible.

Dolor, Lágrimas, y Sufrimiento

Erika Hernandez

Hola.

Mi nombre es Martha Sánchez Martínez. Nací el día 30 de agosto de 1974 en Ixtapan Zihuatanejo Guerrero, México. A los 12 días de nacida tuve la mala fortuna de perder a mi madre la cual perdió la vida a causa del parto. A causa de esto, mi padre sin saber que hacer conmigo recurre a la ayuda de su cuñada con la que duré 7 meses viviendo despues me recogió mi abuelita madre de mi madre con la que viví hasta los 2 años. Mi padre con la ayuda de mis hermanos dicidieron regresarme al hogar donde nací ahí pasé mi infancia junto con mis 7 hermanos. En ese entonces deseaba tener a mí madre junto a mi para que me apoyara y me diera su cariño ya que de mis hermanos no tuvieron ninguna de las dos cosas, me mandaban a la escuela y al regresar me ponían a hacer los que haceres del hogar lavar, ropa, hacer comidas, tortillas, etc.

Todavía recuerdo que mis hermanas se la pasaban con sus novios y se empenzaron a ir una por una hasta quedar yo solita. Me acuerdo que lloraba porque me sentía muy sola ya no sabía que hacer con mi vida así trascurrió el tiempo y al llegar a la secundaria en mi grado escolar e imité a mis hermanas y me fui con un novio que conocía a la edad de 13 años y esto fue a causa de que no aguantaba a mis hermanos y el maltrato de mi papá pensé entonces que al irme con el me iba ir bien en mi vida.

Emigramos a los Estados Unidos y mi eulocausto se guía igual pero me equivoqué ya que a los 14 anos me enbarajé por primera vez y al cumprir 15 años ya tenía a mi primer bebé al que le puse por nombre Marco Antónío, pero mi sufrimiento fue el mismo porque me seguían maltratando.

Regresamos a México de vacaciones un día estando en una fiesta de cumpleaños mi esposo él embriagado tomo una pistola diciendo que nadie lo queria se dio un balazo en la cabeza.

Yo me quería volver loca en ese instante pero agarrando fuerza de no se dónde decidí seguir adelante con mi vida y decidí irme a vivir con mi suegra junto con mi hijo pero se portaron muy mal conmigo me quitaron todas mis pertenencias y aparte de eso me querían volver loca ya que me ponían debajo de mi cama ropa ensangrentada de mi esposo porque me culpaban de su muerte.

Al trascurir un año dicidí emigrar nuevamente a los Estados Unidos y junto con mi hijo recibí desprecios de la gente y hasta mis propios hermanos ya que no tenía el apoyo familiar y muncho menos de los amigos.

Pasó el tiempo me sostuve como pude, gracias a Dios, y a las bendiciones de mi madre transcurrieron 5 años después de la muerte de mi esposo y decidí juntarme a vivir con un hombre para que mi hijo no sufriera el desengaño de no tener padre.

Pero de nada sirvió ahora me trataba mal a mi hijo y a mí lo golpeaba y lo matrataba, al igual que a mí le pedía a mi Dios que me diera fuerzas para seguir con este sufrimiento entonces pense que al darle un hijo a esta persona iba a cambiar todo pero nuevamente me equivoqué todo siguió igual ahora él solamente tenía ojos para su hijo.

Un día pensé para que tanto sufrir y sufrir y me alejé de su lado para nunca más volver ahora quisiera regresar a mi infancia y juventud y volver a estudiar y vivir mi niñez pero al lado de mi madre ya que en tiempo de dolor y sufrimiento siempre está a tu lado.

Por eso les pido que a los que tienen a sus madres que las cuiden mucho ya que es lo más hermoso que nos dio Dios en esta vida porque el cariño lleva una madre no se compara con nada le pido de todo de corazón a mi madrecita querida y Dios que me bendigan en mi nueva relación en la cual espero realizar mi felicidad junto con mis hijos.

The two people you see are part of a *familia*. María Abúndiz is my mother. In another photo I'm in the middle, and next to me is my father Eudoro Abúndiz. These beautiful, and at the same time, historical pictures, were taken on February 6, 2002 by my photographer/teacher. The three of us are getting ready to go to church. Maria and Eudoro have been married for 33 years and have 9 wonderful children. *Sus nombres*: Ramón, Nora, María, José, Trinidad, Jaime, Zoila, Cleme, y Acensión. With their older children married or moved out, María has a daycare at home while Eudoro works in the fields. María's parents, Aurelio y Clementina Espindola, and Eudoro's parents, Acensión y Trinidad Abúndiz, must have brought their children up right as hard working people, not giving up as hard working people, not giving up when the going gets tough. While María is now 53 years old, and Eudora is 54, there's no doubt that they have done a darn good job raising their own kids. The background of the photo is part of their humble home where they graciously open the doors to you and *tu familia*.

For the Love of Her Children

Clementina Abúndiz

It wouldn't be easy, but she knew it had to be done. Her children were first on her mind. Once there was enough money she would send for them. All that she went through was for them. María wanted a better life for her children. This is what happened. This is her story.

María Espindola was born January 6, 1947 in Los Ojos de Agua, Michoacán, México to Clementina and Aurelio Espindola. As a child she lived a beautiful life, even though she unfortunately was only able to go to school only until the 2nd grade. Regularly she would play hide-n-go-seek, dolls, and whatever she could make a toy with, whatever was available.

In her teen years María helped her mother around the house. Hardly being able to ever go out, she made sure to have the house chores done. One and only one time can she remember her dad taking her to a dance with her brothers and sisters. During this period of her life, never did she have enemies. Sure there might have been girls that she didn't like or who didn't like her, but they managed to keep their distance. Her regular daily outfit was a dress. Never did she wear shorts or pants, it was always dresses.

On May 22, 1968 my father's mother's dream came true. María married Eudoro, her childhood friend. María Abúndiz Espindola she became. She was only 19 years old.

In the year 1976 María and her husband took a big risk. They would attempt to cross the border to the United States. Leaving her five children with her mother was hard, but having to cross the border would be even harder.

María, Eudoro, and her brother Jose, attempted to cross during the night. They weren't alone; there were many people that were also following the guide who would help them cross the border. Everyone walked for a good distance until they all got to a spot where they would have to wait for the immigration to trade posts so they could run and cross the border. It was cold. María waited. Everyone waited and waited. The night had passed and still no signs of the immigration changing posts. It wasn't till early morning when they got their chance. It was quite a distance that they would need to run so they had to be quick.

María ran and ran till she could no more. Her legs fell from under her and she fell to the ground. Thankfully her brother and her husband were close by and they were able to pick her up and carry her, one on each side of her. It's as if she was floating on air, she was just moving her legs. Finally they approached a huge brick wall that surrounded many houses. Behind them was the vehicle ready to take them where they chose. This climbing over the fence and loading the little pickup had to be done quickly for fear of the neighbors seeing and reporting them all. As soon as you climbed over the fence you were on United States Territory. María wasn't sure whether to shed tears of joy or of sadness. Happy to have made it, but sad to know her children were so far away.

In the little pickup that had to fit fifteen people in the back, María and Eudoro made it to Dinuba, California. When María and Eudoro first arrived some ladies thought they were runaway boyfriend and girlfriend since they had all of a sudden appeared without any kids or anything. From there they went to Mabton, Washington where they stayed for 2-and-a-half months, and then permanently moved to

Yakima, Washington. Occasionally they moved for work, but they came back always to Yakima.

Before María ever crossed the border to the U.S., she thought of the country as being beautiful and very different from Mexico. Boy was she right. Remembering back, the first thought she had when she crossed over to the U.S. is this: *gusto que ya estaba en este lado.* At the same time sadness because her children were far away from her.

The first job she had when she came to the United States was picking asparagus. Her back would kill her after a day's work in the fields, and when she first started, all she had for shoes was sandals. The first thing she bought with her first paycheck was a pair of tennis shoes. One of the most embarrassing moments she lived through was when she got her first check-up with a doctor in the U.S. María wasn't used to being looked at and examined. This is something she would have to learn to get used to and up to this day still needs to.

One very special *lucha*, or struggle, that she was able to overcome, was when she was studying to become a citizen of the United States of America. María remembers studying long and hard for it. All the studying paid off in the end when she received her citizenship. Now with each child she had she felt happy, *contenta, gustosa por ya tener mi hijo e hija que estaba esperando.* Overjoyed to have another child *y más que nada contenta, agradecida con Dios porque salieron todos mis hijos bien de salud.* If María were given the chance to go back to the past and change something she would probably go back to her youth and change things so that she wouldn't have any family problems or health problems now in the present time.

A dream that María still holds dearly in her heart is to see that all her children finish their studies. This way they will have a better future than she and her husband did.

María went through all of the hardships for the love of her children. If it weren't for the sacrifices she made for us, I probably wouldn't be here right now. Though right now I can't repay her, I still have a whole life ahead of me where I can thank her for all that she has done for me. *Muchas gracias madre, que Dios te guarde y te cuide, por todo lo que has hecho por tus hijos, por el gran amor que tienes por ellos.*

My mom, María Luisa Cortés and I are the only people in the pictures. In one picture I have my arm on my Mom's shoulder, like having a conversation with my friend. We are laughing and having a good time together. In one picture I'm hugging my mom very strong, a little serious, showing that I love her a lot. She is hugging me from my hips. In the other one we are continuing with the conversation. We are looking at some old pictures, reminding me when I was little, when she was working at a restaurant in Mexico. She is always working at restaurants, having a lot of friends and doing the best that she can do. She is letting me go to school to get my education. There is a picture of me taking my first communion. I was 10. We lived in Manzanillo. The church is called Sagrado Corazón. My godparents, Aurora and Mauricio Barela, took me to a restaurant before the ceremony. We came here in 1999 from Madric, Colima, Mexico. After finishing my secondary school the objective of coming here was to come to my brother's wedding. My mother, father, brother and I were expecting just to come for vacations and go back to Mexico, but my mom liked it here, and she decided to stay with her family in California until we came to Yakima, Washington.

"Estamos Reunidos Aquí"

Francisco Galeana

Mi mamá nació el 3 de Noviembre de 1959 en un pueblo en las costas de Michoacán, llamado Achotan. Mi abuelita me contó que cuando ella nació era tan pequeña que cabía en una caja de zapatos. Cuando mi mamá nació ella tenía el pelo lasio y color negro, los ojos color cafe y su piel era muy blanquita. También era muy travieza y le gustaba jugar canicas desde niña. Siempre fue muy inteligente y cariñosa con su madre Maria M. Guadalupe y su padre Juan Cortés. Era muy consentida y caprichosa ya que era la primera hija de aquellas humildes personas, la "familia Cortés" para ese entonces vivian bien. Nada hacia falta, pero, poco a poco la familia fue incrementando hermanas y hermanos. Incrementaron la familia, mi mamá como toda niña normal iba a la escuela, jugaba y se divertía como cualquier otra niña, pero con la llegada de más hermanas tuvo que dejar sus estudios por que sus padres no podian sequir pagando para que ella fuera a la escuela. Ella era la mayor, entonces tuvo que trabajar para que sus hermanos lograran lo que ella no pudo logar. A sus 6 años ayudaba a su madre lavando y planchando ropa ajena para sacar dinero ya que su padre solo tenía unas pequeñas tierras las cuales cultivada y cosechaba para vender una parte y la otra dejar para comer en la casa, pero esto no era suficiente para los 6 o7 hermanos en su familia.

A los 16 años empezó a trabajar en la cuidad de Manzanillo Colima. con una amiga a la cual le pagaba renta. Limitandose así a salir y divertirse en bailes, conciertos, y cines. Su felicidad solo era el ver a sus hermanos graduados de la escuela con buen trabajos y que no sufrieran lo que ella estaba pasando.

A los 20-22 años conoció a un hombre el cual esperaba. Se enamoró, se casaron y ella ya no trabajaba. El ayudaba a su madre y hermanos cuando llegaron los hijos, ella solo se dedicaba al aseo y cuidado de sus hijos. Los problemas y plietos surgieron por ellos.

El tiempo pasó y su marido fue despedido a causa de una disputa entre él y su capitan. Fue despedido y le dieron poco dinero de pensión, al ver esto mi mamá decidió cruzar de nuevo la frontera, pero ahora con sus hijos y esposo y con mucha ayuda de sus hermanas. Nuestros familiares nos ayudaron y nos consiguieron un trabajo. Otra discución hubo entre mi mamá y mi padre porque él se emborachaba varias veces y por causa de eso tuvieron que separarse. Mi padre salió a México. Todo fue peor para él y decidió volver a Yakima con nosotros y hasta ahora todo marcha un poco mejor. Mi mamá está un poco más felíz porque todos estamos reunidos. Yo la quiero mucho y la quedre siempre por todo el esfuerzo y cariño que nos a dando.

My parents are visiting from Tepic, Mexico. They arrived a few days ago. When I look at these pictures and I see my parents and me together, I feel like I can express my feelings to them, especially to my dad. Since I was little I was very affectionate with my mom. I used to kiss and hug her but I never did that with my father. It was different, and difficult, not only for me but for him too. I loved him but I was embarrassed to tell him how much I loved him. They are just visiting, but now things have changed. I'm mature enough to tell him that I love him and I am not embarrassed to tell him. My parents are going back to Tepic, Mexico in about 15 days. I don't want them to leave but they have to. I have these pictures with me, and even if they are going back away from me, it is like if they are going to be closer than ever.

Los Recuerdos de Mi Madre

Antonio Ruíz

I met my mother again this spring after two long years. She was getting off of the plane that had just arrived from California. I started crying when I saw her in her long dress with a scarf around her neck. *Qué felicidad*, I said in a low tone. I can't believe I'm with her again.

I have been here in Yakima for almost three years, living with my brother and two sisters, going to school and thinking abut her, about what she is doing in Mexico. She has been working with my father in those big plains, *los llanos*, that my father had bought for us, so we could spend our lives working them. My mother was coming from these fields where my father wanted all of his sons to grow and to harvest the sugar cane, the chilies, and the corn. My brothers and I were waiting anxiously for them to come. We were working part-time here in Yakima, and attending school, so when they came they would have a place to live.

187

There are no words to express the love for a woman, especially if this woman is your mother. The love for your mother is the most precious thing in the world, and if you lose it, you will never get it back.

My mother was born in Tehuantepec, Michoacán, on June 14th of 1956. Her parents are Antonio Martínez and Eliza Lazo. They lived in a little town with a population of approximately 100 inhabitants. Almost everybody was related, one to each other, except for a very rich family that owned a *hacienda* at the *orillas del pueblo*. When my mother was born, she wasn't born in a hospital. A woman called a *partera* helped my grandmother to deliver her. My mother was the eldest of eight brothers and sisters. My mother's childhood was as everybody else's in her town. Like any other girl of her age, my mom played with dolls made up of old rags that my grandmother didn't use any more. The girls that were very, very poor had to play with toys made out of pumpkins. The *trastesitos* that she used to play with were pieces of broken glasses from some windows. Mud was one of her favorite things to play with. She and her friends used the mud to build castles and dolls to play with after jumping on the *charcos de agua* on the streets when the rain was over.

School was a problem for her at that age. She never liked school and never got good grades. But her dream was to become a nurse and work in the hospital helping people. She attended school in the morning and for about two hours in the evenings. Some of her best friends were Hilda, Elva and her cousins. Since she didn't like school, she and her friends would skip classes and go to eat some guavas at a nearby creek. She was a little wild, and one of her hobbies was to go and visit dead people at the cemetery.

When she was eight years old her family decided to leave the town and look for a better place to live. They moved to a different state. Her mom's family moved to San Luis de Lozada, Nayarit. My grandparents, my mom, and her brothers and sisters, together with my grandfather's family moved to Comala in the State of Colima. They lived there for about six years. When they were living in Colima, my grandfather came to the U.S. and started sending them money. My grandmother was very busy doing the home labors, so my mom had to take care of her younger siblings.

In Colima she went to Benito Juarez Elementary School, and her dream about being a nurse was the only thing she had in mind. She graduated from Benito Juarez Elementary School and the same year my grandmother received a letter from her dad telling her to move to

San Luis de Lozada. They left Colima and went to Nayarit when my mom was 14 years old.

Her life in Nayarit changed radically. She didn't attend school any more and instead, she would help my grandmother with the house chores. Her responsibilities were more now and one of them was to *sacar agua* from the wells. She was very naughty one time. She said, "I was hungry and didn't know how to cook very well yet, so the easiest thing for me to do were enchiladas, but like I was still learning how to cook, and I put the tortillas to fry in water instead of putting them in oil. My mom was angry and after making me eat the enchiladas, she grabbed a cord and spanked me on the calves until I cried." But even that wouldn't stop her.

My mom was beautiful and had a lot of boyfriends when she was young, but the only man that she really loved was my dad. After dating for about a year, my mom ran away with my dad. My grandparents were angry and after she returned with my dad to the town, my grandparents wouldn't see her or talk to her. Finally, they forgave her, and they planned the wedding. My mom was 21 years old, and when she was 22, she had her first baby. My mom had two other children and then me. I was the fourth, and the last one.

When my mother was 28 my grandparents moved to the U.S. with all my aunts and uncles, but not my mother because she and one of her brothers were married with families of their own. Her brother was living in the U.S. already. She missed her family lots and it wasn't until one of my uncles got his citizenship that she was able to see them again. Then my uncle helped my grandparents to get their Resident Cards, so she could travel to visit them again. That was the happiest day of her life. Unfortunately, she couldn't see all of her brothers and sisters because not all of them were legal yet, but she was happy to see her part of the family again.

These photos were taken in my living room, a living room decorated by my mom. There are plants all around the room. There are also photos of the whole family, of cousins, aunts, and other relatives. There's pictures that were taken many years ago. There is also a black sofa with maroon curtains. There is a big cloth embroidery of the Virgin Mary hanging on the wall. There are two photos on the wall that contain two special persons in my life. The first one is my mother, Maria Ana Mendoza, a mother who loves and helps her family when they are in need. The second person is Marino Mendoza, my father, who has had a tough life. There is one special photo; it's the one where my mother is holding a picture of my quinceañera, which was on Feb 13, 1999, a Mexican tradition, and a date that I will never forget.

The Life of Two Wonderful Women

Laura Mendoza

In the countryside of the State of Guerrero, Mexico, there is a little town known as Los Sauces. In the 1920's the town was really small. Everyone that lived in that little town knew each other. On July 2, 1925 Pedro Fernandez and Josefina Brito had a beautiful little girl by the name of Petra Fernandez Brito. She was raised in the same house where she was born. Petra only went to the second grade because there were no federal schools.

At 8 years old she enjoyed singing and dancing. Soon her favorite food became beans and tortillas. While entering her teenage years she felt it was time to help her mother with the house chores. She helped her mom clean the house, and cook. When she reached 14 years of age she fell in love with her neighbor, whose name was Pedro Barrera. After a year of dating they decided to get married. She was only 18 years old when she had her first child, and went on to have ten more, but 4 died. Then on December 26, 1960, they had a baby girl. They then decided that this beautiful little girl would be the last baby they were going to have. They named her María Ana Barrera Fernández. Time went by and Petra still couldn't get used to the major change of getting old.

María continued growing and played with balls, rocks, flowers, and *olotes*, or little dolls, made from husks of corn. Just like her mother, she also grew up in the same house where she was born. Just like any other child she also had dreams. She dreamed of becoming a pre-school teacher. During her teenage years, she enjoyed going to *posadas*, dances, parties, and playing basketball at the park. It was traditional for the mother to escort her daughters to the dances. In order for her to go out to have fun she had to do all the house chores. She had to go get water from the well (about 10 minutes away from the house), feed the pigs, water the plants, and sweep the house patio. Like any other teenager she continued going to school. She loved going to school and had dreams of being very successful in life. Finally she was close to making her dreams come true by going to college, which was named "Escuela Normal Particular Jesus H. Salgado," where she was going to get her degree as an elementary teacher.

This college was private and she had to pay for tuition. Her older sisters and brothers would send her money to pay for the cost of tuition. It was a big change to her mother because the college was about 30 minutes away from her town. But all that Petra wanted was for her daughter to receive an education she never had a chance to get. She stayed in a dorm room with other girls. Every weekend she would go to her home town to see her mother and father. While she was there she would clean the entire house, change the beds, wash the floors, wash all the clothes, and cook. Then at age 18 she fell in love with a man by the name of Marino Mendoza. They then decided that they wanted to get married, so Marino asked his mother to go ask for Maria's hand in marriage, but his mother didn't want to go because they didn't have the money to organize a wedding. So they decided to elope. They then decided to live at his mother's house. María then decided to leave her school behind even though she only had 6 months more before receiving her degree. About 15 days later they got married by the law. It took them that long because María's mother didn't want to give her her birth certificate because she was still mad at María's actions to leave with Marino.

About 1 month later they decided to go to the United States to make more money. On February 1981 they crossed the border for the first time. They had to walk about 3 hours, then run across the sierra for 30 minutes, then ride on the trunk of a car for one hour and a half. Then they would open the trunk and be put on the front seat of a different car, then from there the guy would drive them to their house where they were going to pay a total amount of 300 dollars. Maria wanted to see if what she was told was true *El dinero se barre en los Estados Unidos*. But soon she found out that it was all lies. When she started at her first job she only got paid $3.35 an hour, which was not much. When she received her first paycheck she was really happy because it was money that was made from her own sweat and hard work. It was because her parents never wanted her to get a job as a teenager; they only wanted her to dedicate her time to her schoolwork.

They lived in California in a town known as Santa Ana, in a small room in Marino's brother's house. They lived there for four years. In those four years they had 2 kids. They then had to return to Mexico because Marino's mother was really sick. While in Mexico they decided to get married by the church. That was because according to the Catholic Church they had to be married by the church in order to go into the room of the sick person, because if they were not married then it was a sin. So on April 1986 they got married by the church. About four months later they had already spent all the money they had so they needed to go back to the United States. Since the two kids had been born in the United States, Marino's sister went to pick them up in Tijuana and drove them through the border.

However, Marino and María still didn't have papers so they had to pass the border the same way they did the first time. But this time the Immigration saw them and told them to go back. If they decided to go back they would be at risk of getting arrested by the Mexican police who would hurt them. So they then decided to try crossing, but got caught and put in jail for a few hours. As soon as they got out they tried crossing again because they had to get to the other side to their kids. They finally made it across and gathered with their children who were in Santa Ana. They lived there for a few years. Maria had a dream of buying a house of her own. In 1988 they had another baby boy. Then in the year 1989 the company "IE Sisten" closed, which was the company where Maria was working so she lost her job. Without a job she then applied for unemployment, which she received for about a year.

They managed to live a normal life with little money. Then in 1990 the company where Marino was working filed for bankruptcy. Then a few months later Marino got really sick and was in the hospital for about two months. In those months María was worried because they didn't have much money to pay the hospital bills. He was able to recover from his illness and was able to return to his daily life. Then in March 1990 Marino and María decided to move to another city where there were more job opportunities. They moved to Buena and worked in the fields. When the season of work ended they decided to go back to Mexico, because they didn't have a job. Then in 1991 they moved back to California until the work season in Yakima started.

In September 1991 they moved to Yakima. They didn't have any family except for one of Marino's brothers. So they stayed in his garage for a few months. Then on November 1991 Maria's dream came true. They bought a house and have been living there for the past 10 years.

Later in 1993 they had another child, and in 1998 they had their last baby girl. María only had one big dream, which is that her kids be successful. The one thing she would change from her past was to go finish her career because she felt like she let her parents down since they had big hopes for her. She lived every moment of her life facing all those challenges coming her way. The biggest challenge was the death of her loving father, Pedro Fernandez, who died in December, 2001. She felt like it was the end of the world, crying and suffering, but at the same time trying to go on with her life. She soon learned to go on with her life keeping him in her heart.

In these pictures are my mother (Graciela Farias), my father (Miguel Farias), and me (Cesar Farias). In one picture my mother holds a picture of our family. I stand next to her proudly (by her, meaning my mother). I'm also proud to be a part of this family, where there are lots of us. One of my favorite pictures is one with my father. We both stand together with one hand hugging each other. This picture says a lot to me. My dad is smiling in this picture. He never smiles in pictures. My dad has worked since the day we came to Washington. He gave me everything I have needed and wanted. He disciplines me at the needed time which helps me. In these pictures I feel proud holding one part of my family in my hands and the other part in my heart. I love every single person in a different way. We get mad at each other, but knowing that we carry the same blood in our veins, we are always sorry.

With My Mother, Graciela Farias

Cesar Farias

Visiting the place where my mother was born and raised was fun. It was the first time I had gone back to Mexico since I was brought to the U.S. Now 17 years old and seeing the land, the ranch where I was born as well. I met some of my relatives for the very first time. El rancho was not what I had in mind. I liked it though.

This ranch was not like any other. It was like opening my eyes for the very first time. The two weeks that I was there seemed like just a couple of hours. There can never be enough time to see everything I had missed. I stayed in the same house where my mother was raised. When I was there it was *el tiempo de las aguas*. This time means the rainy season. The land was really soft and muddy. Riding the horses was the funnest. I would go and help my uncle, Antonio, bring the cows every night to get them ready to milk the next morning. Milking cows for the first time ever was really interesting. I had never done it or even drunk the milk straight from the cow. I had the best time while I was there. I will go again.

My mother was born in a small ranch near Coalcoman. Tehuantepec, Michoacán, México to be exact. Her full name is Graciela Sánchez Reyna. Interviewing my mother was difficult for me. *No se porque, pero no puedo explicarlo.* I asked many questions. Some were answered and some were not.

As a little girl, my mom was *morena* with curly hair and *gordita* too. Playing marbles with my uncles was one of her favorite things to do when she had free time, which was not very often. The other was to play baseball. We would fill a sock with sand and use it as a baseball. We didn't have enough money to buy or waste the little we had for stuff we didn't need. *Asi nos decía tu abuelita.* I guess my grandma was very corajuda. My grandma's full name was Soccoro Reyna Gomez. She and my grandpa, Roman Sánchez Leyva, had 11 kids. Seven girls— Adela, Yolanda, Virginia, Martha, Ofelia, Esther, and my mother and four boys, Antonio, Ramon, Fernando, and Jorge.

My mother met Miguel Farias who is my father. My mother was only 17 years old. It was two years that they were together before they had their first son. In my family there are nine members. Three of the children are girls, Patricia, Mayra and Darlene. Then there's us, the six boys, Francisco, Miguel Angel, Oscar, Cesar, that's me, and David and Fredy. We were all born in Mexico, except for the three youngest, David, Fredy, and Darlene. They were born in the U.S.

Yo no me acuerdo de mi abuelito. I was a small child when he was alive. Mom says he was very nice, especially to her. My mom really liked to spend time with him.

When my mom first came to the U.S. she was only 29 years old. I asked her why she decided to come. "Like all the other families that came, I wanted to give all my children a better life, to give all you guys what I didn't have... an education that was given for no price or any struggle." My mother only went to the 10th grade. She didn't finish high school because she had to travel too far every day. First she went by horse, then by car, every day just to get to school. Then the same way back. It got too expensive for my grandparents to pay for their commuting so they finally decided not to go anymore. My grandma chose some of my uncles and aunts to go and live in the ciudad so that they could keep going to school. Unfortunately my mother was not one. Out of four of them, only my uncle Ramon took advantage. He is now a history teacher at a high school in Morelia, Mexico.

When my mother first got here to Washington it was hard for her to find a job, not knowing a word of English, and with a 10th grade education. My father had come first to find a place for us to stay and he began to work in the fields picking apples, cherries, and all the other field work. I was only eight months when I came to the U.S. I crossed into the U.S. with my mother. I guess I was asleep when all this happened. Now I'm an18-year-old senior at Davis High School, where the rest of my family members have graduated from, and will always, until one decides to break the tradition.

I asked my mother the final question, knowing the answer already. Do you regret coming to the U.S? She stopped talking and there was silence for minute. "Yes I do," Why? "Because I came here for better things. Some I've found and some I haven't. I left my parents and everything I was raised to. It seems like I can't live anywhere, not here, not in Mexico. My parents died, so what can I go back to?" The second reason she regrets coming to the U.S. is because of what happened to one of her children. One of my brothers is in a federal prison and will be there for 10 years. That was the hardest for my mother to go through. A part of my mother is locked up with him. I want my mother to change her mind. I want her to say that coming to the U.S. was the best thing that happened to her. So I work hard, then I forget, and seem not to care.

In the picture you see my mother Lidia Gutierrez and me, Marco Gutiérrez. A whole lot of things passed before that picture was taken. I remember I was getting ready, putting gel on my hair, my Mom was taking a shower; my brother, Yair was in his room, also getting ready. My little sister, Lupita, was running all over the place. Suddenly I heard the bell ring and when I opened the door my teacher was out there, waiting for me to tell him to come in. Once inside I offered to him to sit down. My Mom was still in the bathroom, my brother was embarrassed to come out, my little sister got along well with my teacher and began a conversation. When my mother got ready I presented her to my teacher. It was outside, so we decided to take the pictures outside. After the pictures were taken, we went inside the apartment again. I offered my photographer-teacher a glass of water, and when he tasted it, he smiled and said, "Oh, jugo de uvas." My mom, Lidia, doesn't like to live in Yakima. There are many reasons. One is because it is too far away from the border, which makes it harder to travel to Mexico more often. Second is because finding work is also complicated, and the weather here is crazy. She said, "Sometimes it's warm, sometimes it is freezing and when you don't even expect it, it's snowing." My mom says that Yakima is boring, and there are not many places where you can go on Sundays to enjoy. Of course Mom is from Guadalajara, one of the great cities in the world. My family is a split family. My mother, my brother, little sister and I live in Yakima. My other sister, Lidia, lives in Mexico, and my Dad is in Arizona because of job circumstances. My mom is waiting for me to graduate so we can all go to Arizona and live together like a family.

My Mother Is My Treasure

Marco Gutiérrez

My name is Lidia Gutiérrez; I was born in a small town called Sánta Crúz de Las Flores, Jalisco on August 3 1966. My parents' names are Benigno Espinoza and Genoveva Espinoza. My husband's name is Marco Antonio Gutiérrez. I am the mother of 4 sons—their names are Marco, Lidia, Yair, and Guadalupe Gutiérrez. I remember that as a child my dad would take me to work in the fields at the age of 6. I would help my dad one season working the land, and next season I would help my dad make bricks. At six I began to go to school. After school I would have to go to work with my dad, helping him out to *regar abono,* to irrigate and fertilize, and to farm, until seven o' clock when I would come back from the fields. When we returned, my mom would have irresistible home-made tortillas and hot beans. After dinner I was allowed to go outside and hang around with my friends. With my friends and sisters we would play *a los encantados,* with dolls, and *a la tiendita* or we would just sit down and tell jokes and scary stories. At nine o'clock I would have to go inside the house and go to sleep.

On the weekends I would work for my Aunt Luteria who had a small restaurant. My job was to wash the dishes and to clean the tables. I kept the same routine until I was twelve. I come from a big family. I have five sisters; their names are Silvia, Adriana, Carmela, Beatriz, and Lorenza Espinoza. I also have three brothers; their names are Jorge, Gildardo, and Gabriel Espinoza. I'm the fifth out of nine children. I'm 35 years old right now. I cannot believe how time passes by without even noticing it.

Like I was saying, when I was 12, my older sister Carmela got married and moved out to Guadalajara, where I had to move too, because instead of having one baby, she had twins, so I had to help her out with one baby. Every two weeks I would go back to my town and visit my family. Living with my sister I had the opportunity to go to a special school where they teach you many useful things. There I learned cooking, ceramics, and to cut hair. At that time I took ceramics and hairstyle courses. I went to middle school and finished. After two years of my graduation, I moved out from my sister's and went to live with my brother Gabriel. He wanted me to take care of his two sons. At that time I was 14 years old with a lot of experience on how to clean the house and to take care of children.

I would still go visit my parents every two weeks, but when I didn't go, I would go out with my brother, my sister-in-law, and my nephew, to the swimming pools and to the movies. During my times with my parents on the weekends I had a lot of fun, too. My dad worked as a *mesero, or* waiter, for the town's Holy Days.

What I liked the best about the Holy Days was *El Novenario de La Virgen* was celebrated with big parties that lasted nine days. There was a mini fair that had some good rides and games, like foosball and bingo. In the mornings after a 5 o'clock mass, my family and I would go and buy *ponche* and *churros* with sugar outside the church. In the evening many crusades from different towns would gather up in my town to celebrate and to pray for the *Virgen*. In the evening there would be a dance, music, fire crackers, and a *serenata* was offered to the *Virgen* in *la plaza*.

On the weekends there were always dances going on in my town. I liked to go with my dad because he worked there as a *mesero* so I was able to go in for free. At the age of 16, I left Guadalajara and moved back to Sánta Crúz. In the mornings I worked with my parents and in the evenings I hung around with my friends and sisters. We would play volleyball, make piñatas, and play games like *encantados, a la culebra, los listones*, and *hide-go-see*. When I turned 17 I met Marco's dad. He was from the other town called *Tepehuaje de Mórelos, Jalisco*.

At 18 I got married and went to live with Marco, my son, at his mother's house. When I was going to have Marco, I moved back to my parent's house because Marco, my husband, was in California. When Marco was born, my husband came back. That was in October, 1985. After three years I had a daughter. I named her like me, Lidia. After that my husband wanted us to go live with him in California. Then we traveled to Tijuana to cross the border. My husband crossed the border with Marco who was two, and Lidia within just months of being born. They crossed like legals, but only my husband had documents. I had to cross with a *coyote* through a park in Tijuana. We lived two years in California. At that I had already applied for legal documents. After I received my documents, we went back to Guadalajara with my mother. We decided to leave Marco and his sister with my mother.

In California, my husband and I worked in the lettuce, cauliflower, and blueberries. We work for six months without resting. We worked from April to October, and then we would go visit my sons and my mother in Guadalajara. We did that for several years and then I had another son, his name is Yair. He was born in Salinas, California, in 1989. When Marco was in third grade we decided that it was better for them to move closer to the border so that I would be able to see my sons more often. I really needed them to be closer to me, to give me strength to keep working hard and not feel lonely in the other side of the border. So they moved to a town called San Quintin.

In 1997, when Marco finished elementary, I decided to bring him and his brothers to Salinas, CA. At that time I got really sick from my right leg. It was inflamed, and it felt that my leg was going to explode. I went to the hospital in Tijuana and stayed there for one day. Then the hospital released me and gave me a whole bunch of medicine. I wasn't able to walk for over a week. In 1998 I had my last, and definitive, daughter. She was born in Salinas. That moment brought me a lot of joy because she was the last baby, and because it was not in my plans to have her. After two years of living in Salinas I moved to Yakima WA, where my brother told me that I could find a lot of jobs, but when I came it was winter. I couldn't find any job. Yakima turned out to be a mistake to me. I had to go back to California and leave Marco in Yakima to finish his high school. I didn't want to leave him but I understand that it was because of his education. My husband and I stayed in California to work. My other sons went back to live with their grandma.

While I was working in Cali I would send money to my sons in México and to Marco. I only had one hope and it was that at the end of the season I would meet with Marco in Yakima. Right now I am living with Marco and his brothers in Yakima. I am waiting for Marco to finish high school so that we can all move to Arizona where my husband bought a house, and for once for all we can live together like a family.

Elvia and Cristal Manjarréz stand outside of their Yakima apartment. Cristal is very proud of having her mother beside her. Cristal feels admiration for her mother and would like to be as strong as her mother is. "My mother is a good example for me to follow," she says. "One of the things that I admire in her is the way she taught us to face difficulties in life and never give up. She is one of my teachers." Cristal's mother is a woman who has helped Cristal and her other children keep trying to reach their goals. She is a very good example of a Mexican mother. "She has suffered to support and give me an education. She has helped me to overcome the obstacles in my life and urges me to keep trying to do the best that I can do."

"Mi Heroina"

Cristal Manjarréz

She fights everyday against poverty to give her children a good future. To give them the opportunity and support to accomplish their dreams. She wants to see her four little girls reaching the pinnacle of the mountain.

Elvia Manjarréz was born on August 11th of 1964. She was born in Los Sauces, a little town in Guerrero, Mexico. Elvia grew up with her parents in a very poor home. "A veces no teníamos ni zapatos para ir a la escuela" she said. They were 12 children. Their parents did not have enough money to give every one of their children a good economic way of life.

As she grew up she learned to live in poverty, but never accepted it. She had dreams. She dreamed of a better way of life. When she was 14, she wanted to be a ballerina, one of those who dance in the theater. That was her biggest and most impossible dream.

Elvia went to school in Los Sauces. She finished la secundaria there. That's the last school she attended. After she graduated from la secundaria she married Bulmaro. She was 17 years old when that happened. Bulmaro took her to the United States for the first time. They crossed the border without legal papers, "de mojados". After they stayed in the U. S. for around six months, they went back to Los Sauces. A few days after they arrived there, their first girl was born. They were living in Bulmaro's parents' house at first, but then they moved to their own house, right next to Bulmaro's parents' house.

As time passed by, Elvia stayed at home and Bulmaro came to the United States every year to work and earn money to support his family. They were still poor, I mean very poor. *Comíamos puras papas todos los días,* she says.

The second girl was born when the first one was four years old. Elvia named her Dianna. Six years later the third one was born, Jaqueline. After she was born, Bulmaro could made them legal residents of the United States. So he brought Elvia and her daughters to the U. S., to Yakima Washington, to be specific. Elvia was depressed. She wanted to go back to Mexico, but she knew she had to work hard to live better. Bulmaro and she worked at the field almost the whole day, every day.

After six months they went back to Mexico and kept coming to work every season for three more years. The second year they came here, Elvia gave birth to her fourth girl. She was born here in Yakima. Elvia named her Esmeralda.

The fourth time they came to the United States they stayed here, because their daughters were attending school. Since that time, Elvia works to support her children, while they are attending school. "Quiero que sean mejor que yo" she tells them everyday. She lives happy with her husband and daughters, but she couldn't reach her dream of being a ballerina.

I believe she is the best mother in the world. And I am very proud of her, because she is my mother. If I could choose a mother I'd choose her again. I am my mother's *bailarina* and I'll reach the stars for her to accomplish her dream and make it real.

La Historia de Mi Padre,
Através de Los Ojos de sus Hijas

María y Antonia Caro

Sr. Padre mío, con el debido respeto que le tengo, me dirijo a usted. No sin antes decirle lo mucho que lo quiero y me hace falta. ¿Qué palabra tan hermosa y llena de amor, ternura y seguridad: *Papá*? ¿Qué felíz me siento cuando pronuncio esta tierna palabra; me siento el ser más afortunado por Dios porque te tengo a ti papá? Le doy las gracias a Dios por haberme dado la dicha de saber lo que es un padre y por dejármelo vivir y le pido a Dios papá que te deje vivir muchos años más.

Es una persona que ocupa un lugar especial en mi corazón y en mi vida al que admiro por ser un padre ejemplar y amigo. Su historia dio inicio en junio 13, de 1942 en Villegas, Jalisco. Lleva por nombre Antonio Caro en honor de su abuelo paterno Antonio y porque nació el día de San Antonio. Su padre Pedro Caro originario de Villegas y su madre Rosa Ortega de Chiquilistlan. Hijo del segundo matrimonio es el segundo de 7 hermanos y se casó con mi madre María Isabel a los 32 años de edad y tuvo 5 hijos. Sus padres en el

203

primer matrimonio tuvieron 2 hijos cada uno y enviudaron ahora desafortunadamente; ya están muertos.

Un hombre ranchero, humilde y alegre de corazón grande así es como describo a mi padre Antonio Caro. Vivió su niñez hasta los 10 años de edad en el rancho de Villegas en el cual estudió hasta 3° grado de primaria Tenía un sueño de ser maestro o sacerdote el cual nunca logró. Recuerda que su niñez fue muy triste que no tenía juguetes ni tiempo de jugar. Sus juegos eran aprender a trabajar y a manejar el ganado. Su única distracción era ir a ratos a la escuela mientras su papá iba por él para que lo acompañara a trabajar al campo.

Su padre opinaba que no servían las letras para un hombre de campo, que supiera, leer y a escribir era suficiente. Su madre opinaba diferente porque ella había estudiado: su padre le había pagado a un maestro particular para que les enseñara a ella y a sus hermanas a leer y a escribir bien.

Aunque su madre Rosa tenía educación era una persona muy dura y cerrada en sus ideas. Lo educó de una forma muy dura con 3 o 4 nalgaceras al día cuando le iba bien. Su papá pensaba que exageraba al pegarle tanto por cualquier cosa sin motivo pero ella decía, <<yo sé come los educo>>. No podían ni hacerse un gesto él ni sus hermanos porque su mamá ya les pegaba. Cuando daba una orden era de hacerla inmediatamente. Cuando peleaban los hermanos en la escuela, si se dejaban que les pegaran no se le entendía a su mamá y si se defendieran estaba mal también. Era una persona que no se le podía contradecir. Lo que ella decía eso se hacía.

Mi padre Antonio siempre solía acompañar a su padre a trabajar al campo. Su padre lo enseñó desde muy pequeño a querer la tierra y a labrarla lo mismo que a cuidar al ganado. Su mamá no más contaba con su propia mamá Nicolasa Ríos ya que su papá Aniseto Ortega había muerto cuando ella era chiquita. Mi padre Antonio muy poco se acuerda de sus antepasados por parte de su mamá. Su papá Pedro no los quería frecuentar porque vivían peleando entre ellos por la herencia de su padre que era un cacique muy rico. Mi padre Antonio por parte de su papá, conoció a sus dos abuelos Pomposa León y Antonio Caro pero los recuerda como un sueño porque su abuelo murió cuando él tenía como 5 años.

Cuando él tenía 10 años más o menos de edad se mudaron a vivir a Guadalajara, Jalisco. Sus hermanos y él entraron a la escuela. Él se sentía muy raro por que la escuela era muy grande y extrañaba el rancho y a sus amigos. Su papá entró a trabajar al rastro municipal.

Respeto a las dos hijas de su papá nunca vivieron con ellos cuando su madre murió. Las recogió una hermana de su mamá. En ese mismo año los hijos de su mamá se fueron para los EE.UU. Tenían entre 18 y 20 años de edad. Y de ahí en adelante, ya no supieron nada más de ellos hasta como a dos años después de que escribieron una carta diciendo que estaban bien. Pero respeto a lo económico, nunca ayudaron.

La situación económica en su casa era crítica ya que su padre estaba mayor de edad. Lo que ganaba en el rastro no alcanzaba para sostener a la familia que eran muchos y solamente su papá trabajaba. Las cosas empeoraron. Mi padre tuvo que dejar la escuela y buscar un trabajo en una fábrica. Sus hermanas no soportaron la presión de su mamá tan extricta y ninguna terminó sus estudios. Poco a poco se fueron casando hasta que se casaron todas aunque eran muy jóvenes las cuatro. Después de que se casaron, todas las hermanas se quedaron en Guadalajara. Regresaron al rancho mi papa con sus dos hermanos, y sus papás. Este cambio de vida para él era dificil ya que no estaba acostumbrado al ritmo de la vida del rancho.

Un cambio del rancho a la ciudad, de la ciudad al rancho, y del rancho a otro país diferente, EE.UU. fue terrible. *Los cambios de vida llevan tiempo para adaptarse y resignarse.* Su sueño era de ganar mucho dinero pero no sabía el precio que pagaría, y las consecuencias que enfrentaría. A la edad de 17 años dejó su hogar y a su familia. Su madre desconsolada echa un mar de lágrimas, y su padre se resignaba y le daba la bendición. Era un joven inexperto que quería sacar a su familia de la miseria en que vivía. Partió con rumbo a la frontera de México y los EE.UU. a desafiar la ley. Cruzar la frontera fue el primer obstáculo que desafió con la ayuda de un coyote que fue pagado por uno de los hijos de su mamá. Su hermano le dio posada en su casa en California por un tiempo mientras se alibianaba para que rentara en otro lado. Recuerda lo difícil que fueron para él los trabajos en EE.UU. En las huertas piscaba manzanas, peras y hacía de todo un poco. Y por si fuera poco todo eso, todavía andaba cuidándose de la migra porque era ilegal en este país. Después de Fresno, California se mudó a vivir con unos amigos, quienes le consiguieron trabajo piscando algodón en el Valle De Bly. Esos amigos serían su perdición porque lo indujeron al vicio del alcohol. Se volvió un borracho desobligado que ya no hacía caso a sus padres ni les mandaba dinero y ni les escribía. Su mundo era el vicio del alcohol y los juegos de baraja, y del billar. Había unos de sus amigos que hasta perdían toda su quincena por adelantado en el juego. Fue entonces cuando él serecapacitó al ver esos jovenes perdidos por completo en los vicios y decidió dejar el vicio.

La voz de experiencia dice...

Recuerda que el vicio del alcohol fue uno de los más grandes problemas que tuvo que enfrentar en su juventud. Fue un alcohólico y por mas que trataba de olvidarse del vino no podía, era una sed inmensa que tenía. Su cuerpo le pedía de perdida una cerveza. Era un calor que describía como el propio infierno y que no había como una cerveza para calmarlo. *La voz de la experienciá dice que es muy facil agarrar un vicio, lo dificil es dejarlo.* —Intenté una y otra vez dejar el vicio pero era inútil. Era más fuerte mi vicio que yo. Quería escapar de ese mundo del alcohol en el cual había caído. Me miraba a mi mismo y a mis amigos, unos jóvenes de 18 a 24 años de edad, perdidos en ese mundo de tristeza. No encontraba la forma de huir de ese lugar ni a donde irme porque creía que si seguía con esos amigos, nunca iba a dejar el vicio. En un apartamento al lado del mío, vivía un hombre mayor de unos 45 años. Un día me vio llorando, borracho, afuera del apartamento y le conté que quería dejar el vicio y que me quería ir á vivir a otro lado. Y le di lástima y me dijo que en unas semanas se iba a terminar el trabajo y que él se iba a mudar a Bly. Me preguntó si yo quería irme con él.

Y me fui ahí donde conseguí trabajo en el riego. El patrón me dio una cabina y me informó que ahí habían matado como a unos dos trabajadores. Tenía un machete con el cual, en las noches, salía aventando machetazos por todos lados y prefería por miedo irme a dormir a los campos de riego bajo un árbol. En este trabajo duré dos años trabajando casi los tres turnos. Les mandaba a mis padres los cheques cuando los agarraba y no mas dejaba lo suficiente para mi comida. Después de tres años en los EE. UU., mi padre Antonio Caro regresó contento a México al rancho de sus padres a Villegas, Jalisco.

Sus planes eran no regresar a EE.UU. como por unos, cinco años ni oír la palabra "norte" por razones tenía. Había sufrido mucho en EE.UU. y quería descansar. Al llegar a su casa se espumaron sus sueños. No habían tenido consideración de su sacrificio, ni habían valorado su trabajo. Sus hermanos se daban la vida de lujo. Hacían las labores a base de trabajadores y se la pasaban en fiestas y diversiones. Él se desilusionó al ver que no le habían ahorrado nada de su dinero.

Los años de duros trabajos y sacrificios de él no valieron de nada. Se quedó por dos años en México y se olvidó un poco del sufrimiento que había pasado en el norte.

A los 22 años, mi padre Antonio intentó venir por segunda vez a los EE.UU. Intentó pasar la linea muchas veces, pero no lo logró. Los de la migra ya lo reconocían aunque se cambió de nombre cada vez que lo agarraban. Llegó a tal punto que usó hasta el nombre del tatarabuelo de su tatarabuelo. Después de que quedó convencido que no podía pasar a EE.UU. decidió quedarse a trabajar en la frontera en Mexicali con el hijo de su mamá. Ahí hizo de todos los trabajos venderor de agua, jardinero hasta que consiguío trabajo en construcción. Estuvo en Mexicali por tres años y logró sacar el pasaporte americano para tiempo indefinido el cual se lo robaron. Describe su estancia en Mexicali como una pesadilla, un calor que no se puede vivir. Dice que si pusieran una tortilla en una lámina a coser se cosería. Así es como describe el calor en Mexicali.

El tiempo es un buen consejero

Cuando cruzó para EE.UU. decidió irse para Florida. Llegó de tarde y no conocía a nadie y solo tenía un dólar. Miró una cantina y entró. Miraba para todos lados a ver si miraba aún mexicano. Pidío una cerveza y la estaba mariando y se le acercó una mujer quien le pidió que le disparara una cerveza. Le daba pena decirle que no pero le dijo a ella que no. Se rio un viejo gabacho borrachode mi papá. Le dijo que nunca se le dice no a una dama. Mi padre Antonio no le contestó nada al gabacho y después de mucho rato empezaron a platicar. Mi padre le dijo que andaba buscando trabajo. Él gabacho era el dueño de un rancho y le dio trabajo y donde quedarse aunque era un garage viejo donde echaba a su perro.

<<El tiempo es buen consejero y de los años vividos se aprende mucho. Lo más importante es sacar provecho de los errores. Yo aprendí a valorarme y apreciarme más después que superé el vicio del alcohol y que aprendí a dominar los vicios y que los vicíos no me dominaran a mí. Aunque quería con toda mi alma a mis padres y hermanos, no los apoyé como la primera vez que vine a California. Ya tenía que pensar en mí. Ya era un hombre hecho y derecho. Ya había experimentado lo bueno y malo en cabeza propia y decidí darme tiempo para disfrutar mi vida antes de casarme. Quería ir ahorrando

un poco de dinero para cuando me casara para tener algo que ofrecerle a mi esposa e hijos. Mi patrón, el gabacho, me dijo algo que nunca olvidaré "La vida es hermosa y más cuando la sabes disfrutar.>>

<<Ya tenía 27 años, y no era un adolescente, estaba cansado de vivir solo y en otro país que no era el mío. Estaba cansado de andar de un estado a otro lejos de mis padres. Ahora era Pennsylvania, lugar en el cual estuve a punto de casarme, con una gabacha para que me arreglara papeles. Pero pensé que voy a estar condenado en este país trabajando diario no más por el interés de los papeles. Así que para no meterme en problemas, me fui para New Jersey. Ahí duré dos años trabajando en las huertas y después me fui para Pornory. Yo trabajé empacando almejas por un año y sería el ultimo lugar en el que estaría de EE.UU. y regresaría a México.>>

A la edad de 33 años mi padre regresó a México, al rancho con sus padres. Y mientras encontraba a la mujer que buscaba con quien casarse, decidió pasearse un poco y en su estancia en Guadalajara conoció a mi madre, María Isabel Sánchez, con la que pronto se comprometió. Ya tenía todo lo que deseaba y era muy feliz. Lo único que le hacía falta era irse a vivir al rancho cerca de sus padres. Su madre estaba muy enferma de cáncer y su hijo de su primer matrimonio se la había llevado a Mexicali donde murió. Este fue un golpe muy duro para mi padre, Antonio, porque se sentía muy mal ya que su hermano no hizo nada para alargarle un poco la vida a su madre. Pero por otra parte le daba las gracias a Dios por sus dos hijos.

Cuando nació la última de sus hijas, se mudaron a vivir al rancho de Villega en Jalisco. Su padre estabá ya muy enfermo de leusemia y mi padre Antonio no quería que se muriera. Lo interné en el hospital militar de Guadalajara hasta que los médicos le dijeron ya no podemos hacer nada más por su padre. A mi padre Antonio esto le dolió en el alma. Su padre le decía, <<hijo no me quiero morir.>> Estas palabras de su padre le partían el corazón. Mi padre casi vendió todo lo que un día era el rancho cuando murió su padre. Su padre se estaba acabando y al mismo tiempo lo que había sido su rancho también. Todo esto era muy triste para mi padre Antonio, ver como su padre moría y no lo podía evitar. Sentía como si le reclamara la tierra y el ganado a su amo Pedro Caro. Cuando embarcaba el ganado para venderlo las vacas bramaban como si se despidieran llorando y supieran lo que pasaba, que iban a morir igual que su dueño.

Se respiraba un aire de tristeza. Se miraba el rancho triste. Su dueño había muerto. El ganado que estaba en los corrales bramaban desaforidos, las gallinas chillaban, los perros aullaban y lloraban por su amo que había muerto. El rancho estaba de luto porque había muerto el amo; murió Pedro Caro. Mi padre, Antonio, quedaba desamparado en el mundo pero le quedó un consuelo. Le había echo la lucha a salvarle la vida a su padre, Pedro Caro hasta el último momento.

Después de que murió su padre en 1986, volvio á EE.UU. y arregló papeles con la amnestia. Metío la aplicación para arreglarle a toda la familia. Y desde ese año viene cada año a EE.UU. Para él, sus hijos son el tesoro más grande que tiene aún desde antes de conocerlos, ya los quería. Todos son diferentes. Son como los dedos de su mano, todos disparejos, pero a todos los quiere por igual. Para él, EE.UU es un país de oportunidades, y por eso es que Antonia, Luz y yo, María, estamos aquí estudiando.

…vives con una sonrisa

La voz de mi padre dice, <<hijos, nunca se estanquen ni digan, no puedo—quiero que triunfen. Dejen huella en este mundo pero de algo bueno. Esfuércense por alcanzar nobles ideales. Nunca digan mañana, porque quizas mañana ya sea demasiado tarde. Den lo mejor de Uds. cada día y sean humildes nunca se cieguen por la avaricia del dinero. El dinero no es la felicidad. Nunca se den por vencidos. Si caen, levantense porque un fracaso es un nuevo empezar. Y al mal tiempo, buena cara porque la vida se vive mejor si la vives con una sonrisa. Traten de ser felices, porque vida solo, hay una y recuerden lo que hagan hoy repercutirá mañana. Su padre los ama y los lleva siempre en su corazón. Aunque lejos estén, están a diario en mi mente y en mi oración>> Antonio Caro. <<Hijos, espero que esto que yo viví les sirva de experiencia y que no cometan los mismos errores que yo cometí. Recuerden, no es amigo él que trata de inducirlos en un vicio. Un amigo es aquel que está contigo en las buenas y en las malas y quien quiere para ti lo mejor.>>

María and Antonia Caro conducted their interviews with their parents over the telephone between Guadalajara, Jalisco and Yakima, Washington during March and April, 2002. The format for telling their father's story takes the form of a letter written to their father. María wrote the original in Spanish, and Antonia translated the interview into English. The English version has been abbreviated.

Our Father's Story
Through his Daughters' Eyes

Antonia and María Caro

Dear father, mine with the respect that you deserve. I direct my attention towards you. Not before letting you know how much I love and miss you. You are in Jalisco, and we, your children, are in Yakima getting our education. You have been gone from us since 1999. Such a beautiful word and full of love with tenderness and security: *Papi.* How happy I feel when I pronounce this sacred word. I feel like the most fortunate person of God, because I have you, *Dad.* I give thanks to God for letting me know what *father* means. And for letting you live, I ask God to let you live more years to come.

You are a person who occupies a special place in my heart and in my life. I admire you for being an example, a father and a friend.

Your life begins on June 13, 1942 in Villegas, Jalisco. Your name is Antonio Caro, in honor of your Grandfather, Antonio Caro, because he was born the day of San Antonio. Your father, Pedro Caro, is originally from Villegas, and your mother from Chiquilistlán, a small town in La Sierra, near Guadalajara. You are the son of a second marriage and you are the second of your father's siblings, and you have five children. You married my mother, María Isabel, at the age of 32.

Your parents, in the first marriage, had two children, and were both widowed, and unfortunately, both are dead. A happy and humble farmer with a big heart, this is how I describe you as my dad. You lived your childhood up to the age of ten years old in the village of Villegas where you went to school until the 3rd grade. You had a dream to become a teacher or a priest, which you never fulfilled. Your father's opinion on education held that all a farmer needed to know was how to read and write. Your mother's opinion was different because she had an education. Her father had paid a tutor to teach her and her sisters to read and write. Even with her education she was a very hard and stubborn person in her ideas.

You remember your childhood as one of the hardest times in your life. You were a sad child, who never had a chance to play, not even time to enjoy your childhood. Your fun was to learn how to work and tame the cattle. Your mother taught you in a hard way with three or four *Nalgaseras,* or slaps on your butt, each day when you were having fun playing. Your father thought your mother exaggerated, hitting you a lot for little things without good reason, but she used to say, "I know how to teach them." You couldn't make a gesture one to another. You couldn't argue, either. When she ordered you to do something, it had to be done immediately. When you used to fight at school, you didn't know what to do, *no se le allaba.* According to your mother, if another boy hit you, you were bad, and if you defended yourself, you were bad, too.

You always went out to accompany your father. Your father taught you, from the time you were little, to love to till the fields. The same with the cattle on learning to work with them. Your mom only counted on her mother, Nicolasa Ríos, because her father, Aniseto Ortega, had died when she was little. You, my father, remember almost nothing about your Grandma and relatives from your mother's side. Your father Pedro, didn't want to frequent them, because they always lived fighting for the land. This was the inheritance of their father, a wealthy *cacique.* From your father's side you met the two of your grandparents, Pomposa León and Antonio Caro, but you remember them like in a dream, because your grandpa died when you were five years old.

But he never said, *Go back to the ranch*

When you were ten years old, you and your family moved to Guadalajara, Jalisco. You and your siblings entered school. You felt rare, the school was big, and you missed the ranch and your friends. Your father entered to work at the meat packing plant, and your stepsisters never lived with you. When their mother died, they went to live with a sister of their mother's. Your father, Pedro, didn't like to live in the city, but he never said to go back to the ranch.

When you were 12 years old, two children of your mom emigrated to the U.S. They were between the ages of 18 and 20. From then on, you heard no news about them for two years after, when they wrote a letter saying they were fine. But they never sent any money home.

The economic situation in your house was critical. Your father was old. What he earned at the meat packing plant wasn't enough to feed his family. It got worse. You had to leave school and look for work in a factory. Your sisters couldn't put up with your mom's anger. She was too strict and none of your sisters finished school. Little by little, each one of them got married at an early age. After your sisters got married, you and your two brothers and your parents returned to the ranch. This life change was hard for you because you weren't accustomed to the ranch rhythm.

You were living through a change; from the ranch to the city, from the city to the ranch, and from the ranch to another country. Life changes take time to adapt to. Your dream was to make money, without knowing the price you would have to pay, or the consequences you would have to face. At the age of 17 you left your home and family. Your mother's disconsolation made a sea of tears. Your father, resigned, gave you his blessing. You were an inexperienced young boy whose thoughts were to take his family from the poverty they were in. You left in the direction of the border between Mexico and the U.S to defy the law. The first obstacle you had to overcome, with the help of a *coyote*, who was paid by one of your stepbrothers, was to cross the border. One let you stay at his home in California until you found a job and rented an apartment. You remember the hard jobs in the U.S., picking apples and pears in the fields. And doing *de todo un poco*. And if the hard work wasn't enough, you had to hide from the immigration because you were illegal. After Fresno, California, you moved with some friends. They found you a job in El Valle de Bly, picking cotton. Those friends were your ruin. They induced you to drink alcohol. You turned into an alcoholic, *desobligado*, who didn't care about his parents. You never even sent money to them or wrote them a letter. Your new world became the vices of alcohol, playing cards, and shooting pool. There were some friends of yours who lost the check from the next week by gambling. When you saw those young people completely lost in the vice is when you thought it over and decided to leave the vice.

Leaving the vice

You remember that the vice of alcohol was one of the great problems you had to face in your youth. You were an alcoholic and as much as you tried to forget the wine you couldn't. It was a great thirst you had.

212

Your body asked for at least one beer. It was a heat that you describe like hell and there was nothing like a beer to calm it. The voice of experience says, *It's easy to get a vice, the hard thing is to leave it.* You tried *una y otra vez,* many times to leave the vice, but it was useless. Your vice was stronger than you were. You wanted to escape that world of alcohol you had fallen into. You saw yourself and your friends, lost in that world of sadness. You didn't find a way to run away from that place, or where to go, because you thought if you stayed with those friends, you would never leave the vice. In an apartment adjacent to yours lived an older man about 45 years old. One day he saw you crying and drunk outside the apartment. You told him you wanted to leave the vice and go live somewhere else. He felt sorry for you and he told you that in a few weeks the work was going to end, and he was going to move to Bly, he asked you if you wanted to go with him.

And you went. You found a job watering the fields. The boss gave you a cabin and informed you there had been a murder of two workers there. You had a *machete* which at nights you would throw from here to there, and you preferred to sleep under the trees because of your fear. You worked for three years, almost completing three harvests. You sent your parents your pay checks and you would hardly have money for your food. After three years in the U.S. you returned happily to México to your parents ranch at Villegas Jalisco.

You planned not to come back to the U.S. in the next five years. You had suffered very much and you wished to have some rest. Arriving home your dreams vanished. Nobody cared about your sacrifices nor appreciated your effort. Your brothers lived a life of luxury. They had workers to do the chores. They lived in parties and *diversiones.* You were disappointed when you saw they hadn't saved any of your money. All these years of hard work and sacrifices were useless. You stayed for two years in Mexico to forget the suffering you had in the north.

Time is a good counselor, and from the years, you have learned much. And the most important thing is to learn from the errors. You learned to value and appreciate yourself. After you conquered the vice of alcohol, you learned to overcome other vices, and not let the vices overcome you. Even though you loved your parents and siblings with all your heart, you didn't help them like the first time you came to California. You had to think of yourself, you were a man, *hecho y derecho,* made and true.

You had experimented with the good and the bad in your own — *en cabeza propia*—your own head, and you decided to take some time to enjoy life before you got married. You wanted to save some money so when you would get married, you would have the capital to offer your wife and children. Your boss, *el gabacho*, told you something you will never forget, "Life is beautiful, and more, when you know how to enjoy it."

You were already 27 years old and no longer a teenager. You were tired of living alone, and in an another country that wasn't yours, going from one state to another, living far from your parents. You were in Pennsylvania, the place where you were going to marry a white woman, so she could give you citizenship. You thought that you were going to be condemned to the U. S., working everyday, just for legal papers. So you didn't want to have any problems, and you left to New Jersey. You worked there for two years in the orchards. Then you left for Pornory, where you worked packing clams for a year. It was the last place where you worked in the U.S. before you returned to México.

At the age of 33 you returned to the *rancho* with your parents. You searched for the woman you would marry. And during your stay in Guadalajara, you met our mother, *María Isabel Sánchez*, the one you would soon be engaged to. You were so happy, and had all that you desired. The only thing you needed was to live near your parents. Your mom was so sick; she had cancer. Her son, from the first marriage, had taken her with him to Mexicali, where she died. It had a great impact on you. You felt so bad, because your brother didn't do anything to help your mother live longer. On the other hand, you gave thanks to God for your two children.

When the last one of your daughters was born, you moved to the *Rancho Villegas*, in Jalisco. Your father was so sick from Leukemia, and you didn't want him to die. You put your father in the military hospital in Guadalajara until the doctors told you that they couldn't do anything else for him. Your father's words broke your heart. You sold everything at the *rancho* when your father died. His *rancho* was coming to an end. You were unable to help him. You felt as if the cattle and the land reproached you for the loss of their owner, Pedro Caro. When you put the cattle into the truck to sell them, they *mooed* as if they were saying *Goodby*, crying, as if they knew what was happening, that they were going to die, along with their owner.

You could smell the sadness in the air. The rancho seemed gloomy; the owner had died. That cattle in the corral mooed, the chickens cried, the dogs barked and cried for their owner, your father. Pedro Caro had died. You were forsaken in the world, but you were consoled. You had tried to preserve your father's life until the last moment.

After your father died in 1986, you returned to the U.S. and you obtained your papers through the Amnesty. You also made application for your family to emigrate. Since that year, you have come to the U.S. every year, because your sons and daughters are the most valuable treasure you have. Even before you knew them you loved them. Each one is different, they are like the fingers of the hand, all uneven, yet you love each one the same. For you, the U.S. is a land of opportunity. That's why, we, María, Luz, and me, Antonia, are here, studying.

My father's voice says, "Sons and daughters, I never want you to be stuck, not even to say, *I can't*, I want you to succeed. Leave a footprint of something good in this world, make an effort to achieve your noble ideals. Never say, *tomorrow,* because it can be too late. Give your best everyday, and be humble. Never blind yourself with greed. Never give up. If you fail, stand up. A failure is a new beginning. In bad times, stay positive. You'll live a better life if you live it with a smile. There is just one life. And remember, what you do today, will count tomorrow. Your father loves you and always has you in his heart."

"Although you are far from me, you are always in my mind and prayers. I hope what I lived through is an experience for you too, and that you don't make the mistakes I did. Remember, a true friend does not introduce you to vice. A friend is with you in good times and bad, and who wants the best for you."

This is the story of our mother in her voice. We just asked her to tell us about her life, and thanks to her, we got this interview finished. She wrote her history in Spanish. This is her *testimonio*. My brother Gastón and I translated her words into English. First, we read it to our classmates in Spanish. And one thing that I learned from my mother when I wrote this history was to keep learning, because we always are learning, to be a good woman and to be strong. I think I have learned what I am from both of my parents, but something special that I have learned from my mother is her intelligence, and she will not let me fall. I want to say thanks to all my family generations, because they are my past, my present and my future. Thanks to Mr. Bodeen, because he is a teacher that made me see who I really represent in this country, and one more thing, for giving me the opportunity to develop my thoughts and to shout out my dreams. Thanks to all my teachers for giving me this opportunity; thanks a lot.

MY CLEAR WAY

Blanca Pérez

As told to Gastón and Paloma Pérez

In a very small town on March 31, 1959, a little girl was born in the middle of a storm, Blanca Esthela Padilla. The storm stayed many days. Those who survived include her mother, a young lady 18 years old, Emilia Velazco, and her father, 32-year-old Julio Padilla Garcia. Blanca was the first child of the couple; she was healthy and looked very strong.

Blanca, who had black hair and big blue eyes at the age of 5 years old, began to go to a small school (kindergarten) where she met more children of the same age. Some of those children were bigger than her because it was not a formal school.

At the age of seven she went for the very first time to elementary school. By that time she began to like drawing and painting which caused troubles for her because she was doing it every single minute at school. When her teacher saw her drawing instead of paying attention to the class, the teacher got really mad.

In those times all the teachers were very strict. They were so strict to their students that the punishments were very heavy for every child at that time. How can you support the pain of ten lashes on the palm of your hand and in front of the class? Also, the teacher would call your parents to tell them that you were being rude to them. Then your father or mother would yell at you and maybe punish you.

When the school year was almost done, I was very happy because every single student needed to do a project in which you had to do it by your own hand. The girls needed to sew or to do flower decorations. Men needed to do carpentry and things like that. Our parents and people from the town came to see what we had done.

At the age of thirteen, I graduated from elementary school. At the end of the school year we would dance the traditional dance called "bals" and we received our certificates. In the following year I received a terrible notice by my father. He said: you cannot continue studying because the girls of your age cannot be outside by themselves. That year I was turning 14, that whole year my mother taught me how to cook and do the chores of the house. On the other hand, my father taught me how to work the land and how to ride a horse. He also taught me how to grow corn step-by-step. I was in charge of my mother's business which was earning a good profit. My father, who was a farmer, also had a small movie theatre and my mother had a small restaurant.

When I was 15, I amazed my mother when I told her that I wanted to keep studying and I told her I wanted to become an artist like those in the movies. My mother told me that I could not become an artist because it required going away from the town and studying away from home. My mother also told me that I was skinny and quite ugly, plus my father would not give me permission to leave.

One day a lady came to my town that had studied in one of the best fashion schools in Gudalajara, Jal. Mex. *Mi madre al ver la presión que le ponía constantemente para estudiar algo,* she went and talked with the lady, and she told her that she would pay her to teach me how to make dresses. The lady accepted and she taught a group of four girls and in eight months I learned *Corte y Confección de Ropa,* or fashion design.

I started to work in my house with my clothes and my family's clothes and I continued to study at a small school and the teacher took me to another school, because I learned very fast. I was 17 years old, and my parents let me go out of town to continue my studies. The teacher sent me with the principal when I entered that school, and she asked me where I had studied, and what method I had studied. I answered every question, and when she asked why she hadn't given me a certificate, I answered, "Because she didn't have permission to give it." The principal told me, "If you can learn to do *sastreria* for men and *bordados* on the machine and by hand, I promise you that I'm going to give you the certificate, but you need to put in a lot of effort, because the ladies that are going to graduate this year are very advanced, and they just need 6 months to graduate."

I paid a lot of attention and at age of 18 I got my certificate *de alta costura en corte y confección.*

I opened a little business in my house and I was *La Modista del pueblo.* Pero también tenía que divertirme. I liked to ride horses and do dances with the horses, maybe because I saw my grandfather every day he rode his horse, and he taught the horses how to dance and how to do different things, and all his life he was *entrenador de caballos,* a horse trainer. Another thing my grandfather, from my mom's side, showed me, was how to dance a horse, and *a tratar los caballos.* When I was 18 years old I knew how to ride a horse. I told my father that I want to make a group of *Charras.*

After a month I started a group of charras and we had shows in many places of the state of Colima.

At that time I was considered the *queen of las charras* and I made all the dresses that we wore.

Many friends wanted to be with us in our group and our group started to get more bigger. In three years I had a group of charras of 20 girls. All places that we went, all the people had respect for us. All the people of the state of Colima knew about us.

Another way in my work of sewing I made the small dresses for a wedding , but I wanted to continue to study more, and I thought about studying design, but my parents didn't give me permission to do it. So I entered a school where I learned to do hand work, like flowers, with a material called *migajon* and ceramic.

I liked gastronomy so I entered the University of Colima to learn how to conserve fruit, vegetables, cheese, yogurt and ham and how to do all that kind of foods.

When I was 22 years old I met the most wonderful man in the world, and he is my husband now. I got married with him eight months after I met him. I made my wedding dress and all the things that a bride has. We went to Tijuana to honeymoon because he was working there, but after four months we came back to Colima, because I missed Colima a lot. We opened a small market of vegetables and fruit.

At the age of 24 I had my first son, Gastón Pérez Padilla, and at the age of 26 I gave birth to my daughter, and last child. Her name is Paloma Pérez Padilla.

After that, at the age of 27, I wanted to continue to learn more so I enrolled in cosmetology classes.

One day, I arrived at the town where some people were asking for me. They showed me a class of cosmetics and then I started to sell by myself.

I did high sales, and at the age of 30 I met with other people to show my products. In three years I was number one in sales in all the state, and I received a lot of gifts from that company, but ultimately we had to come to the U.S. to meet my husband, because he was here working. I had to leave my business and my hard work to come here, and that was so hard for me.

When I came here, it was another life, another language, another culture to start again, but *yo no me arrepiento*, because my parents told me that all that I had learned in the past, would benefit me in the future. I am actually here with my family and with my blood in my veins.

I took some courses in decoration of cakes and pastry, and how to do chocolates.

Now I am working in a Mexican store called "La Petunia" and "La Morenita" where I develop all that I learned in Mexico. And one more thing, I will never forget what my parents taught me:

In this life we have to learn the most necessary things and go on with all the things that we have learned, and can't forget that every time, every where, we learn something new. And from the most insignificant person, we learn something, because all of us have our own histories.

With all my heart, Blanca Esthela Padilla Velazco

Me (Erika Cruz) and Mom (Asención Espinoza). That day we were getting ready to go to my friends' wedding. The mass started at 2:00 pm in Toppenish. We were in a hurry, but you couldn't tell. This is one of the few pictures of my mom and me together. We hardly spend time to take pictures together because of the falta de comunicación. I wonder how this picture would change if my father was in it?

No Questions and No Answers

Erika Cruz

As I write these words there are no questions and no answers. They come from the heart and mind. The reason for this is because as I became a teenager. Things started to change with my mom. Love was turning to hate. Words turned to sharp blades that hurt my heart, and the communication was getting lost.

The things that I know about my mom are because when I was small—*ella me agarró como un pañuelo al cual le podría decir muchas cosas malas y pensaba que no me dolería—oh me estaba lastimando y danando mi corazón.*

She grabbed me like a handkerchief, and she could say a lot of bad things too, and that it wouldn't hurt me, for example, she said that my dad was a bad man.

220

She once mentioned that she was born in Campoelcielo Guerrero, on August 15th 1947. That gives her 54 primaveras—54 springs, *primaveras de la cual*—*she said that the years were really bad from the time when she turned thirteen years old.* My mom's mom and dad were very wealthy in the beginning. They had many cattle and other animals.

My mom probably went through exactly what I am going through. We never had to suffer for shelter or food, but we didn't get the love that was needed to stop the suffering. Someone has to break this chain of suffering, and that's my job.

Asención (mom), was the 9th child of 12 kids. Only three survived: my mom; my Aunt María Espinoza, 52 years; and my Uncle Zistos Espinoza, who died at the age of 38; that was about 21 years ago. The rest died before they saw daylight. My grandma's name was María de Jesús Farias De Espinoza. *Ella pasó a descansar con Dios el 19 de Agosto de 1999.* She never knew how old she was because her parents died when she was small and they didn't have a birth certificate.

My grandpa's name is Alberto Espinoza de Farias. He is still alive. My mom never told me much about him. All I know is that they haven't talked for about ten years, and he won't talk to my mom on the phone because he said he doesn't like to talk on the phone. Mom had to leave the house at the age of 13 because my dad forced her to live with him. Mom said that she never loved him that the only reason she stayed with him was because my grandpa didn't want her back home. They felt they were backstabbed since they gave her everything she needed and more. My dad's name was Felix Cruz de Espinoza. He died on August 31st 1997. Mom and dad had 12 kids. I was the 12th one. My mom was 37 years old when she had me.

My mom doesn't say nice things very often, and when she told me that I was a miracle I felt very special and I will never forget what she said. The reason she told me that was because after her 11th kid, the doctor told her she shouldn't get pregnant again because of health issues.

Since I was small, I had to stick to my mom's *faldas*, or skirts, because I had to read the prices for her at the stores. And when we got here, well, she needed me to translate. I think that I have been a big help in her life but her *orgullo* doesn't let her see that, but it's ok as long as I do what I can to help her, and God knows it, that's O.K. I can continue to be the *buena para nada*.

We migrated to the U.S. on June 1st 1990 for the first and only time for me because since then I haven't gone back. They emigrated from Tijuana to California. Me and my nephew Julio crossed through the border line, but the rest of the family had to cross the *cerro*. My mom had no hope that my dad would change so she had to come over to the U.S. to fulfill our dream.

At that time there were only 3 girls left who were single, the rest were married and with families of their own. It was hard for her to *acostumbrarse a este país, pues era algo muy diferente, pero mientras nos beneficiara a nosotros ella no le importaba que le fuera difícil adaptarse a este país.* There is another thing that is not clear in my mind. She used to say that she wished my dad the best in life, and that even though he hurt her, and ruined her life, she did not wish him anything bad. What could be worse than to get your own daughter to hate you? Because that's what she did, she turned me against my dad.

When my dad died they brought his wallet for a *recuerdo,* or a memory. My mom showed me the wallet and it was full of pictures of me and my sister Maribel, the second to the youngest. That really broke my heart. I found out that he did love me, he did care for me, and I had hated him. The man was just a little irresponsible. *Pero ni modo la vida sigue, ahora la familia no más crece y crece de una pareja que no tenían esa chispa de amor y el fuego que se necesita para tener una familia. En total somos 7 hijas y hijos, 6 nueras y yernos, 19 nietos y nietas, y finalmente, dos bisnietas.*

I really thank my mom for showing me moral values, and how to be a responsible, respectful person; and best of all, she showed me the importance of my religion and believing in God. *Cuando estaba chiquita, me llevava a fuerza a la church pero ahora le doy las gracias.*

A la mejor mi vida no fue de maravilla, o un cuento de adas, pero yo voy a amolar el resto de mi vida agarada de la mano de Dios para que de ese modo pueda romper esa cadena de rencor, odio, y inmadurez que hay en mi familia.

The hard moments that I have gone through aren't going to stop me. That's going to come back in a good way sooner or later, if I learn from my mistakes and I realize what the people surrounding me are doing and imitate the good actions. Like I've said before, PROBLEMS and SADNESS are not to get you down, they are to get you stronger and to motivate you to try harder and aim higher, to prove to yourself and others that you can go beyond your obstacles and achieve your goals.

The situation in our family hasn't always been too easy in the past, especially the first ten years we spent here in the U.S. I've seen many of my friends fall into the temptation of drugs and gangs. I feel fortunate that I didn't end up in their shoes. Like many families, we've had many conflicts with each other. What has helped us overcome all that is the fact that no matter what happens, we will always be united as a family. A strong family produces strong individuals. What matters is not how many parents or the size of the family, but rather that there is unity within a household. I credit my parents with keeping the family together even during the worst of times. By completing the follow-up to my dad's original interview, I wish to give my parents the recognition they deserve for being able to raise three rowdy boys who are now responsible young men. So here is my conclusion to the original interview about my father Rafael Rosales.

The Voice of Reason in my Father

Oscar Rosales

As a youth, my father had to work hard and show self-reliance. My grandfather, Antonio Rosales, passed away when my dad was six years old. To this day, whenever I speak to him about his father's death, he still has trouble speaking about it in full detail. Although he now had the obligation to help care for his family, he still found the time to fit in some school and sports into his life.

To this day he still follows his favorite team "las Chivas Rayadas del Guadalajara." Sometimes I also see him watching pro wrestling on the T.V. I wasn't aware of it at first, but when I joined the wrestling team at Highland my freshman year, I unknowingly continued the wrestling tradition in my family.

It seemed to go well for him until the 1980's. During the first half of the decade, the standard of living in Mexico took a nosedive and among many other things, his grandfather died. A year later, we would make the trip *al norte*.

We had to pack light and bring only what we could carry. We practically left our whole history behind. All my early memories are nearly wiped out. In fact, my earliest memory is that of the border crossing back in 1986 when I was four.

By conducting this follow up, I also hoped to learn about the past before it was erased from my young memory. It is a means of uncovering the past, like a lost city in ruins, my history that unfortunately stayed in Guadalajara.

An Interview with Rafael Rosales, Part II.

When you lived in Mexico what other places did you visit outside our home state of Jalisco?
When I was about your age, I visited Mexico City. I also took a trip to Obregon City when I was a kid.

So which year did you visit the Federal District?
It was right around 1970, a few years before I married your mother.

How was the city when you went to visit?
Well, it's not as bad as most people say. I really enjoyed myself when I went to visit Chapultepec Park and the Colonial Plaza.

What do you think about what happened in Tlatelolco in 1968?
It was very bad. The students who were murdered were merely petitioning the government to be accountable for their actions and to stop the corruption. Unfortunately the ruling party gave the go-ahead to the police to open fire on them.

In your opinion, what must a person do to be successful in life?

Study! Stay positive and don't give up on anything. It is also important to stay away from negative influences. Sometimes it's your so-called friends that can do you more damage than even your worst enemy.

Who's the person who has influenced your life the most?
It was my grandfather. His name was Juan Guerra. I believe he moved to Texas when he was about three or four. His parents had already passed away when they took him to fight in WWI. Fortunately, the fighting had already ended when his ship arrived in Europe. Afterward, he would go on to California, where he would meet my grandmother. About three years later, after my mother was born, they decided to move to Mexico. That was around 1923 when they did that. They moved to Guadalajara where most of the family still remains. He taught me the value of hard work and to be proud of the work I do. It was the year before we moved here that he passed away. It's a shame you didn't get to know him that well.

In your opinion what defines a successful person?
What a person has done with their life. The way they act, think and live their lives.

If you were able to get to know a historical figure, who would it be, and why?
It would be the first indigenous Mexican President, Benito Juarez. He instituted a variety of reforms during his time in office that helped out the less fortunate. I'd probably ask him for advice, because he was an intelligent man and a great leader.

What is something that you still want to do in life or that you want to accomplish?
To see you and your brothers make it big in life. Also to help you and your brothers the best I can.

When I have kids of my own, what's the most important thing I need to know in order to care for them better?
Remember that they always come first. You must also try to understand their situation and help them solve their problems.

Now that I'm nearing graduation, do you have any good advice that may help me when I get to college and start making that transition toward life as an adult?
I can only tell you to be your own leader. Don't go around following people who don't take their lives seriously and who just smoke and drink their lives away. Just remember, "Don't do bad things that look good."

La Voz de Razón de mi Padre

Oscar Rosales

En años pasados la situación de nuestra familia no ha sido tán facil, especialmente los primeros diez años que estuvimos en los E.E.U.U. He mirado muchos de mis amigos caer en las drogas y en otros problemas graves. Me siento afortunado que no me pasó lo mismo. como muchas familias, nosotros también hemos tenido nuestros problemas. Lo que nos ayuda a nosotros es el hecho que pase lo que pase, siempre estaremos unidos. Una familia fuerte, produce gente que tiene una mente fuerte y que no se dan por vencidos. No importa si la familia es pequeña o si sólo hay un padre, lo importante es la unidad. Sin la unidad, no hay familia. Mi padre, Rafael Rosales y mi madre, Angelina Rosales Castañeda, son los que mantuvieron la unidad en nuestra familia y nos enseñaron a tener orgullo en ser trabajadores. Ahora,aquí les va mi entrevista con Rafael Rosales, la parte II

¿Cuándo vivía allá en México cuáles otros lugares visitó fuera del estado de Jalisco?
Cuando tenía más o menos tu edad yo fui a la Ciudad de México a visitar por allá y también cuándo era más pequeño visité a Ciudad Obregón.

¿Cuál año era cuando fue al D.F.?
Creo que fue en el año '70, unos cuantos años antes de que me casé con tu madre.

¿Cómo se le a figuró la ciudad cuando fue a visitar?
No era tan malo como dicen unos. Sí me gusto la ciudad. Todavía tengo recuerdos de cuando fui al parque de Chapultepec y a la plaza de la Colonía.

¿Qué opina de lo que pasó en Tlatelolco en el en Tlatelolco en el '68?
Era muy malo. Los estudiantes sólo pidieron al gobierno que tomen más responsabilidad por sus acciones y que sirvan mejor a la gente pero desgraciadamente el gobierno actuo en tal manera.

En su opinion, ¿qué debe hacer uno para tener exito en la vida?
Estudiar! Tener mente positiva y nunca darse por vencido. También es de suma importancia alejarse de las amistades que sólo estan allí de vagos y que no estudian. En veces, son las malas amistades que te hacen más daño que tus propios enemigos.

Para usted, ¿quien fue la paersona que influyó más su vida?

Fue mi abuelo. Se llamaba Juan Guerra. El se mudó a Texas a la misma edad que tu tenías cuando nos venimos a los E.E.U.U. Ya se le habían muerto sus padres cuando lo agarraron a que vaya a pelear en la primera Guerra Mundial. Afortunadamente ya se había acabado la guerra cuando su barco aterrizó en Europa. Luego fue a California y conoció a mi abuela. Un año después de que naciera tu abuela en Santa Bárbara, decidieron volver a México se mudaron a Guadalajara. Él es el que me enseñó a trabajar y a tener orgullo en lo que uno hace en la vida.

En su opinion, ¿qué es lo que define a una persona exitosa?

Su manera de ser. Mejor decir, la manera en que actúan, piensan y viven.

Si podría conocer un personaje historico, ¿quien sería y por qué?

Sería el Presidente Mexicano, Benito Juarez. Él era el primer presidente de raza indígena en México. Él defendió contra la invasión francesa e instituyó reformas para ayudar a la gente humilde. Si pudiera, le pedería consejos. El era muy inteligente.

¿Que es una cosa que todavía le falta hacer en su vida o que quiere lograr?

Mirar que tú y tus hermanos tengan éxito en la vida. También ayudarles lo más que pueda.

Cuando tenga hijos propios, ¿qué es lo más importante que tengo que saber para poder criarlos mejor?

Que ellos vienen primero. Tienes que tratar de comprender sus situaciones y ayudarles a solucionar sus problemas.

Ahora que me voy a graduar, ¿hay un consejo que me pueda dar que me ayude cuando llegue a la universidad y cuando empiezé hacia mi vida adulta?

Sólo te pudo decir que seas tu propio líder. No sigas a gente, que no toma su vida en serio y que siempre andan por allá bebiendo y fumando mota. Acuerdate lo que dice un pasaje en la Biblía, "No hagas cosas malas que parezcan bien."

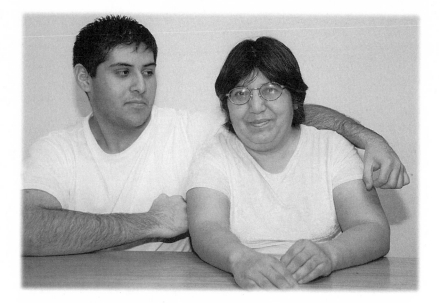

Angelina Rosales Castañeda, pictured here with her youngest son Oscar, is a native of the small town of Santa María de Los Angeles, Jalisco. She is now 46 years old and lives with her husband in Yakima. The impact she had on Oscar's life was immense. He credits her with giving him hope and always encouraging him, even when he was having hard times. She is the one who, along with his dad, helped Oscar develap a personality that has both their influences, yet is uniquely his own.

The Dispenser of Strength and Courage

Oscar Rosales

In life, no matter how bad our situations get, there is always a positive aspect. When we are at our lowest point and feel isolated from the rest of the world, there is always one person there supporting us, giving us the courage and strength to pull through. For me, such a person has been my mother, Angelina Rosales Castañeda. She's been there for me, literally, since day one. I credit her for giving me all my courage, and above all else, for not letting me go down the wrong path.

A native of Santa María de Los Angeles, Jalisco in Mexico, my mom, was born to Ramón and María Auxilio Castañeda on the first day of October in the year 1956. My grandfather, who just recently passed away, moved the family to the city of Guadalajara back in the

60's. Coincidentally, they moved in right next door to my dad's family. Since both my mom and my dad had to work during the day, they had to take classes in the evening

At first they seemed like polar opposites. My mom enjoyed dancing and being around friends, whereas my dad was more into his job as well as being into athletics. My mom goes on to tell me that her initial impression of my dad was that he was a bit of a "show off" and that he was in her own words *muy creído*, because according to my mom, he had a bunch of women there watching him during wrestling practice. Even though my dad was always hanging around my mom's older brothers, he was a bit shy about asking my mom out on a date, that is, until an event occurred that would change both their lives.

It was around 1975. My mother was all set to come over to the U.S. with my grandparents. It was at this time that my dad finally came out and told my mom how he felt about her. Somehow, he was able to convince her to stay with him. A short time later they got married. They were both relatively young, my mom being 20 at the time and my dad being 22. Like many married couples they've had their ups and downs, but they've always managed to resolve their problems.

They have been together for over 26 years now. They still look like they have a lot of left in them, even after raising three boys. Now that I'm headed off to college, my parents can breathe a sigh of relief. Finally the last one is on his way out. Everything got easier for them after my older brothers Eduardo and Edgar graduated, so now it's up to me to make it a complete "sweep."

I still remember when I was a little kid that I didn't like my name. Oscar, it sort of sounded to me like I was a spokesperson for the company that makes hot dogs. So I took advantage of this opportunity to finally ask my mom how they arrived at choosing my name.

At first I thought I was named after the Academy Award, coveted by the best performers in film production, but according to my mom, they arrived at my name almost by accident. In her account, my mom tells me that she and a few of my aunts came together to think up a name for me. They were thinking of Jose, Antonio, Ramon, Ignacio, and my dad's name, Rafael. When my dad came in he was opposed to naming me after him. In his version he told me that he wanted me to be my own man, and not an extension of himself. So they arrived at Oscar because, supposedly, it wasn't too common.

In concluding my interview, I thanked my mom and went about doing the rest of my homework. I applaud both my mom and my dad's efforts in raising me. At times I know I let them down with my attitude and behavior. It is now that I'm more mature that I understand the sacrifices they made for me. They haven't really told me in detail their plans for the future. I still remember a promise I made my mom when I was about nine years. I said that one day I'd buy her a house when I become older and that she and my dad wouldn't have to worry about anything any more. I intend to keep that promise and make sure they receive what they deserve. They've paid their dues, and now its time for them to enjoy life. I'll always remember what my mom used to tell me when I was younger: *Ponle ganas al estudio, Oscarito, no te dejes por vencer.*

In these pictures, you can see the powerful connection between my father, Lucio Robles, my mother, Josefina Robles and me, Rosa Robles. By being close we demonstrate our strong relationship and love for one another. I am one of the fruits that my parents' love has given. You can see the resemblance there is between my mother and I. Let me say that I am proud and I thank God for still having my parents right by my side.

My Root

Rosa Robles

My name is Rosa Isela Robles and I am 17 years old. I am the daughter of Josefina Robles. In the following paragraphs, you will hear about my mother's life from her childhood until today. It is written in a form as if my mother wrote it herself. It is an interview that I made with her in the last month of the year 2001. I have entitled it "My Root" because to me, a root gives a sense from where one comes from and what one has created.

The earliest I can remember is when I was seven years old. During this time, my mother, Celia Amador, had sent me away to another town with the name of "Palo Verde." Here, I stayed with my grandparents, María del Refugio and Chano Ramirez. They were my father's parents. My mother's parents were Juventina Camacho and

José Amador. My mom had sent me to help and cheer up my grandma because she was sick. These times of my childhood were the happiest times of my life.

My grandparents were very rich. They owned cattle and land, and my grandma even had gold coins. I would go and play in one of the rooms where there was gold and I played with the coins as if I was taking a shower. I was the spoiled one in the family. They bought me a lot of stuff. As time passed, I grew older and I began to help wash clothes. In order to do this, I had to take water out of a well in buckets where sometimes a line of ladies would be waiting for their turn. I was such a brat that in order for me to go first, I would yell at the ladies. When I arrived home with the buckets full of water, I would get to work and wash on a flat rock. This was very fun.

Ironing clothes was another job I did. My aunts were so lazy that they asked me to do it. At the age of 12, my father, Santos Ramírez, came back to the town to take me home to "El Crucero de Santa María." I was very sad and inconsolable. My parents were very poor. We all lived in a small house with only one room. Imagine ten of us all sleeping in the same room on the floor.

My mom had married my father at the age of 13. Both of their parents took about six months to forgive them. But my mom's brother since then and until today, does not talk to her. At the age of 14, my parents were not that poor anymore. My father now owned two meat markets, land, a creamer store, a coal shed, and a beautiful house. At this time, I had a boyfriend. His name was Vicente. I was seeing him without my father's consent. My father was very jealous. Jealousy is an old tradition. Guys could not ask permission because to him, women were not objects that were to be lent out. I met this other guy named Lucio at the same time I was seeing Vicente. They were both from the same town that I was. I was scared of Lucio because he was tall and his look was strong. My boyfriend was also scared of him. Whenever Lucio saw us together, he would tell Vicente off. There was one time when he grabbed him from the neck and told him to stay away from me. Poor Vicente, he was shaking. At the time, it was scary but now it is funny. There was another time when Lucio and his friends tried to steal me. They tried to put me onto a horse and kidnap me, but thanks to my friends that pulled me away, they were unsuccessful.

A while later, I began to like Lucio. But still, I did not leave Vicente. I was with both of them. To see them, I had to hide from either one or the other depending on whom I was going to see. I also

232

had to be careful with my dad and my brothers. As I began to like Lucio more and more, I broke up with Vicente. It hurt him so much that until today, I hear rumors saying that he still loves me. But like I said before, he was too scared of Lucio. I remember the sweet and romantic things Lucio would do. He would go outside of my house in the middle of the night and sing to me with a guitar. He always sang the song of Vicente Fernandez, *Aquí tienes las llaves de mi Alma*, or, *Here you have the keys to my soul*. He would also give my sisters money to take me out to see him. *(When my mother told me all these crazy stories about her boyfriends, I could not stop laughing. It was quite amazing how she made me imagine these funny incidents.)*

There was one time when dad caught me talking to Lucio in the back porch. He grabbed me from my hair and hit me as I walked back to the house. This was very embarrassing for me because Lucio saw. I did not go out for about two weeks. I also remember when I went to a dance without anyone knowing, but I had such bad luck that my brother was there too, and saw me. He also grabbed me from the hair but thank God that Lucio was not there. That would have been embarrassing, too.

At the age of 15, was when my life made a big step. You can say it was my doom. My dreams were to go back with my grandparents. Those years were the happiest for me. One night when I was asleep, my cousin Paz came over. She invited me to dinner but I refused to go. My mom convinced me so I finally went. It was only to destroy my life. They had it all planned. She would leave with her boyfriend and I would leave with Lucio. I did not want to, nor Lucio, but we listened to them, and left. The truth is that I was so innocent that just because I walked four meters with a boy, *I thought I was dishonored*, so I left. The next day, our parents were angry. My mother told me that my father asked her where was his *Barbie*.

My mother regretted letting me go out, but it was too late. Lucio's mom, whose name was Rosa, was very mad. She did not like me at all. She wanted Lucio to go to the United States and immigrate. Lucio was a teacher and so I left with him to another town. Afterwards, we got married. We got married early in the morning and there were hardly any people.

This day was a disaster. There was this guy that tried to act smart and he asked me to run away with him on the day of my wedding. Like I said, I am very aggressive so I grabbed a brick and broke it on his head. He bled and fainted. My brother went to go see if he was okay. We were worried that I had killed him.

One year after our marriage, we had a son. I was 17 and had a big responsibility as a mother. My son's name was Francisco Iban. He died three months later. He now would be 24. I would cry like crazy. It hurt me so much that it took me over three years to calm down. I thought that us women could only have one child. My mom told me that if that was true, then how was it that I had more brothers and sisters?

There was one time when I heard my son crying in the room. My mother told me that I did not let him rest in peace, so I stopped crying. One year later, I had another child. It was a girl so I named her Maria and she is now 23 years old. She was born in Guadalajara, Jalisco. We then left to the United States. We had to cross the border as immigrants with the help of a *coyote*. A *coyote* is a person who takes you across the U.S. with the price of about one thousand dollars for each person.

The first and second time we were caught. It wasn't until the third time that we crossed. We then came to a place with the name of Moxee and then later to Yakima. As time passed, Lucio and I worked, rented a house, and had another child. His name is Lucio Jr. and is now 21 years old. Two years later, we had our second daughter. Her name is Nancy and she is 19 years old. My husband was now the supervisor of where he worked. We then bought our first house and had another child. Her name is Rosa Isela who is now 17 years old. Seven years passed and we now had two more houses, another one here and one in Mexico. My kids now went to school and we continued to go to school.

When Rosa was ten years old, I had another son whose name is Christian. He is now 7 years old. He looks like a *gavachito*. Blonde hair and blue eyes.

We suffered a lot as a couple. His family did not like me and they tried to convince him to leave me. At first Lucio listened to them. We were going to get divorced until finally he snapped out of it and put an end to it.

Being a mother was tough for me. I took half of my children to school and the other half to baby sit. After work, I picked them up and watched after them, making sure they did their homework, were clean, and healthy. My daughter, María, left the house with her boyfriend at the age of 14. I felt like a piece of my heart was taken. Because I got married young too, a lot like me, my daughter did not have fun. After this, each year we have gone to Mexico. We finally fixed papers. In other words, we have now immigrated. We are

234

citizens.

In 1994, we moved to Yakima, the place where my children were born. I did not like it because it was more dangerous for my kids. There were too many gangs, crimes, and fights. And my fear was right, the city was more dangerous. My husband got sick and got operated and now has a pacemaker. My son, Lucio, had a car accident and went to jail for 4 years. At the same time, my other daughter Nancy left with her boyfriend at the age of 15. Rosa went to Mexico, and my husband and I were left alone with Christian. I felt like I was dead but living. I lost three of my kids but now everything is different. I am now a grandma with four grandchildren. We are all together and I am once again alive. My grandparents have now passed away. My dreams are to go back to Mexico forever and be with my people.

•

My mother was born in "El Crucero de Santa Maria," Jalisco. She is the only one out of four sisters that does not have a college degree. She also has four brothers but only two of them have professional careers. My mother might not have finished school, but I consider her career to be a great mother that she has always been. One thing I would like to say is that my mother has always been there for us. I am very proud and honored to have shared this part of my mom's life with all of you who were interested in reading it.

Today, the 25th of January 2002, my family is here in Yakima, Washington. All of my brothers came from California and my father came from Mexico. My father's name is Israel Barriga and my mom's is Guadalupe Hermosillo. They are happy, because we are together and because all three of us are abrecaminos. First my sister María was an abrecaminos, and last year Jessica became an abrecaminos. This year it's my turn, and it's the third time we've interviewed our mom, and my interview gets to go in the book. By 3:00 pm just two of my brothers were at home, Israel and Angel. The other two are not in the picture. My mom was happy for us that day and for my other sister, too, who is in the picture, Bertha Alicia. She was going to be married the next day, Saturday. My mom was nerviosa also because on the 28 of January 2002 she was going to have a surgery on one of her legs because of her *artritis*. But she had hope and our love. All my siblings were happy. I enjoyed my family and they enjoyed this, too. We have our roots with us. One rule is that we have to eat together at the table. At night on this day we made menudo and we ate together as the family that we are.

The Wonderful Mother

Rosa María Barriga

In this world each person has different experiences in life. A person's life depends on what they do, or where they belong, for Latinos as for Chicanos or Americans. All of as have different customs and *raices*. Even my mom, Guadalupe Hermosillo, has different ways than mine.

My mom belongs to a little ranch whose name is *La Lechuguilla*, in *the municipio de Aguililla, Michoacán*. That's where she was born in 1940, on July 24th. She lived there until she was 21 years old. Her life was difficult and kind of sad because as a child she had to play with *olotes* of corn wrapped with *garras viejas* instead of dolls. Her dolls were made of corn cobs wrapped in old rags. Her family was from a low social status, and she couldn't go to school because they lived on a ranch and school was far away. She had to stay at home to do her chores.

My mom had to make tortillas and food at the age of 10 years old, because the woman is born to do that, my grandpa said that. Also my mom and her sisters had to go to *Parages*. Here their father and brother had to work for days. My mom and her sisters went to make food for them. They had to do *tortillas moliendo el nixtamal on the metate* and cook the food on the *comal* with wood.

My mom grew in that world and with time she had fun too. Her parents used to take them *a la plaza* (to the plaza), or garden in Aguililla, Michoacán, a place where the girls walk to one side around the garden and the boys walk to the other side. It is like two lines, one of girls, and the other of boys. In that place is where my father met my mom. He gave her a flower and she received or accepted the flower, and that meant *Yes*. Then they talked, and she told him where they could see each other, because my grandparents, Feliciano Hermosillo and Rosa Villalvaso, were really strict with their daughters. They didn't let them have boyfriends. That's why my mom had to see him when she went *a acarriar* the water from the river to her home. She *la acarriaba en cantaros de barro*. She carried the water in clay pots. She saw him many times when she went for the water.

My mom says that she thinks that her parents were really strict, maybe because they were from La Granada, and they were born and grew up there. On this ranch, *La Granada Municipio de Aguililla Michoacán*, the people were really strict with the girls, or women, and the women who didn't respect her parents were called *bocona, desobediente and malportada. Loud mouth, disobedient and badly behaved.* But my mom didn't think like that. She told me that she always thought, *How come they don't want me to have a boyfriend, even when my mom was married two times?* But she never said anything to them about that, because my grandma knew more than her. She just continued seeing my father without their permission.

The time went faster and the day came when my father, Israel Barriga, asked my mom if he could go to her home to ask her parents if they could get married. My mom said yes because they had a year going out. My mom says that she would never forget those days when my grandparents told him no, that he wouldn't get married to her, because his family was really poor. Then they told my mom how her life would be if she married him. My grandpa said, "Do you want to live like that, poor for your whole life? Look, for example, at their poor situation. They don't have a permanent place, they live from place to place, and also, you know as I do, José Barriga, his father *golpea* (hits) his mom. Later on, he will do the same thing to you. So I decided that you are going with my sister Gloria to Uruapan, Michoacán. Next week you will be there to forget those *absurda*s ideas that you have in your mind."

And it happened as my grandpa said, but she just lived there for a month and came back with my grandparents. She had to come back, because in Uruapan, while she was with her Aunt Gloria, a man tried to rape her *por la fuerza*, while she was going out to the store. By that time my father knew that she was back and went to see her again, and they continued seeing each other until my father had to ask for her hand three times. Well, *asking for her hand* means to ask her parents' permission to get married, but after three times, he received the same answer, *no*.

My grandma told her one time, "If you marry him, forget that I'm your mother." They sent my mom with my Uncle Miguel, her brother, to tell my father that she wouldn't get to marry him, ever, and to stop asking. But my mother, instead of doing that, she got married to him that day. In her wedding there was nobody from her side, and some of his family. Then, at the end of the wedding, my mom asked my father if she could go a week with her family before they got together. My father said yes, and she went home, but her brother knew what happened. He just said, "That's your problem because I didn't know anything about it and I wasn't there either. So you resolve your problem on your own."

When they got home my grandparents were there and she told them what happened. My grandpa said, "If that was what you wanted, good, good for you, but don't come and tell us when he ends up beating you a *garrotazos*. She didn't worry much about it because they had talked before about it, and my father told her that he would never touch her with that intention. By that time she was 21 years old and my father 20 years old.

By the way, she was pregnant at the age of 22 years old. They named their first child Jesús, who died at the age of 3 months from fever. My grandma didn't do what she said at all, because she was with my mom all the time when she was pregnant and she also helped my mom to be a mother, showing her how to take care of kids and so many things like that. My mom had another boy and later 4 girls. By that time they were living in Aguililla where all of them were born.

In 1976 my parents arrived in the U. S. A., and they had to live through a lot a bad things on their way to the U. S. They had to come through the hills of Nogales, because they weren't legal in this country. And also because the *coyote* charged less and they didn't have much money. They came with my oldest brother and my 4 sisters. On their way, one of my sisters was thirsty and she wanted water, but my father told her "We are almost there. Don't speak, and we will give you water as soon as we get there." My father was carrying the youngest of my sisters, Bertha, and my mom had Carmela with her. The others were walking with them. My mom says that she felt bad for her children and also scared for them, because they were just children and had to go through this.

My parents lived here in Yakima, Washington for six years, where they had three boys and two girls. My father had been working in the fields of Yakima. By this time in 1983, my parents had to go back to Mexico, because my grandma on my father's side was really sick on her way to die. My mom was 42 years old and she was pregnant with her 11th child. She was 7 months pregnant.

I was born on November 1, 1983, in Aguililla Mich. When I was born my parents were worried because my mom was 43 years old and it would be hard for one of us to survive. But nothing happened and I lived there with my parents until the age of 16 years. While I was growing, my brothers came back to the U.S. on their own and then all my sisters, too. So I was the only one who lived with them, and we were just waiting until migration called my parents to come for their passport to Cuidad Juarez. That happened pretty soon and we came to the U.S. to be with all my sisters and my brothers living in California where we passed to see them, before we came to Yakima, Washington.

Here is where my mom and my father came to live with me and my sisters because I'm coming to school and learning English. At the same time I'm growing, my mom's dreams are the same as my sisters. My mom always wanted to go to school and learn English and Math and to have a career. She didn't go to school but she knows how to read and write in Spanish (not professionally, but she knows) and she learned as an older woman.

I love you mom, you are a wonderful person, and I admire all your qualities and efforts and because you have put up with my father, an alcoholic, God bless you, mom. Thanks for giving us a whole family with my father and you together all our lives instead of leaving us without a father, because it was hard to be with him drinking all the time and being a *mujeriego*. He is *cariñoso* too, and he took care of us. He didn't leave my mom and us for another woman. He gave us the most he could. He is a good father and I learned a lot from him, and my mom, she is the best mom. She is sick now, but I hope she'll be better from her arthritis in her legs.

The day we took this picture was the first time my mom really gave me a hug. There was a closeness that me and my mom never have shared. The relationship between my Dad and I also became closer. My dad and mom were a little embarrassed but they got over it. This picture means a lot to me because me and my parents have never taken pictures together, all three of us. My parents don't like to take pictures. They say they will break the camera. I love my parents, they're pretty special.

Towards a New Life
Hacia una Vida Nueva

Beatriz Rivera

In the state of Michoacán, in Mexico, there is a small town by the name of Coyota. This is where my grandparents are from. Simon Sánchez and Ignacia Mejia. All of their 12 children were born there. My mom was the fourth out of twelve. Her name is María Irene Sánchez. Together they lived in a small house in the *Colonia de Los Mejias.* My mom, every single day, would walk to the town of Coyota to go to school. Then came the time when my mom had to stop going to school because there wasn't enough money. So she ended up going only to the sixth grade. From then on she had to stay home and help with chores and take care of her smaller brothers and sisters. Every day she had to get up early and wash the dishes, sweep the patio, carry jugs of water from the *ojo de agua* (water hole). This had to be done three times a day. She also worked in the fields with her dad, planting the corn.

At the age of eighteen she went to work in Mexico City as a *trabajadora domestica* (maid). This was to help out her parents economically. At the age of twenty she returned to live with her parents. One day she was washing the clothes at the water hole and a guy was passing by and introduced himself by the name of Jaime Rivera. He said that he lived in the next town. He also asked her what her name was. She said, *Me llamo Irene.* Then he asked her if she had a boyfriend and she said no. They kept seeing each other and eventually they became boyfriend and girlfriend. After two months of knowing each other, my mom decided to leave with the man who is now my dad. She decided to leave with my dad because one of her cousins told her that at her age of twenty one, if she didn't decide to marry then, she would never marry, because by then she would be too old and no one would be interested in her.

"*Nunca se me va olvidar ese día que me fui con tú papá. Los perros ladraban y ladraban y no paraban de ladrar. Cuando se hizo noche y acabamos de cenar yo me fui para mi cuarto y agarre mis pocas cosas y me fui. Cuando llegue al lugar donde me estaba esperando tu papa se levanto me agarro de la mano y nos fuimos caminando para La Cortina donde vivia tu papa. Luego tomamos un taxi para Zitacuaro a la casa de tu abuela.*"

Here is a translation of what mom said: "I will never forget the day I left with your dad. The dogs barked and barked and they wouldn't stop barking. When it became dark and we had just eaten dinner, and I went to my room picked up a few things and left. When I got to where your dad was waiting for me, he stood up and took me by the hand and we starting walking to where he lived at "La Cortina." From there, we left in a taxi to your grandma's house in Zitacuaro."

After that she went to live with my dad at his mom's house. She didn't like living there because they didn't like her very much. Then my dad made her a house out of adobe. He built it near a small stream. This way they could have water for all the plants they were going to have. Then my dad left to the U.S. to work in the fields. While he was over there my mom wrote him a letter saying that she was pregnant. The months passed and he returned. After his return his first daughter was born and he named her Beatriz .

Then one day my dad decided he wanted to leave to what he calls "el otro lado"—the other side, but he wanted to take my mom and me. My mom didn't want to leave. She was scared of moving to a new place. She was also scared because she was five months pregnant with her second child.

Finally my dad decided he wanted to leave for the United States, but this time my mom and me were going. My mom didn't want to go because she was scared of going to a new place and leaving her mom behind. She was also scared of crossing the border and at the same time being five months pregnant. Then my dad convinced her and she crossed to the United States for the first time through Ciudad Juarez in March of 1985. She remembers walking through the desert at night and how cold it was. They walked many hours. They walked until they got to the other side and a car picked them up. They came to the City of Yakima where my dad's brother and sister-in-law lived. They lived at their house for some time and moved to Mt. Vernon, where my dad worked picking cucumbers and strawberries. Then one day he got deported by the immigration. So my mom was left alone and worried that my dad would not be there when the baby was born. He did make it on time. That very same night he returned, my mom gave birth to her second daughter and named her Brenda.

After that they returned to Yakima and worked in thinning, picking pears, picking cherries and apples. My mom decided that she wanted to live in a house that would be hers. She was tired of living in an apartment or in a house so close to so many people. So my dad looked for a house which they could both afford to buy. They did buy a house in which they still live today. They both worked hard in the fields to pay off the debt. Later my mom got a job at the Snokist Warehouse in Terrace Heights peeling pears, which is still her job today. Years passed and she got pregnant with her third child, another girl. Her name is Esmeralda; and next came Ruby, who is the baby.

Now at the age of forty-one she is still working hard to maintain what she has worked so hard for. *Ella dice que ella trabajará hasta que coseche lo que plantó.* "I will keep on working until I harvest what I planted, which is you." Now she only awaits the day she will retire and go live in Mexico with her family.

My name is María Trinidad Padilla. My parents' names are Antonio Padilla and Margarita Maciel. On March 27, 2002, we were waiting for my teacher at 6:30 p.m. While we were waiting for him, we were talking about the differences between Mexico and the United States. Those two different cultures contain and enclose a lot of conversation. One example is the difference between Mexican farming and United States farming. In Mexico, a farmer owns about four acres of corn, *trigo, sogo, garbanzo* or *frijol,* and buys the *fertilizantes* at a very high price. It is very difficult because they don't receive pay from anybody. They do the work by themselves. At harvest time, buyers pay a very low price for the crops which don't satisfy the farmer. It doesn't cover expenses for the sowing. That is why many Hispanic people, especially Mexican people, come to the United States. We immigrate to this country to seek better pay and a better future. At the time my teacher arrived at our home, he was talking with my parents while I was brushing my hair. Then he started taking some pictures. We had so much fun, because we had never done this before. We used to take pictures, but on other kinds of occasions. For me it was an incredible moment. I couldn't believe at this moment I was with my parents again, and all my siblings, too. How many times in lonely moments I wished to have them all with me! When my teacher gave me this opportunity, I was so happy, because all my family had just came from La Cuestita Michoacán México. Now for the book, I would be with my parents in the picture. Later, when we finished taking pictures, it was a pleasure to share with my teacher some cheese and pumpkin seeds, toasted on the *comal* that my parents brought from México. We were showing him how to open the pumpkin seeds when my mom said, *"Yo recuerdo que cuando era una niña no podía pelar las semillitas y pues yo me las comía con todo y cascarita para mas facíl."* Everybody laughed about it *a carcajadas.* My teacher left for home after we had fun in the beautiful afternoon. A week later he came back to give us the pictures. We invited him to come in to eat the favorite food of the family. It was *mole* with rice. But he was going to the movies with his wife. So we told him, "After the movie you come back to eat O.K?" He was very excited that we were cooking especially for him and his wife. When he was at the movies, my mom, my sister Maggie and I were finishing cooking the *mole.* My mom was *dorando los ingredientes* and grinding the *chili.* My sister Maggie was preparing the *carne,* and I was straining the *chili,* using the strainer. When my mom was in México, Maggie used to do the *mole* because she learned very well from my mom. I didn't learn it. I just helped, but I really don't know how much of each condiment they use to make it. We used all the condiments so the *mole* would be so delicious. It was very delicious. It had the flavor of México. Or I will say, it tasted the way my mom cooks. Mr. Bodeen arrived at home then, we got everything ready. The tortillas, lemon, salt, refrescos. While we were eating at the table, we were listening to my mom's favorite music, especially the song she likes the most. It ís a song from *Los Relampagos del Norte.* The song is called *Un Día Con Otro.* My mom says that this song gives her a lot of memories from her teen life. That is why I like to play the song. I feel like I like it, too. We had a nice moment all together. We were talking about the classes for parents who want to learn English. My teacher gave my mom a special invitation to go to school. He wrote it on a napkin. She still has the napkin written by him. My family and I give thanks from all the Hispanic people. It is an *orgullo* to know that there are people like our teachers at Davis who know how to value our culture. Thank you, everybody. We really appreciate your dedication. And thanks for encouraging us to be *abrecaminos* and to make a way where there is no way.

Tesoro De Raices Seguidas Por El Tiempo/ Treasure of Roots Following the Time

Trinidad Padilla

This is the story of my *más* precious *tesoro, my most precious treasure,* my parents. Their names are Margarita Maciel and Antonio Padilla. They were born in La Cuestita Michoacán, México. My mother was born on December 19, 1950. My father was born on May 11, 1947. They have been living together with the same intensive love since they met for the first time.

It is April 27, 2002 as I make this interview. My parents are very special and they are the most precious *padres* in the whole world. They have a beautiful big family. We're seven girls, and one boy, who is the little one in the family. All the members are Lety, Martha Imelda, Maggie, María de Jesus, Triny (that's me), Rosy, Claudia, and Antonio de Jesus Padilla Maciel. We all love each other. We are not fighting as in the usual families. I think we don't like to do that because we have never seen our parents fighting, or even yelling to us. Of course they used to say something when we were wrong, but they never tried to hit us. Both of them are wonderful. They are always giving us good advice.

Both of them have little secrets as I just discovered on this occasion. For example, my mother never told us about several letters that she got when she was like 14-years-old. It was at the time when she started to have a boyfriend. This is the only part of her life that we didn't know, because she had already told us about her childhood. She said, *"¿A ver que quieres que te cuente?"* I answered, "Pues, your adventures and more about your life since you were a child. And about you as a teenager going out with boyfriends. *¿Como le hacian para platicar con los novios cuando sus papas no las dejaban salir?*

"Oh! My!! *It feels good in here, huh mamy!*

"Sí, Triny, está muy agusto aquí. — It was better to come here to the park and feel the air *fresco* and not being at home. "A ha! Here we are laying down on the little *sarapito* that we put on the ground. A lot of voices from many people are interferring with our *charla,* our little conversation. There are three baseball games going on with little kids playing in the Elk's Park. That is why it's too loud in here. That is O.K though, it appears like there is something going on!

—"Well mom, tell me!"

"O.K. Triny, pues mira. One time, like today, but in 1957, I was only seven years old. I used to like to be with my mother, *tu mama, Trina.* I always wanted to be like her. I wanted to be grown up. But little by little, I discovered that the most beautiful lifetime is when we are kids. If you see, we used to take life as a game and didn't realize that the time is a treasure, even though, my childhood was very hard. I was just seven years old when I had to make *tortillas* from *masa. Tu mama, Trina, pobrecita de mi mama.* She had to go get water in big *cantaros.* The lake was very far away from home. I had to make the *tortillas* because my mom had to go at the crack of dawn, so the sun wouldn't warm up the way making it too hot. I didn't even reach the

comal, but I had to *tortiar*, (make tortillas), because being the third one of six siblings, it was my responsibility. Esperanza, my older sister, used to be the *manda más*. At 5:30 a.m. she used to get up to break up the *nixtamal* and get the *masa*, so then she can put me to making *tortillas*.

"One day I thought, If I break up the *nixtamal*, Esperanza is going to make the *tortillas*. But it didn't work out. Esperanza got mad so at the end, I had to finish doing everything.

"I got lucky when Esperanza got married when she was 15 years old. I was now the older sister. I was then 14 years old. At this time, I was getting letters from a lover. He was the first boy I liked and the only one. His name was Antonio Padilla. *We have been in love since we met for the first time*. It was *chispas* to have boyfriends at those times. As I was a *catequista*, someone who teaches little kids *God's things*, I used to get out from home with my friends and used to go to church. After teaching doctrine, we had time to write letters and send them to the boys. And when we used to go to get water in the big *cantaros* made of *barro*, we wore our new *guarache*s so the boys could see us dressing nice. I still have the little letters that Antonio wrote for me 38 years ago. If you want, I can show them to you!"

—Oh yeah! That will be exciting and very interesting. "Ah! Mama, I can see in your eyes and your smile, you are still in love with my dad, ah?"

"*Oh! Claro que sí!* I am reading those letters and I feel like it is 38 years ago." "Look! Mama, they still have this dust. What is it?"

"Hummm! It was perfume in dust. It is almost gone. He put it on the letters so they could smell good."

"*Ooh! Haa! Papa tenía bien conquistada a mama verdad?*"

"*Usted que cree!*"—"You better believe it!"

"Mama, where did you put those letters so that nobody could see them before? What about every time we painted the house? You used to save them very well, ha!"

"*Oh pues, sí, pues que creen mis niñas que no las iba yo a guardar!*"

"Well yeah, but not too much time.

"Look! *Chiquillas* in all the letters, my dad drew a little bird with a little letter in the *pico*."

"Oh, yeah! And in all of them he put the *verso* that says, '*Vuela, vuela palomita anda y dile a esa muchachita del reboso ralladito que la quiero mucho.*'"

"Look at the dates of the letters! This one was written *Agosto 20, 1964*. This one was from *Agosto 23, 1964*. All are just one day after another, aren't they? That is *chispas*, Mama, and how did you use these small envelopes?"

"People used to sell them in different colors."

"Wow!"

"Mama, and when did you get married?"

"Umm! I got married in 1970 when I was 19 years old."

"Since you were 14-years-old you just had my dad as a boyfriend?"

"Yes, he was the only one. We were going out for 4 years, and we broke up for two years. But then we got married and got all of you. My beautiful seven girls and my baby Antonio."

"What is my dad's story?"

"Well ask him. And see what he says."

"Hi, Papa! Hi! How are you doing? Because I am making a way where there is no way. Mmm!—You are watching the Chivas against Las Aguilas de la America.—Hah? Yea! —Who is winning?

"Oh, pues America."

"Ok! Papa, tell me about your childhood."

"About my childhood, what do I tell you?"

"A lot of things we don't know."

"Well, since I was a child I had to help my parents work in the fields. My brothers and I had to wake up in the crack of dawn and go to work all day. The shift was very difficult and tiring. After all day at work, we used to return back home at night. Sometimes when it rained, we got home very wet. My mom had to stay awake until we returned, because she had to wash and iron our clothes. It was very hard because we only used to have one set of clothes and we were going to need them for the next day. And so my mom, your Mama Chuy, often times had go to bed after midnight. *Pobrecita*, she always put the iron on to get hot before we got home, so when we got there the iron was already warmed up. The iron was made of *fierro*, heavy iron, and to get it hot it needed to be placed *brazas bien caliente*. Also when the clothes were torn, she had to *remendarla*, or to patch them with another piece of cloth.

...a quarter of a bag of corn

"In the fields where we were working. when it was lunchtime, we could only have one taco, *and that was when we were lucky!* Because even my mom had to mix a lot of *nixtamal* to make *tortilla*. We wouldn't

248

get enough tacos to eat. Everyday at 12: 00 p.m., she had to go where we were working to bring us lunch. That time was very hard but at the same time, it was enjoyable because we used to eat *bien agusto* at the fields.

"Passing through the years, we were helping your grandfather more. Maurilio Padilla Pinones. He was born in 1917 and died on June 27 2001. He *si que* suffered while trying to support all his family. He worked his whole life since he was a little boy. He used to tell us that when he was working all day, he used to have only one taco in his stomach. He had to work since the crack of dawn until night, *de sol a sol*, or from sun to sun. The pay for the whole week's working was *only a quarter of a bag of corn.*"

"My grandmother, Guadalupe Piñones Zamora, your grand-grand mother, used to feed my father and his brothers with *espigas* from the top of the corn plant. She used to get it when the corn wasn't enough for everybody to eat.

"She was born in 1871 and died in 1986. She was 115 years old when she died. Maybe you still remember her, do you not, Triny?"

"Yea! I remember her. I used to like to go and buy candies from her small *tiendita* that she used to have when I knew her. She always was saying, '*Tu, muchacha, ¿Eres de Antonio and Margarita, verdad?*' "Oh she used to have a very good memory, even when she was 115 years old."

My father told us he didn't like to see his mom suffering because there wasn't food to eat. When my grandmother was asked by everybody to give them tacos to eat, he used to take *un montón de chiles,* a pile of chiles, and eat them all, so he wouldn't be hungry any more. He heard and saw his brothers hanging from his mom's *mandil* (apron), and telling her '*mama taco, taco mama*'. She answered, *esi mis niños ahorita esperenmen.* It was when she used to mix a little bit of *nixtamal* with some *espigas* from the corn plants in order to give them a *taquito.* And your grandfather used to eat *chilies to get hot and not ask her for another taco.*"

"Oh! My God! Poor grandpa, *he si que suffered didn't he*? The taco he needed to take, he preferred to give it to his brothers.

"Now I see Papa, that you are like my grandfather, Papa Maurilio. *Always fighting to obtain the best for your children.* And now I would like to tell you, THANK YOU SO MUCH for everything, for all your time and support that you and mom always have for us. Also thanks for telling us when we are wrong. We need all your *regaños* to be good persons in this life respecting each other."

"Pues bendito sea Dios ahora que estamos todos juntos. Vamos a luchar todos juntos con muchas ganas para salir adelante. Debemos ayudarnos, uno a otros, y ustedes ponganles muchas ganas a estudiar todo lo que puedan, y que siempre contaran con nuestro apoyo."

"Well, Triny, thank God we are altogether right now, and let's fight hard to continue being good. We have to help each other, and we want all of you to put a lot of desire in your studies. You guys know that you can count on our support in your studies."

This image of me and my father, Ricardo Estrada Mendoza, really means a lot to us, because we get to see our faces through all the years we have been living together. We know ourselves very well, and my father has taught me plenty of things in life, like how to drive a car, and how to do all the chores outside the house, like yard work. I have also learned other things in detail that I wouldn't expect from anybody else other than my father. My father has always been good, and sometimes a little hard, when I disobey him, but I still love him with all my heart. He really loves the way he dresses, especially with his black cowboy hat in which he looks very good.

My Dad—A Library of Experience

Uziel Estrada

[Author's note: When my Dad talked to me during this interview, he spoke in Spanish. I have translated his story into English. These interviews were conducted during the winter and early spring of 2002. I have also included some stories that I have remembered that he has told me through the years we have been together.]

My father, since he was a little boy, has suffered through stuff he would never recommend anybody to have to pass through—family problems, poverty, illness, and working real hard like a burro, only to survive, but never prospering much. As he remembers from the time

251

of being a kid, he's worked his butt off to survive, and lived by himself, mostly.

"Mijo tu estás rico a comparación en mis tiempos que yo vivía. Aquí en los Estados Unidos lo tienes todo, solamente que estudies con ganas y salgas adelante, pero no tanto esfuerzo como yo lo hacía para sobrevivir," says Ricardo Estrada Mendoza.

"Son you are rich now compared to my old times I have lived. Here in the U.S. you have all the opportunities, all you have to do is go to school and study hard and keep going forward, but not hard work like I used to have to do, to survive.

"My name is Ricardo Estrada Mendoza, and I was born in Tepalcatepec, Michoacán, México on October 22, 1960.

"This is how things went when I was little. My father woke us up in the *madrugadas* to go to work far from where we lived. He wouldn't give a damn if I had little sleep, or I was sick. When I didn't get up he would grab his old ugly belt and get me up by spanking me hard. The thing I most hated was that I didn't have any shoes or anything to cover my bare feet. I would get thorns in my feet. I had bruises and cuts. I never gave up and demonstrated to my dad that I could work. And all this work helped me for my own good.

"Hunger in my times was a big issue that many people suffered. Sometimes I was really hungry, wishing for a loaf of bread, or anything that would make my belly happy, but instead I went to sleep, and, perhaps, when I woke up the next morning I'd find something to eat.

"One really big obstacle happened when I was about thirteen years old that left me nearly dead. I saw this wonderful fruit tree that was tall and ugly and I decided to climb it. The tree was called *anona*. While I was reaching to get the fruit, the branch I was standing on cracked and went down with me. I fell on the side of the river. The bad thing was that I had hit some rocks. I was totally unconscious. Some girls along the river that were washing their clothes, saw me lying on the ground like I was dead. One of the girls was my brother's girlfriend. She picked me up and took me home.

"When my mother saw me, she began to cry out loud saying, *Mi hijo, Mi hijo, se murió que le pasó?* Then, my brother's girlfriend explained the whole story of what had happened to me. She didn't know what to do, only to start praying for me, and she saw the miracle that God had done that brought me back to life. At the time this happened, my father was working far from where we lived. When the accident occurred, my youngest brother went on a burro to tell my father. This took a long time. When he was coming, it was dark and my dad was desperate to see me as he had gotten the news. As he was getting near to our house there was a small hill to go over, and this is what my father said, *'Si las luces de la casa están prendidas y hay gente es que mi hijo se murió.'* As he went over the hill, he saw those lights on and started crying like a baby, thinking I was dead. But when he arrived at the house my mother told him I was doing better, and that she saw God's hand put on me, and bringing me back. His heart got really happy after she told him that. And this is what he said, *'Que bueno es El Señor.'*

The Years Pass Like Water

"As time passed, I got better and I began to work like always. The years passed like water. I was about seventeen when I heard my oldest brothers talk about the United States of America, which they called *el otro lado* or *el norte*. My oldest brother, Manuel, said to me, 'You're going with us'. I never was afraid because I never cracked if they talked about work. The person who did not want me to come was my mother, because she said, 'You're my favorite son.' But I told her, 'Mother, I'm going to make some money and send you some, so you can buy anything you want.' With all the sad faces she made, I still decided to come. But I didn't want to come either, because I had left a girlfriend which had cost me a lot of time, *para conquistarla*, and I loved her so much because of her beauty. But I did promise her when I came back from the U.S.A., I would talk to her father and we would get married.

"When we decided to come, in the late 70's, my brother never told me about crossing the border and *la migra*. But I had fun seeing them looking for us in their light green Broncos. The first time I passed the border, it wasn't that bad because all we did was run, and the border patrol luckily did not trap me. When we got to the town of Yakima, my brother right away put me to work picking apples. It was fun for me because I was making more money than in México, and that I would send home for my beautiful mother and father. When I started making money, all of my brothers and sisters were real nice with me and mostly took half of my pay check, but I never forgot about my parents and I hid some money and sent it without my brothers noticing.

"Back in those times, I can tell right now that I had my eyes closed. When the *piscas* were finished, my brother Manuel took us to the worst work I ever experienced, up in the mountains by Wenatchee. It was *en los pinos* in the forest. You plant and cut trees. It was so damn cold that once one of my brothers almost died freezing. But it was us that saved him. We covered him up with our bodies. We even didn't have a place to sleep. Sometimes we got no sleep. Also making something to eat was something terrible, too. We fried something and within minutes it was cold. Although we suffered, we worked there for a couple of months. When my brother Manuel decided to change jobs, we moved to a town called Pasco. It was also a hard job. We worked picking asparagus. It was hot. Plus, you had to work with your back. You leaned all day, it really hurt your back. As time flew, asparagus finished, and we worked again in *las piscas*. A little more than a year passed and we planned to go back to México. When the whole *enchilada* finished a year later, my brother had bought a pickup and we left.

"It was a long trip. It took about four days to arrive. When we got home, I saw my mother feeding the chickens, and, as soon as she saw me, she left everything and ran and gave us all a hug. The next day, my dad killed a cow that he had saved to buy with the money I sent him and celebrated with us for our arrival. The next day, I got a ride and went to see my girlfriend, Bertha.

"When she saw me, too, I could see her heart pound with joy. I talked to her father about marriage, and he said yes and so did she. So we set up a date about getting married in the future, just in case we might change our minds. But in my mind I knew I was going to do this first. I had to work really hard, showing not only myself, but also everybody, that I was going to be able to hold the load of marrying a wife, and, later on, raise children.

"A few months passed and I started building a house with my own sweat. When two years passed, I was 24 when I thought it was time we got married. Then we decided to have children. And you were the first born, Uziel. Also a year later, your sister Bella was born. After a few years, we decided to come to the U.S.A. to live and work, improving and bettering life. The bad thing was to cross the border at Tijuana. There were three *coyotes* and one was going to help us cross the border. The *coyote* who was going to cross us was a really mean man. He didn't want to let us go until one of my brothers from *el norte* would pay him. The advantage we had was that the *coyote* had crossed us, and we were now in the U.S. I didn't want to cross the border again with you and your sister, Bella, which was a nightmare, having to hold you two infants and running from the immigration.

"The thing that broke my heart was when your mother fell

with your sister and I couldn't help her. Some really nice teenagers, about nineteen, helped us with your sister. It was a miracle of how we got out and escaped from the *coyote*. The wife of one of the three *coyotes* was the one that was so nice to us. She took us to her house. She bought clothes for all of us and she even let us sleep in her bedroom. She had to go to an appointment and asked if we wanted to come with her, and I said, 'yes.' I saw a big chance to escape without paying him, and I did, even though she was a nice woman, because the *coyote* who crossed us was such an idiot. You were small and you and your sister were crying. It was full of cigarette smoke where he had us in a tiny room, and he didn't even want us to get fresh air from outside. The thing that angered me was that you and Bella were crying because of the smoke, and you were hungry as they hadn't given us any food.

"I ran from the *coyote*. I knew some family members in Tijuana, U.S.A., who I can thank a lot today for bringing us to this country. We were then brought us to the Tri-cities, where me and your mom worked so hard to survive. But we did prosper working in the fields, in apple warehouses, and cutting meat at I. B. P. We worked really hard, all of the jobs were really hard work. The thing I liked most was that we always took you to work with us in the fields. Although you did some really bad *travesuras*, like turning on the car and moving it, spinning the tires in the mud, and leaving us with nothing to eat because you scrubbed our sandwiches all over the windows of the car. The *rancheros* never said anything but one time we went to a job and started working there for a week, and when the boss saw you, he fired us because he said that there were no children allowed. That was the only one that didn't want you. But we never put you to daycare. It was only once, but somehow you broke your nose and we had to pick you up and take you to work."

[Interviewer's note: My father got his papers during the amnesty in 1988 and he has also documented me, my sister, Bella, and my mom.]

"As years have passed, so quickly, we are here in Yakima, Washington where you have lived most of your life. And I say there is no other way to get a good job than to go to school. Because with no education you're going to be like me, working in the fields, or in butcher shops like Washington Beef. That's why I encourage you to get an education. That's pretty much all our history of what has happened throughout the years from México to the U. S."

This image, or photo, is very important to my mother Bertha Estrada and me, her son, Uziel Estrada. It shows us standing having my right hand over my mom's shoulders. I'm not doing it just to take the picture. I do it with pride and happiness. I see my mother as if I was holding on to a reina, a queen. She is the one who is my savior, my survivor and my love. I think this is a good memory since it's a picture and it lasts longer than just watching with your eyes, and then forgetting. My mother and I are real proud of being together in this wonderful memory.

SOMETHING RARE AND SPECIAL: INTERVIEWING MY MOTHER

Uziel Estrada

INTERVIEWING MY MOTHER WAS SOMETHING SPECIAL, IN ONE WAY BECAUSE NEITHER SHE NOR I, HEARD ABOUT THIS INTERVIEWING BEFORE. ALTHOUGH SOME QUESTIONS WERE DIFFICULT FOR HER TO ANSWER AND FOR ME TO ASK, I TRIED MY BEST AS A JOURNALIST, AND GOT EVERYTHING I NEEDED PUT ON PAPER.

My beautiful mother was born on a rancho called San Gabriel, Colima, México. The rancho is full of dirt and rocks that I couldn't stand when I went there for the first time. She was born on October 20, 1962, to Miguel and Esperanza Acevedo. Her full name is Bertha Acevedo Negrete. During my mother's childhood everybody was poor. She didn't have all the supplies as a little girl that she wanted, but my grandpa never let her and the rest of the family starve.

She says that being a girl sometimes is difficult because men sometimes are really machistas with them. As a little girl she saw many family problems such as my grandpa being a womanizer and *traicionando a mi abuela*. But my grandma did support all this womanizing of his. Her childhood wasn't that bad for her until the age of 15 when the biggest barrier occurred. Usually women sometimes go get water from the well. When my mother was sent by my grandma to get water in the night she went, and as she was getting some water, a fox appeared to her and she screamed so loud it got her really scared. She dropped the water and started running home. A couple days later she could hardly walk, and then she was paralyzed. By now, my grandpa had sold everything he had including the cows, to pay for the doctor's fees.

There was nothing else to do than to take her to the doctor but the doctor said that there was nothing possible to cure her. When my mother heard this she totally felt like she was worth nothing and asked God to help her get back on her feet. A little less than a year later, that terrible barrier was knocked to the floor. Since my mom's family are Christians, they believed God could heal her, and it happened when some Christian brothers in God prayed for her and told her that if she believed in Christ she would be healed. And my mom said yes, and they told her that in two days she would move her big toe, and they were right. My mother was healed by the Lord.

At the age of 17 she met a guy named Ricardo Estrada Mendoza and they became a couple. My mom says, *Lo terminé varias veces pero era tan rogón que me volvía a conquistar.* "I broke up with him many times, but he was such a beggar, that he made me come back to him. He asked for me and he talked with my dad first about it, and dad said it was fine for us to get married." At the age of 22 my mom got married. She says it was easy getting married. A year later I was born, and a year later my sister was born. "Raising children is priceless and also a pain." But she still loves us with all her heart.

When I was about 2 years old my dad decided to come to the U.S.A. Mom says, "It was a struggle crossing the border, especially those damn mean *coyotes,* but we still made it to your dad. That was our destination. Your dad did get pissed with the *coyotes* when they told him that they were going to throw him back to Tijuana and leave me with them. They made us suffer, especially with you and Bella.

"Since I've been here I have worked in the fields where we took you with us to work. You were such a *travesuriento.* But we never put you to daycare. One time we left you in inside our first old Datsun wagon your dad bought. We had no experience and never thought you were going to do a bad thing. We left the wagon keys and you turned it on and put it to drive, pressed the gas and you were scrubbing tires in the mud. Luckily one of our friends saw you and got in the wagon and turned it off. You sure were lucky, because you could have gotten killed by hitting an apple tree. One time your dad hit an apple tree and the wagon rolled over many times. Luckily nothing happened to us, especially you, who were riding in the back. That, and many other experiences, we passed through. I worked in warehouses, at I.B.P., and at Washington Beef. They truly are hard working jobs, but I never gave up on one job and I don't want you to work in those jobs.

"Here in the U.S life is better than in Mexico because you have the opportunity to work and succeed in life. You have the opportunity to be in a brand new car too."

My mother has started a daycare recently, where she enjoys working with children. That's pretty much the interview I made with my mom. I discussed this with her for hours and about those 39 years she's been living. I put it together in one interview. Over the years my mom has suffered because of my father sometimes being with other women. But my mother has been brave and has succeeded in life. She's been learning English for a little more than a year.

"When I first got here to the United States I thought I would never speak a word in English but now I am learning a lot of English. *El mundo da muchas vueltas. The world has many turns*, she said. She and I agree that the U.S.A is a country where you can "come, work and prosper, and show the *gringos* you can do anything that you want by working hard on what you want to become."

My mother, not once in my life, has spanked me. That's why I love her so much. But I never have caused her problems. "Uziel behave yourself always with everybody you meet and they will get along with you and even like you as friends."

This is a picture of Josie Guapilla and Margarita Venegas. Even though they do not appear in the picture, Josie has a sister named Eva and a brother named Luis. This photograph was taken in the kitchen of her house. It's one of her mom's special places because it's where we all gather up and have a good time when we eat. The moment that this picture was taken became a very special moment for Josie because never before had she taken a picture with just her mother and herself.

The Life of the Woman with Dreams, Hope, and Courage—La Mujer Incomparable

Josie Guapilla

The life of the woman who left everything behind in search of her dreams begins on February 26, 1960. It all began in a small town called Guanimaro, Guanajuato when a woman by the name of Angelina gave birth to her second daughter, who she named Margarita.

José and Angelina always tried to give the best to their kids, even though they didn't have much. Margarita was given the opportunity to go to school, but unfortunately she only went until she was in the third grade. *Al empiezo de su niñez ella dejó sus muñecas para empezar a trabajar para ayudar a sus padres. Ella junto con sus padres y hermanos vivieron en un rancho called Sapotito de Mancilla.* Her grandparents Angela y Jesús also lived there.

At the age of 11 her family moved to a small town called Pinozuares, Jalisco where they would start a new life. She remembers not wanting to move away. She didn't want to leave behind the memories of her childhood as well as family. She was also scared because she didn't know anyone. But after living for a few weeks in her new home, she soon adapted to her new life. A life in which many things were about to change.

When she finally thought that happiness had knocked at her door, something unexpected happened. She was only 14 and was already going through the roughest part of her life. Her mom passed away after giving birth to her last son. At that point of her life, Margarita thought that she could no longer go on. She let go of many dreams, because she, along with her sisters, became the mother of the child that had been left behind.

But things just didn't end there. Three years later her youngest sister, Sofia, also passed away. Margarita doesn't remember the cause of her sister's death. The only thing she remembers is that she died in her arms. At a young age my mom went through a lot of pain, a pain that made her much stronger.

The following year of her sister's death, Margarita decided that it was time to move on. She, along with some friends, decided to try a new life. And the only way to do that was if they crossed the border. Margarita was very lucky. She crossed the frontier at her first try. She wanted to live in California. Once in California, she worked very hard to help her family back at Mexico.

Even though she felt lonely, she made it through. Margarita went through three marriages in which she didn't have much luck. In those three marriages *ella concebió a sus tres hijos*. At age 22 she had her first daughter whom she named Eva. Two years later she had me, (Josie), and at age 28, she had her first son, Luis. She doesn't regret going through three marriages because she learned many things and she also learned to value herself more as a woman.

After her third divorce everything seemed much harder for her. She was a single mother with three kids. She went through a lot of struggles, but she always found a way out. Margarita never gave up and she has always tried to give her kids the best. Now, at age 41 things are much easier for her. As a mother she has given the best of herself. She's also learned that being a single mother is hard, but it's something to be proud of.

Now that I'm old enough, I understand everything that my mom has done for my sister brother and me. I want to thank her for making us who we are and for setting aside many things to become a full-time mother.

The Heart of Our Family—El Corazón de Nuestra Familia

The two people in the picture are my mother, Martha Alfaro, and, of course, me, Martha Gamboa. The dining room I believe, is the heart of our family, the place of *grand valor* (great value). Our dining room is the room with all the power. This room is the light of our home. To me it has a great meaning; my grandmother had a *Velorio* (Rosary/Viewing) here. This room makes me feel like my grandmother is always here with us. Our dining room brings the family together once a day. Every night we gather here and say grace before eating dinner together. "This table and these walls capture so many images." During the evening after eating dinner we can all talk to each other about what happened that day, or what was funny about something we watched, or even what happened that day at work. We tell a few jokes and then every one goes their own way. The table in the dining room brings us together as a family; we have a lot of communication. This room, I think that this is more than just simply a room—it is like the heart of our family, the unity between our busy lives.

You Can See Life Two Ways:
The Easy Way or The Hard Way

Martha S. Gamboa

Let me take you back in time to a place called Tijuana, Baja California. The time is January 6, 1968 just a few hours into the day, about 3 a.m.—a gift from heaven had just arrived to my grandma, Raquel Zarate. A very powerful woman was born this day, my mother, Martha Reyna Alfaro. This was *El Día de Los Reyes* that is celebrated in many ways, mostly in Mexico. This was a great day for my grandmother and her newly born child, a gift from the kings, *Los Reyes*.

My grandmother had four children, (oldest to the smallest by name) Silvia Zarate, Ana Zarate, Rafael Alfaro, Martha Alfaro. They all lived together in a single parent home for a while when the oldest was about 16 years old.

But before my grandma could register her daughter, the child/baby was kidnapped when she was eight days old, from her own home, leaving an empty cradle behind. This gift that was given to my grandma was taken away by some people. The new family registered her by the name of Martha Broski Padilla. The family lived and raised her in San Diego, California while my grandmother did everything she could to find her missing daughter.

A very close friend of the family helped to find my mother. Time passed and my mother was two years old and still no one knew where she was until my grandma received a call.

The voice on the phone said, "I know where your daughter is at now. You can come and find her. She lives in San Diego, California." The kidnappers gave my grandma some directions, but no real address, to find her daughter. She quickly went to San Diego to go look for her missing daughter. She could not find her, but she remembered once going to a house in San Diego from her husband's side of the family, and she went there first.

To her surprise, she found a little girl outside the house about the same age as her daughter. She went inside the house and talked to the people and it turned out that the little girl outside the house was her daughter that had been missing for two years. The family had her the entire time. They really didn't like my grandmother and wanted to make her suffer, and what better way than to take her daughter from the crib that night two years ago. They gave my grandmother her daughter. Mother and child were now reunited with the rest of the family.

My mother's life was complicated at a young age, but now at age 16, she had many new challenges. She lived wondering what her father must have looked like. She had never seen picture of him or even knew his name. The name my grandmother gave my mother was "Buck Robinson." There was never any record of him anywhere.

A man that was living with my grandmother at the time. His name was Ismael Alfaro, gave my mother her last name. This man is the only man my mother has seen as a father figure. It was always hard for my mother as she grew up without a father, but when Ismael was gone, it was even harder. My grandma was always gone; she wasn't at home because she would work two jobs to support her children to keep them alive and well. She felt like she had no one to turn to when she had problems. She only wished that maybe one day, for only a moment, she could see her father. She didn't even know if he was dead or alive. She was always wondering about it, and it made it harder because her sisters had a picture of their father, and knew his name.

But since my mother and her brother didn't know much about their father, my mother just wanted to do things for herself. She always wanted to become a model, a pediatrician, or even a flight attendant. But her mother was beyond strict. She didn't want her to do anything. Grandma would always say to my mother that she'd probably end up going off with some boyfriend instead of studying. Every time grandma said that, she'd crush my mother's hopes and dreams of ever wanting to be somebody in life. My mother would have only wished that her mother had encouraged her do nursing or something. But since that didn't happen, my mother was driven in the wrong direction. Seeing no support from her mother, she went off with her boyfriend. My mother never really got to finish school because she got pregnant. But even then she always wanted to control her life.

My mother, now at age 22, always wanted to do something different than her sisters. She didn't want to stay at home with the kids, with the same routine day in and day out.

My mother always got a good paying job, even though she didn't have a high school diploma. My mother was working for an aerospace division called V-SHAN in Englewood, California. She worked there for three years as a laboratory technician. After she got separated from my father, she realized then that she had to raise four children on her own.

She decided to move to Yakima, Washington on May 5, 1994 to my grandma's apartment. She thought her kids needed a better way of life. This was a small town compared to the town we came from. We lived with my grandma when I was about ten years old. My sister, Leticia Gamboa, was eight, my brother, Jose Gamboa, was two, and my little sister, Alberta Gamboa, was eight months old. My grandmother was just recovering from her kidney stone surgery. I stayed home with the kids and got everything my grandma needed. My mother was never really happy living under her mom's roof, so she tried even harder to find a place for us to live.

She found a place, a four-bedroom house with a big yard. She then received a phone call from a store to work in a pharmacy. Since she was bilingual, they hired her on the spot. She worked right across the street from where we got the house. So everything worked out fine.

The money she made there was not enough to pay the rent, the bills, buy the food, and to buy us clothes for school. She had to get another job, and over the summer, the whole family went to work in the fields and picked cherries. The younger ones would go and sell things like pop, tamales, or *ceviche* to the people that were working there to raise money for back-to-school clothes in September.

At the end of that year I was 12 years old and my mother wanted me to go to LA on the California Express bus to go buy school clothes for the family. It was hard to go because my little sister was always moving around and didn't stay still. My mother sent me off with my little sister that was two years old. My aunts didn't know her, because when we left, she was just a baby. My aunts lived in LA and when I got there, my Aunt Silvia went to go pick us up. She was so happy to see my little sister. We rested the first day, and then went the next day to go shopping. To my surprise, my little sister wouldn't let me do anything. She was always attached to my leg like I were her mother. My aunt was surprised that I took good care of my little sister at the age I was, like she were my own child. Well, I bought everyone a pair of shoes, five or six pairsof jeans, and six tee shirts to match the jeans, and, lastly, I bought socks and underclothes. It was time for me to go back home. When I got home again my mother was very happy. She said she was very proud of me for going to buy everything she asked for.

When I got back home on the California Express bus my mother soon started her second job at a restaurant during the night to get enough money to pay for rent and bills and worked in the pharmacy during the day. When my grandmother recovered from her surgery, she helped my mother out with the kids, since my sister and I had to be at school. These times were hard for all of us. We would hardly ever see our mother, because during the day we were at school and mom was at work. During the evenings our mother was at her second job.

While all that was going on, my mother tried to find time for us. She said, "We need each other to succeed. If we don't trust each other we will never get anywhere in life." She said, "My daughter always knew that every Sunday morning after 10 am was a time for us to be together and do something." The whole time my mother was working I would stay home with the kids, but Sunday was our day. No matter how tired my mother was, she would always find the energy to be with us and do things unlike other parents who did nothing with their kids.

"Some people aren't there for their kids," she would say, "and then they wonder where their kids end up." She knew that kids are always going to be just kids. They always want to do everything and if you don't let them try things out they will do them behind your back anyway. Mother always let us experience things for ourselves. I asked her once to let me go to a kickback (a house where teens go to drink and socialize with people their own age), since all my friends were going. Then we were going to go to a dance club in Toppenish. She let my sister and me go and my sister said, "This is a kickback? It's a waste of time." She said, "Let's go dance already; all they are doing is getting drunk." So we left.

The next day my mother asked us, "So how was the kickback?" We were like, "Boring!" My mom said, "Well, at least now you know that it isn't fun." My mother trusts us to do many things. We go out to parties and dances, but when my mom says, "I want you back home at a certain time," we are back, so that next time we can go, and maybe for a longer time.

Mother always said, "My daughter knows how much I struggle but she knows that no matter what happens, family will always come first. It is just us and if we don't help each other who will help us?" She would remind us, "Your father isn't going to come and give me money to support you. Since that isn't happening we have to help each other as much as we can."

That's why, I, Martha Sandy Gamboa, say, "I don't want to struggle like my mom. I want to finish school and go to college, so I can make life easier." My dreams are to get an education and build my own home one-day. At the rate I am going, it will come true.

Now I don't have to live my life the hard way like my mother. Now I can live life the easy way. My mom says, "Now, I have showed my kids that there are two ways to live life. The hard way, like me, or the easy way, like going to college and then having your kids, because then you have a higher paying job to support your family and you do not have to struggle like me with two jobs to pay for things."

I listen to my mother and have made up for some of her mistakes. I am 17 years old now and I am not pregnant. To me, it shows that I have changed the way I want to live my life. I have already I started a new beginning. Even though I don't have the same goals and dreams as my mother did when she was in school, I have made my own decision to pursue my higher education. Now, with my mother's help, I can change the way she was brought up, because as an individual she changed how she raised us.

Part VI

Testimonios

…with the pen in my hand writing
about myself in the loneliness of my room
remembering my life's story, without
wanting to remember, maybe because
I have never known how to live and
appreciate what God has given me:
the opportunity to exist.
Why have I always
felt that I had nothing? Why, having
people beside me who love me, haven't I
known how to appreciate them? Maybe my
heart hasn't known how to open its door
to them.

Antonia Caro

Who I Am

Roberto Méndez

In this world, in this time, there are many people who *tiene que vivir* their own lives. Some people have many problems and other people

don't. If you want to be someone in your life you have to study or work so hard and do it. But if you or somebody asks me,

Who are you, young gentleman? I couldn't say who I really am. Right now I think that I am just a simple student studying and *preparandome* to be

someone in my life. I have had some difficulties because I didn't have a childhood like other children because I never lived with my mom and

father together like a real family. But I didn't have a sad or bad childhood. I think that I had a wonderful childhood because I lived

with my grandparents. They are wonderful persons. They are like my real parents. I have their *recuerdos de ellos* in my heart. I never *podria*

olvidarlos. I love them so much. I love my *primo*, Paco, also because he is like a brother for me. He's older than me by a week. We studied

always together at the same schools. Me and my *primo* have something similar, we like to play soccer, but now that I am living in another country, I *recuerdo a ellos*, every day. I will keep going studying in this country and get a college degree. *I don't let anyone stop me.* I will do

it. You know, *if you want to realizar something you have to try.* There aren't *barreras* just try, *try and do it.* In this life all *se puede lograr*

luchando poniendo esfurzos para realizar todo lo que queramos. I think if you are climbing a montain and if *te caes o te trompiesas subiendo a la montaña,* listen to me. *Don't say I can't.* Try two, three, many times, until you do it. That's what I think. *I never pararé. Lograré*

todo lo que me proponga in my life. Let my dreams come true and be happy when I do it. I want to have a good job and *poder ayudar to my grandparents*, because they helped me in my childhood.

El Granero de Mi Padre

Jesus Barriga

I am in the kitchen making tortillas for my dad. Ohooh my god. He is hungry already, and I haven't made the chile that he always asks me for. I have to hurry up. I am toasting the red chiles and the smell is making me sneeze. My mother is helping me cook the meat and beans.

I hear my dad's foot steps coming down the hallway to the kitchen. My mom rapidly served the plate of food and set it on the table. And I put the salsa of tomatoes and some tortillas for him. The first thing my dad said was, "Where is the water at?" *"Este vato toma agua"*. "And your tortillas has holes. I am going to hang them outside en el patio in the front yard for everyone to see."

That way I was going to be embarrassed and I would learn how to make them better. As I tried to make them better they were worse; maybe because I was nervous every tortilla burned or tore.

Something must be wrong with my dad. He was yelling at me like always, but I saw his sad eyes looking down, and his sad look too. His eyes were down and my mother got close to him. Before she asked what was the matter, he said, "The granero is going down. The corn is almost gone. What are the cows going to eat?" He was sad. *"Si la pastura se está secando…"* the plants of corn are turning yellow because it doesn't rain." My mother said, "Pray, viejito, pray!" And the weather is going to be better. "We always want things but we don't even ask God for help."

"Vente a resar el Rosario!" my mom said. Llama a tus hemanos también. After we got done praying, my father went to the parcela or his tierras where he had his cultivo. The plants were almost dead; he started to cry. After seven hours of crying without stopping, he made a river with his tears. He took water from there and watered the plants. In that moment I took the last corn from the granero and I told my mom, "Este es el ultimo nixtamal que siento!" It was the last corn that I cooked.

I heard dad's whistle. He was coming happy with a big smile, and he said, "The plants revived, *vieja, ya tengo pastura para las vacas.*" We all said, "Thanks God." My mom said, "*Viejito,* now I can see the granero crowded with corn."

My dad was saying his story when he was in Mexico. He's from Puebla, where the famous battle was fought against the French, and he was saying that this is where we get the celebration for Cinco de Mayo. We were sitting at the dinner table talking. My dad was a *viajero*, a traveler. He was a *viajero* from the time he was about 15 years old. He knows and *conoces* most of the *pueblos* and cities in Mexico. He was telling his story and Mom was listening. He told how he didn't have a father. He had a mom, but he didn't grow up with her. Changes in his life started when he decided to come to the United States. He said that he likes to travel a lot. He also knows many cities from the U.S.A.—including Chicago and Miami. He is also working in the fields and he works the whole year around. He always works. These photos were taken during *Semana Santa*, before *Pascua*, on Good Friday. My mom says we *were "...cara a cara y frente a frente,"* or *face to face.*

My Principles, My Dreams To Be One of the Leaders of the Latinos and Chicanos Breaking Chains...

Lilia Nava

I want to. I have to. I am able. These are my principles to guide me on my path.

Mis principios son muchos in my life para poder seguir saliendo adelante.

Estos son mis principios—los que queremos tenemos y los que tenemos podemos. I know these are only three phrases, that might look or sound simple, but they are very strong when you have them in your hands and don't let them slip away for any significant thing. They are *principios* for *anybody*, and phrases are the code to accomplish any dream or goal in mind that we have. *"We have to, want to, we can. I know we can!"*

Hello, my name is Lilia Nava Perez. I'm a student at A.C. Davis High School. I'm a senior ready to graduate and sad to leave this campus because I don't think that I will ever find more friends like the ones that I have now. It's been fun, interesting, and a lot more. For me, it's like my second home. But that's the part of life that keeps on going, and we just have to keep the memories in mind and never forget all the fun moments.

I was born November 24, 1982, in the city of Puebla, Mexico, a nice and pretty city. It's a city that I'll never forget, because it is the one that saw my birth. It is the city where most of my family is from. It's also the city that I'm proud of and thankful for, because of the family it gave me.

But the other part of my life is this—I also have a baby boy, whom I have named Angel Nava. He was born January 5, 1999, in the City of Yakima. Right now he is three years and two months old. At this moment my life, he is the one that gives me power *para luchar* against everything. He gives me *ánimos para salir adelante.* I want him *to be proud of his mom, me, Lilia Nava,* and to know that she was a *Latina abrecaminos* in the United States of America. To follow in my footprints, he not only has to be like me, but more than what I am. I would want him to have more *entusiasmo* and more dreams than the ones that I have had in my mind. He is the one that is always at my right side when I think of doing something. In my life I have had many ups and downs, but until now I have always found my way out of it on my own. I don't think that anybody is going to come and find it for me. I think that life is fun but you have to know how to live it. Because if you don't know how to live this life, it's always going to be hard, and I mean hard— where you are not going to find a way out, because if you don't succeed and find a way out, you will forever doubt your luck. But in reality that's not how it is.

I have four brothers and one sister, and of course, my parents, my mom and my dad. My mom's name is María Florinda Pérez Gonzales, and my dad's name is Jaime Nava Huerta. My mom was born in Puebla, Mexico. She was born on August 3, 1954. Her mom's name was Lilia Gonzales Rojas, and her dad's name was Odilon Pérez Rojas. My grandparents have five sons and five daughters, including my mom. They are all alive at this moment. They all get along as a family, helping each other.

My grandpa was with another woman at the same time that he was married with my grandma. She didn't know anything at that time and she didn't notice until later after eight kids were born. And the funny part about this was that he would get both my grandma and the other woman pregnant at the same time. So that's why his kids from both women were kind of the same age. The farthest that their kids were apart in age was a maximum of three months. With the other woman that he had, he also had four sons and five daughters.

As time passed, my grandma noticed, and she didn't want to see him at her house any more, but he still went back to see his children and gave them support. And they stayed like that, separated for almost two years. He always kept on going back for forgiveness, saying that he wasn't going to do it again until he convinced her to forgive him and she did. She pardoned him and he came back to the house.

He still gave support and food to the other woman because he always liked to be responsible. As years went by they were all happy because finally my grandpa was back again as a daddy and a husband. Years passed and their kids grew up until my mom was about 14 years old. My grandma started with *dolor de cabeza*, (headache), for two days and also with a fever. So they took her to the doctor and he said that it was only *dolor de cabeza* and maybe a little bit of fever and not to be worried about it, and to take pills for the pain.

However the saddest part was that she went to sleep and the next morning she didn't wake up because she was dead. The doctors didn't know why because she had never complained of anything. The thing that made my grandpa even sadder was that their kids were small. The smallest was three years old and the oldest was fourteen years old.

At that time my mom was in school. She was in 7th grade. Her dreams were to become a nurse or doctor. But after my grandma's death, she had to drop out of school and take care of her little brothers and sisters and help my grandpa, because he couldn't handle it by himself. But she is proud of this. By helping her dad raise her smaller brothers and sisters, she was able to give them the education that she wasn't able to get.

So as years passed and time went on, he met another woman. After seven years they got to know each other. He told her his story and she understood him, even though her kids were already grown. After he had talked with her, he went and talked to his kids. They said it was O.K. because he had the right to make his life over, but they would treat her like an aunt, not like a mom, because there wasn't going to be anybody else like their mom.

He went back to her and told her what they thought and she said that it was O.K. because it was true what they said. So they decided to get together and not marry, *nada mas se juntaron. Y fueron felizes hasta que él murió.*

My grandpa died June 11, 1999. We all loved him and even though we weren't with him all the time. After we came to the United States, we would hear from him by phone. I personally didn't get to see him until eight years later when I went for a vacation to Mexico. And even though years had passed by, he was *gustoso* for my *quinceañera*. He wasn't expecting me when I got there. He was expecting me months later.

When I first saw him after that length of time, I had missed him so much that we both started crying de tanta felicidad. *¡Que sintíamos los dos! What we felt, the two of us!* Those are moments that I'll never forget. I will always have them in my mind. Then, a year later, he got sicker. Since he had worked all his life to give everything to his kids he *se enfermó de muchas cosas unas ya no tenían curación,* so *por eso me siento tan orgullosa de haber estado con él, el ultimo año* of his life. When he was getting really sick, all of my uncles, aunts, and my mom went to Mexico to see him. After they all got there he only lasted for two more months. I think that his death was the saddest part that I have ever lived in my life. For all of us it was really sad to lose him.

My mom said that her life in her *niñez* was really fun. She really enjoyed it even though she didn't have as many things to play with in those days. Back then, they didn't have sufficient *dinero* to spend. She said that she only had a couple of dolls, plus the ones that she made of her imagination, you know, out of stuff that you find at home, her life as a *muchacha* of 15 years and above, she told me that she went out on dates, but not too many, and whenever she wanted to go to a dance her dad would take her. So yes, she really loved her dad, because she didn't even have to ask him to take her to a dance. He would tell her: "You better be ready for the dance tonight when I come back."

And she met my dad at a dance when she was 17 years old. My dad's name is Jaime Nava Huerta. They became *novios* for almost three years until they decided to get married. My dad's story is he doesn't know much of his mom nor his dad. He only went to school up to elementary because his mom was working at a place an hour from where they lived. They didn't have sufficient money to pay for school and his mom died when he was about 8 or 9 years old. About his dad, he doesn't know anything because they never told him anything. He doesn't even know if he is still alive.

He told me that his *niñez* was really sad, not only because they didn't have any money, but because he didn't have a mom or dad *que lo quisiera y que le diera cariño cuando más los necesito.*

So he had to drop out of school, and he had to start working. Years later he met my mom and they got to know each other, and years later they decided to get married.

For their honeymoon, they went to Mexico City. When they returned to Puebla, they stayed there for two years.

Then they moved to Monterrey to live. And when my mom was 20, she got pregnant. She named her Alicia Nava Pérez. After two years she had a baby boy. And of course she was happy because she had a boy and a girl.

On her third pregnancy, she was waiting for a baby girl and it was a boy. She was happy but a little disappointed. On her fourth pregnancy she said that she was really excited because she knew that it was going to be a girl, and she bought pink stuff for a little girl, and a lot more stuff. But once again it was a baby boy; and so she had to go to the store and buy baby clothes, but this time for a boy.

She thought that she wasn't going to have any more girls other than the one that she had. On her next pregnancy she bought clothes for a baby boy and guess what, it was a little girl *La mas travesurienta de la casa, me, Lilia Nava, (la que está escribiendo esta historia).* And on her last pregnancy she had a boy, what she expected. So in total she had two daughters and four sons. She says that she is really proud of us and we are proud of her because she has always tried to help us the best she can.

I admire her because she *is one of the Latina women.* It seems that her life has been one of constant struggle and suffering. For example, one of her struggles was when she lost her mom and she had to give up school.

Another challenge in her life was when my dad decided to come to the United States. We didn't come to the United States with legal papers, we came, *como se dicen, de mojados.* Of course it was hard, because they—my dad, my oldest brother, and two uncles—came with the *coyote.* They had to walk, I don't know how many hours, in the desert. Other things happened too They endured hardships such as hunger and mother nature, plus other things while they crossed the border to get to the U.S.A. They almost made it through the crossing, but when they got to that place where they were going to be picked up, immigration arrived and they sent them back to Mexico.

For them it was another *sufrimiento*. In order to come back they had to walk again and the worst part was that they couldn't take any water with them.

My mom and the rest of the family were worried for so many things that could happen to them—remember, they couldn't take anything with them, but they had to cross the border in order to make their dreams come true.

The Sueño Americano—everybody is looking for it in the United States of America. It's a dream that not everybody gets to realize, because some people make it through the border, and some only get half-way, which is very sad. Some die because of the *sufrimiento que pasan y que no llegan ha lograr nada y cuando todo lo que hacen es solo para que les puedan dar una vida mejor a su familia.*

My mom struggled on, not knowing their whereabouts, wondering if they were all right or not. Her struggle ended when she heard from them. They told her that they were in the USA. That's why I think that these are the two most difficult struggles that she had to pass through her life.

That's why I think that my mom is a Latina woman, the one that I admire. I don't think that I'm going to find a better one than her in this world. She is always behind me, pushing me wherever I go, and even when I get stuck. She always tells me that if she made it, maybe with not too much, why shouldn't I make it, *para que todos nos trajeran y vivieramos con ellos*

The first time my dad, brother, and uncles came to the USA was in July, 1986. *Después de todo el sufrimiento que pasaron ellos se establecieron en Los Angeles, California, con unos amigos.* He said that they were really nice to them and a couple years later they started working. After two years, my dad went back to get my two brothers and my older sister. They said they had trouble, but not as much as when my dad came the first time. He kind of got an idea of how it was on the border and probably they were not going to get cheated like the first time.

A year later my mom, my little brother and I came over by ourselves, but since my dad didn't want us *que sufrieramos al pasar como ellos entonces el busco la manera de como hacerle. Y unos amigos le prestaron las actas de sus niños que tenían más o menos la misma edad que nosotros. Mi papa les pago dinero, a cambio de los papeles. Y que nos recojieran en el otro lado de la frontera.*

That's why I think that we also crossed de border as *mojados con un coyote pero ya no con tanto sufrimiento como él que todos ellos pasaron aunque ha mi papa le costo un poco caro para que nos pasaran. Pero el no le importo eso, porque lo unico que él quería es que llegaramos bien y estuvieramos todos juntos.*

So 1990 was when we all got together again as a family. And my mom said that for a while we were separated, but everything was for us to have a better life, *"... and for you guys to have a better education."* After that we were all in Los Angeles. They decided to move to Fresno, California, and we stayed there for about three years. But the house where we lived burned down, and my dad *se decepcionó,* so he decided to come to Yakima. We started working. He liked it in here because he said that it reminded him of Mexico.

As time went on they decided to buy a house and we still live there. In our family my dad always wanted my oldest brother to follow his dreams, to always do what he thought was good for him. But now my brother wants to follow his dream.

Since my dad didn't have a dad, he thought he was doing the right thing to my brother, not knowing it was the worst thing he was doing. He never asked my brother about his dreams of what he had in mind for himself. My dad would always push my brother into doing something that he wasn't really interested in doing.

My brother didn't like doing what my father wanted him to do because he had dreams of his own. And he didn't want to accomplish my father's goals. This caused my brother to go away from us, to withdraw from the family. Eventually he married an older person which made my dad and mom mad. After a while they understood what he wanted and they saw his happiness.

So what made the whole family happy was that my dad changed, and now all that he wants is for us to get an education and make our dreams come true and be proud of ourselves. He did notice that what he did was wrong.

My brother has three kids and the oldest one is named after him. He had to make his own life with his family. My dad realized that the best thing to do was to keep us *unidos,* not separated. He now calls my brother, and my brother calls my dad, which is good for all of us.

Because my dad's changed, we are now not only together, but *unidos.* A good thing to say is that my older brother graduated from IKE High School. He said that he had fun and really enjoyed going over there, which is good. After his graduation, he went to college and he loved it. He has already finished his two-year degree and he is working now. He is going to keep studying for the electronic degree. My whole family is proud of him, because he was the first one in our family to graduate from high school and start college.

I'm following him. I'll graduate this June 2002, and my brother, the baby of the family, is graduating next year, which is June 2003. We just can't wait until those dates get here.

Then we must take advantage of these opportunities and use them to benefit our dreams and goals. We must grab them with our hands, hold them in our hearts no matter what, and not let them go.

Because if I do that, then I have *fuerzas para poder y sacar adelante a mi hijo para que sea u niño de bien*, because I wouldn't want my son to go the wrong way. I would like him to be an example, like his mom, as I am a *luchadora*, a fighter, even though it's hard. I know that I will make it because *my principles are many*. They start with my dreams, those dreams that I have in heart. Some dreams I have already realized, and some are also in my mind and in my future. Hopefully, these will be my son's dreams also. These dreams hold to many things. They include my A.C. Davis High School graduation and my graduation as a professional cosmetologist. They include being able to help other people that need it, especially people that have just arrived in this country and that don't even have any idea of how the things work in this country. As for me finding my own way in life, I want to continue breaking chains, doing something better than what I do right now, being able to reach the goals that I have written, and more, nothing rich, only what I want for my son. I am struggling for everything that I can reach.

When I first started this class of Latino Literature my dream was to climb the Macchu Picchu mountains, and when I climbed them and came back, my life changed in some way, in my way of thinking, in the way of being an abrecaminos.

In this life we have a lot of stuff to go through. We have to struggle for what we want and what we need. Challenges, struggles, problems, and difficulties is life, because life without these *pruebas*, it's not true life. *Pero tenemos que sufrir primero, para luego merecer algo.*

Sometimes this life gives us a lot of opportunities and we don't *aprobechamos* and we let them go. Then we realize that those opportunities are gone, and it's too late because they are not coming back. That is why I suggest to not let go of any opportunity, even if you think that it doesn't benefit you, take it, no matter what.

All I can say is that I have learned a lot of things from this class and also from my friends, teachers and fellow ABRECAMINOS. One of the things is this—most of us have some struggles in our lives, but with these struggles we have dreams. And also on the way to realize the dream, there are going to be times that people might get stuck, but we have to learn how get out of it, and to keep on going and make it all the way through.

I also learned that most of the ones who struggle are Mexicans or Chicanos, and all of them are trying to do something with their struggles. They are trying to make the difference, and they are also trying to change the indifference of other people. They are also trying to help some of the other people that come from different nations, who also come looking for the *Sueño Americano*.

I learned that everybody who came to the United States wants to do something better with their lives. This goes to show that we, the Latinos, could be better than what others think.

SO BE AN ABRECAMINOS AND LET YOUR DREAMS BECOME TRUE!

Soldaderas Republicanas #180

Mayra Rodríguez

My house is in the capital of Michoacán, in the colonial city of Morelia. There are many ghetto parts in Morelia and I live in one of them El Realito. El Realito is famous, and not for being a great place to live, but because it was said that here they'd kill or rape without a motive, for free.

When my family and I moved in, taxi drivers were just finding the courage to drive into El Realito. To avoid being robbed or killed, they'd leave their passengers on the colony or district's limits.

My house was on the corner of Soldaderas Republicanas and Avenida Huaniqueo which was a dirt road. Everyone that lived on the opposite side had no running water. There were a couple water holes along that road and when the water did finally come out you would see everyone carrying it in buckets to their homes. At first I felt terrible to see them doing it. I remember I'd think to myself, water? Everyone should have it. After seeing them do that for months, I realized that was their way of life and that's the only way they knew how to live. So it didn't bother me much anymore they were use to it and so was I.

A lot of houses in El Realito are made of cardboard. Compared to these homes my house is fortunately made of brick and has running water. I remember very vividly the first time I saw my new home. I was so embarrassed to know it was mine. All it's windows were broken the side walk was made from dirt, and it had no paint except for the places where spray painted names were put. My kitchen had no cabinets. It was just an empty room. I was ashamed to tell people where it was I lived because I was always looked at as some type of criminal and in the end I'd say "I lived in El Realito y que?"

My Friends

But I got used to living in a place that at the time I thought was the worst place in the world. I wanted to have friends so I began to talk with a group of guys that hung out on the corner of my house. They were called Los Angelitos Locos.

Los Angelitos Locos were weird at first; they all used words I had never heard and they had nicknames. Like some I remember were, Frijol. He was called that because he was dark brown like a bean. Guito, Caguama and Pitti were also called Los Monstrous. They're three brothers, and well, they're not that good looking. Then there was Chinto and Mascaras. Once I got to know El Mascaras, he became my best friend.

Los Angelitos were made up of about fourteen guys. Most of them at the time were between fifteen and eighteen. They smoked and drank a lot. I was twelve but I did none of that.

My neighbors hated them. The women living on my street seemed as if they lived from looking out their windows and from getting into every one else's business. To us they were *gente chismosa*. The more I hung out with my friends the more I felt as if they were beginning to hate me, too.

To my neighbors I was seen as a bad influence because of the people I spoke to and they began to tell my family not to let me speak to Los Angelitos. In the beginning they tried to make me understand something I couldn't get myself to even hear. One day my sister told me, *los cuidas como si fueran oro.* I think maybe I did take care of them and defend them as if they were gold. My friends helped me by letting me fit in, in a new world I never thought I'd get to know. And all I wanted was to be heard, like they did. And I was, and they were.

Ignacio M. Altamirano

This wasn't a school. It looked more like a prison. There was a high brick wall that surrounded the school with a fence you could see along it and it had barbed wire along the top.

All the rooms were identical. They had many wooden desks that we sanded down at the end of every year. The teachers taught from a table. A table so shaky that if you sat on it would surely enough break. They only had one computer in the whole school. It was really out-dated too. We had a library, but it only kept old school books. You couldn't even borrow books.

Physical education and all other sports activities were performed on a cement area that had four basketball hoops. I didn't like it at all. There was no grass to walk on. The science labs were decent but it was rare when a class used them. I think it was to keep it new some thing they failed to do with other things. This school only had one television and it was kept in the library.

There are many secundarias in Morelia so I know I could have chosen a better one. There are more than one hundred there. There was even one where I lived in El Realito. We use to call it "la de mil palitos." The school of a thousand sticks. It was very long and made from small pieces of wood that still had bark on it. To see the school was very sad. Compared to that one, I'm glad I went to la nueve.

People would tell me it was a bad school. I'd tell them, it doesn't matter where someone goes to school. If you have a desire to learn, you can learn anywhere.

Maestro Abel

El maestro Abel, my Spanish teacher, spent the whole hour talking about anecdotes. All his stories were hysterically funny. He'd never want anyone to laugh; we'd always say he was crazy.

One day he made us laugh like always but this time I had an intoxicating laugh. I laughed so hard I stomped at the floor almost wanting to roll upon it. And then he said to laugh at my mom instead. I laughed harder and harder. I started to cry I laughed so hard. I laughed so hard ,no longer laughing at his jokes, but at him. By this time my stomach hurt from laughing so much. I kept laughing. I couldn't stop.

He'd keep making me laugh telling me I reminded him of a person he met that was in a mental institute. I didn't need him to say something to make me laugh anymore. All I had to do was look up at his angry face and that was enough to keep laughing.

He kicked me out but I didn't care. I kept laughing. Even after I was walking out I kept laughing. Even after I was walking out, I kept on. I guess my laugh was contagious because my friend Diego was kicked out right after I was.

When I returned to class everyone told me how he said he was going to have me kicked out from school. He also said he would tell my mom that I had mental problems. The next day he didn't even say anything. I guess he had forgotten it but I'll never forget the laughter he brings me every time I remember him.

Physics

I remember many of my teachers. El maestro Rincon is one of them. I remember one day he walked into class. We greeted him like we had to do with everyone of my teachers and then waited to be seated. He was talking to one of my classmates, Guadalupe Leticia. While we were still standing, he kept talking. I felt stupid because I stood there out of a sign of respect and he didn't care. I asked him, "Maestro Rincon, can we sit down?" and he said, "No not till I say so.".

I acted as if I didn't hear him and sat down as he was looking at me. Surely enough, he kicked me out. His class was Physics.

Soon I started to hate him because he talked about Americans. He would say that Americans were stupid, that they'd put their garbage outside waiting to sell it. He was trying to explain a yard sale.

I don't know why he spoke that way, knowing his son is a successful doctor in Seattle.

Never did I pass his class. Those two semesters I spent more time outside and trying to find a way to get kicked out than sitting and listening to what he tried to teach.

A Face I Cannot See

One night as I was coming back from La Colonia La Industrial, like always, I stopped at La Curva, which is where my sister spent most of her time.

When I got there, my sister told me that she was gonna fight some girl. She asked me if I would go with her in case someone jumped in. We called that *hacer esquina*. So I went just like that without knowing why she was doing it.

There we went, my sister, her two friends, and I. We were meeting up by *la barranca del muerto*, that's what the type of ravine was called. It was off to one side of Prados Verdes where La Curva is. As we walked up, I would be the one to get in the fight, not my sister. And I guess, to look good, I said, "All right."

Now I didn't even know why we were fighting. I had never seen the girl in my life but we fought anyway. While kicking, punching, and scratching one another, she fell. After a couple of days, I realized...she could have died, as she fell down the ravine. I still think of that, to this day, and I wonder, "Does she ever think of that day?" I guess I'll never stop wondering.

If one day she walks by me I wouldn't know her name, and when I try to remember her face, I can't see it.

Bere's House

I was bored in my house. For a time I was fed up with everyone there. I guess maybe it was the craziness of adolescence.

My mom hated the idea, but I think I was in a type of phase where everyone was wrong except for me. I always argued till I made them see what I saw or until they were sick of listening. And I got what I wanted.

I moved into my niece Berenice's house. We all called her Bere for short, she was seventeen. It was an apartment with a bedroom, a small living room, and the kitchen. I had never seen one as tiny as that one. It was the size of the bathroom.

Bere and I weren't the only ones living there. Her parents lived there with her dad's sister and all my nieces and nephews. All eight of them Fatima, Eli, Elisa, Miriam, Jose, Danny, Lupe and Florecita the youngest. We all lived in this tiny baby blue apartment.

There was always something interesting to do with the kids. We'd go to the park everyday and on the weekends we'd visit the zoo. It was fun.

I felt good to be a part of a large family, but I also thought of my cousin and how I was probably just another mouth to feed when it came down to what were the facts. I was her responsibility and I felt bad. Even though she never showed her feelings toward me staying, I know she saw that things were easier when there was one mouth less to feed.

I don't regret living there because I found out for myself that there is no place like home.

Jennifer

My little sister Jennifer. She's a smart little girl only she isn't small anymore. She's twelve and as tall as I am. We all have nicknames but she has more than we do. I don't know where we'd get all these names. We'd call her Johnny 5 like from the old movie about a robot. We also called her John Luke Bucard of Bucard Enterprises, I think we got that one off of Stark Trek, or we'd just call her J.R. For short, we'd call her by her initials, J.R.

I didn't like Johnny's cat "Chispa's Spark. I didn't like her because she only ate and slept. Okay, well I hated Chip's for being a cat.

Like always, my friend Gustavo visited me. Sometimes he'd take his dog, "Kody." It was a beige and white pit-bull and was very obedient. He'd amaze me when Gustavo would tell him to sit. He reminded me of a statue. When I went out to see who had knocked, I left the door open on purpose. Minutes later, Chispa came out and Kody chased after her. She was left without a choice, so she climbed up a tree to get away.

Jennifer was crying and called to her cat to get down. As she jumped down Kody caught her in the air and clenched down on her body, not letting her go. You could hear Chispa and it wasn't anything but the sound of an animal being slaughtered.

It broke my heart when I turned to see my sister. It was like seeing her in slow motion, dropping to her knees in the middle of the dirt road as she covered her face with her hands and cried.

The Loveliest Memory

Of many things I do remember, I'm glad I kept this memory with me.

Three years ago I vacationed in a small town in Michoacán three hours from where I lived. The town's name is Senguio. My mom was born here and all of her relatives live here. Because this town is so small and was founded by seven families, most of the town is made up of my relatives.

I had gone many times to this place but it was different this time. I went for Christmas vacation and got an unforgettable Christmas present.

On Christmas day I was woken up by my cousin Richard at four in the morning telling me we'd go see the butterflies. I had never gone to see them, which was unusual because most people from Senguio have. So we were off—my cousin, five of his friends, and me. It's a four hour hike there and back. It took us a very long time to even get to the midpoint which is a Catholic Sanctuary. I thought it was lovely being out there in nature, and everything at peace. It was a precious experience.

As we almost reached the top of the mountain, we could not see many, but with every step we took we were getting closer and closer. More and more butterflies appeared, like it was magic. At first I couldn't tell that the trees were completely covered in these little delicate creatures. Just being there reminded me of what someone once told me, that Aztecs believed that butterflies carry the souls of those who have passed away.

It was a long way to get there and home but it was the best Christmas present I could ever have. It's a memory that I will carry with me forever, and there isn't a better gift than that.

Once More

Jamas olvidaré that blue house en El Realito.
I will never forget that blue house on El Realito.

It has had an unexplainable impact in my life. I've become the person that I am because of it.

The experiences I had in this home are priceless and form a part of my life I will hold forever close to my heart.

How much wouldn't I give to go back and live that time once more. Here is where I started to grow as a person; this is where the blindfold I wore disappeared. . . .And I began to find the real me.

My Struggle

I struggled when I left my home last year. I had thought of the day my dream would come true every day for three years, and I was sure that this is what I wanted.

I wanted a better life. I had a good one, but I wanted an even better one. And the only place where this could be was back in the U.S. with my Dad. I knew school would be better, job opportunities would be much larger, and my life would be fuller.

I remember the day I left. I didn't cry for leaving my Mom, or for leaving my sisters behind. I didn't care for saying good-bye to anyone of my friends. To me it felt like any other day, except for this day I would accomplish something that would bring me a step closer to what I wanted with such passion and desire.

I struggled when I left my home. I didn't know if my dream would come true, or if I would have to make a different one, one where I'd wish to come back.

Only I Know It

Liliana Mendoza

A young Mexican female.
Extreme power.
As much on the inside as out.

All eyes on me.
Power to succeed as I proceed.
Power to stay up as I stand up.
Power to know a lady's worth.

Priceless.

Nobody can put a price tag on me.

I walk my walk.
But don't talk my walk.

It's all on me and just me.

No bragging.
No begging.
No approaching.
No ho'ing around.

I'm a lady first.
I know my game.
But I keep it on the hush.

There's a problem with other girls.

They don't know how to act or be a lady.

They let themselves be a victim.
A victim of temptations.
They go crying when the consequences come along.

I can handle the decisions I make
because I know how to make decisions.

I'm a lady first.

Many guys have a problem, too.
Most guys.
Almost all guys.

They think they got all the game.
Talking about, *I got all the bitches.*

Maybe.

But that's all they can get
Bitches...

They can't handle a real lady
because they don't know how to approach one.

A lady can only be approached by somebody who can be *a man.*
Not somebody who tries to be *the* man.

There's a difference.

I'm satisfied with my game,
so I don't need to talk about it.
I know what I got.

And I can handle it.
I'm like a black cat.
I walk lightly and swiftly.
Noticed by everybody.
Not only by my appearance,
but also by my uniqueness and heart.
I'm intimidatingly feared by other cats.
Saco las uñas when I need to.
Superstitiously feared by the color of my skin.

I walk like no other.
It attracts the unseen eyes.

Head up high.
Eyes wide open.
No talking.

I don't need to experience
in order to learn.
I just keep my mouth shut
and learn from others' mistakes.

I know what I know
because I watch what goes on around me.

I know what I'm worth
and I don't live my life off of temptations.

I'm a lady first.

That's how I walk my walk.
Only I know it.

My Life

José Garibay

When you are living in a different place far from your town or your city, you always think about how your life was when you were a baby, and how you grew up with your family and your friends.

I was born on April 22 in a little town named Aguililla, Michoacán, México. When I was a little boy I liked to play with my friends and my sister. I always liked to go to my grandma's house because she used to make me some good food, like frijoles con queso y tortillas. When I was a little boy, my mom always used to tell me that I had an *abuelita linda*, a beautiful grandmother, who always took care of me, and who loved me too much with all her heart.

Talking about little boys, I would like to talk about my mom when she was a little girl. My mom was very poor and she had to work a lot because she and her family didn't have all the simple things that you need to have in life. She didn't have shoes to go to school, and sometimes clothes to wear, either. But when God is with us we don't care how the person's life is. There is always a way to go on in life and to have a better future. In this life that we are living now, there will always be obstacles.

When I was 14 years old, my mom became sick and she died. I remember when she was so sick, she was skinny, and she couldn't talk during the last days of her life. When she wanted something she had to write it on a piece of paper. My mom was too sick and we were afraid to lose her, but that happened and we couldn't do anything about it. God took her away from us and we have to face the truth, and live the life, even though my mom is not with us. But she will be always in our hearts. My mom was a good person and she was a great mom and a great friend for us. She always used to go to church every day in the morning. I think that's why she died, because she was like an Angel bajado del cielo. She was like an Angel below Heaven to take care of us, *para cuidarnos, y para protegernos de todo el mal y para ayudarnos en todos los problemas que tuviéramos. Y ella siempre estaba ahí en esos tiempos cuando la necesitabamos.*

My mom was also a good hard worker. She always used to wake up in the morning to open the store and to get all the things out like the canastas and every single thing like that. Me and my family were so frustrated about my mom because she was too sick, and when I say sick, I mean really sick.

Everyone's life has different changes, in different ways. Now I would like to talk about how my life was after my mom died. Me, my dad, and my sisters had to work in the store every single day of our life, as my mom used to do. Sometimes I used to go out with my friends in the night and we always used to play in the street, telling stories about everything that we wanted to tell.

I grew up during the rest of the years with my dad and the rest of my family. It was hard for us to understand that my mom was gone forever, but that's the way it goes, and we cannot change it. After all these problems that I had with my family, I went to study far from home, like two hours away. I was studying really well, but I didn't like it too much because in the school there were just guys. When I came back home from school, I knew that my father had another woman, and the worst thing was that she had four girls. I didn't talk to them because they just wanted my father's money. That's why I decided one thing that really changed my life. I decided to come here to the United States with my sister. She seemed like a good person, and of course, she was my sister, and I had faith in her, and I decided to come with her.

When I arrived in the United States I was 14 years old and I didn't know how to speak English. I stayed at home for a couple of weeks and then I came to school. It was my first time in class and I didn't know what to do because I thought I was the only Mexican in the whole school. When I saw more Mexicans I was a little bit scared anyway. The first day in class I had classes in Spanish, and it was easier for me because during that time I started to learn how to speak English. It was hard sometimes because the teacher used to talk to us in English and sometimes I didn't know what he was talking about. I am still learning English and I am studying hard every day and playing soccer at the same time.

When I came to literature class I was kind of scared too because I thought my teacher could just speak English, and I was scared. But then I was reading and writing poems and I started to like all the poems and the class, too because it was a good class. Then I wrote about my personal life and my real life. I heard different poems and all of them were good with understanding. I liked these poems because they were written by perfect persons in our class, in fact they were written by the heart from every one of us. I heard some poems talking about "Breaking Chains" and I liked them because the writers wrote them with their hearts in their hands, and with good feelings like the person really feels it, and that they had reached for their poems to get them better than ever.

While I was living with my sister, I thought it was going to be easy living in the United States, just doing your job every day of your life.

Now that I am living with Lisa, Jose and Ty, I am happy because they are just like my parents and they are really kind people and I am proud of myself because I got a good family here and I am just really happy about it. José and Lisa are both teachers at my school. They are Mr. and Mrs. Garcia at school. When I need something, they are there where I need them. It's so much different living with them than when I was living with my sister. That's because I've never lived with an American woman, but Lisa is a really good person, and I am really happy living with them.

Sometimes I think that I am a cool person and that I have discovered that I have a good family here. I have done many things in the United States of America that I'd never done before in my whole life. One of the things I want is to graduate from Davis High School. Then I will think about college, because if I graduate from the high school, I would like to go to Mexico, see my family and to breathe fresh air, but I would like to go to college.

When I think about my family that is in Mexico I get sad because they are far from home and I can see them. That's why sometimes I just think about them and I relax. This is what I am feeling now, here, far from home, far from my family, but that's the way it is and I can't do anything about it. There is just only one thing. I will never forget my family that is in Mexico. And I will never forget my mom, even though she is dead. I still love her too much with all my heart, and she still loves me because she is my Guardian Angel. This Guardian Angel will never forget her son that is on earth, because this son loves her too much, and he will never forget all the good things that lived with that Angel on earth. That Angel will be always in my heart, forever.

It's Little, But it's Pretty

Cristal Manjarréz

It was 11:27 p.m. when we crossed the border. We spent three hours trying to get a permit to drive our American car in *La Republica Mexicana.*

My parents kept driving after we got the permit at 2:30 a.m. My father and my Uncle Juan Carlos were anxious to arrive to the little town in Guerrero. I didn't have that feeling. The bumps on the road remembered that I was not the same child who emigrated to the U. S. five years ago. *No tenía nada en Los Sauces, solamente una casa.* My family was established in the United States, my friends, my school and my life. Why should we go back every year?

My parents are Mexican, my family is Mexican. I'm Mexican, but my soul belongs to another place. All the time we spent on the way to our town, I thought about what I left in the U.S., and even though I knew that I would return, I was missing my life, the things that I love and that I wouldn't see. I was missing my friends from church, my Jewish friends. I took several books with me, those books about Jewish history that I love to read. I have been studying Jewish history and Hebrew language for a few months, that has been one of my biggest passions. My goal was to go to Israel next year. I had been saving money the whole year to go to Eretz-Israel. But that was just a dream at that time.

We arrived in Los Sauces the next day at 11:45 a.m. My little house was still green colored as I left it last year. *It's little, but it's pretty.* It remembers me when I was a child, when I used to play *a la comidita* with my friends. How could I forget that time? Life was so easy back then. All my responsibilities were to play in el patio.

My grandparents, aunt, uncle, and little cousins, were there to welcome us. They're not that little now. Actually they're taller than I am. The town has changed, too. It looks less poor than the last time I saw it.

Going back to Mexico is like going back to my childhood. That calm that I feel when I'm at home is unique. There is no place like my town. Its climate, its smell, its peace. How could I live away from it for such a long time?

The day after we arrived there, we went to Teloloápan to change dollars for pesos, and to buy supplies for our house. That city is crowded. Everybody pushes you and you push everybody to get a spot to walk. They sell fruit and all kinds of things in *el mercado*. The city is known for the *mole* they produce and also for *la Tecampana*. These are stones that sound like *campanas* or bells. The word means *piedra que canta*, "stones that sing." Teloloápan is the closest city to Los Sauces. That's why we go there to buy supplies.

Another city that is close to our town is Iguala. I went there three days before Christmas. It's incredible! You step on the street and start to sweat. Its climate is simply hot. When I was there I remembered the snow on the mountains of Washington, and started to miss it. Iguala is known as *La Cuna De La Bandera*, because it was there where the first flag of Mexico was made.

Two days after we arrived at Los Sauces I met Blanca, one of my best friends. She is the only one that still lives there. My other friends got married and went to Chicago. But Blanca still lives there. She is my age. We went to *la secundaria* together. But now she has two children that call her mamá, and a husband that asks her for *almuerzo, comida, y cena. Pobrecita mi amiga*, she looks very tired.

The 24th of December, when people celebrate Christmas, my mom cooked *mishotes*. I have eaten them in Yakima too, but they don't taste the same as in Mexico. My family and some of my parents' friends went to visit us that night. That's what people do on that day, visit with each other. They really don't know what they celebrate. They say they're celebrating the birth of Jesus, but they get drunk and never talk about God on that special night.

Two days after Christmas, we went to Taxco. Taxco is a tourist place, three hours from Los Sauces. It's known for its cathedral of Santa Prisca. They say it's made of gold, but I really don't believe it.

There is a lot of *plata* there. Silver stores everywhere. Taxco is pretty, its streets, its people, its food—everything is precious to remember.

The night of the 31st of December we celebrated new year. People in Los Sauces wait until 1:00 o'clock to eat dinner. There is a lot of noise and at that exact time, *las campanas de la catedral* begin to ring. Men are shooting their guns, and people are talking outside in the streets. Families get together to celebrate every new year. That's the singular way of celebrating that we have in Mexico.

On the 5th of January my parents made a party for me to celebrate my birthday. Some of my friends came to congratulate me, some others didn't, but my best friend Vianney called me from Yakima. My father said he was proud of me. He said I was his fulfillment, because I was his oldest daughter. The party was good, but the most interesting part was that I realized that my parents have been there all the time, at all my birthdays. I had never thought about it.

We left five days later. In the time we spent there I realized that I belong to it. I lived half of my life there. All my memories of my childhood are from there, from Los Sauces, my little town in Guerrero. But now there are new things in my life, my life in the United States, my passion for Hebrew culture, and my new point of view about life. I like Spanish, English, and Hebrew. I love Mexico, the United States, and Israel, and I would like to be in the three places at the same time. The reality is that I belong to the three of them.

It's a few hours until we arrive in Yakima. I would like to go back to Mexico. I'll miss its warm climate, its food and its people. I would like to live in both places at the same time. I'll miss my house...*it's little but it's pretty*.

Half Way

Marco Gutiérrez

My name is Marco Antonio Gutiérrez Espinoza.
I was born on Octubre the 2d. 1985, in a small town
called Cocula, Jalisco, Mex.
My parents are Lidia Gutiérrez and Marco Gutiérrez.

I'm the oldest of four. My sisters' names are
Lidia Elizabeth Gutiérrez, and Guadalupe Gutiérrez.
My brother's name is Yair Issac Gutiérrez.
My sister Lidia is 14, my brother

Yair is 12, and my little sister,
Lupita, is 3. My mom is 35
and my dad is 41. I was born
in Cocula, because it was the

closest hospital there was. I have never
lived there, they only helped out my mother
to deliver me. Every time I go to my parents' home
town, I only pass by, without feeling

anything that can hold me there. Since
I was two, my parents left me with my
other mother, who really was Geroveva
Espinoza, my mom's mother. My parents had

the necessity of coming to the U.S.A. for
a better job, so they can get paid better,
so we can have a better life than they
did when they were children. I lived

until I was 8 in Guadalajara Jal. Mex.
Because my parents hardly came to visit
us every year, we moved to Sán Quintin
B.C.N. We traveled on train for 3 days

until we got to Mexicali early morning.
From there we traveled on bus for 8 hours
to Sán Quintin, where my mother
had relatives, and it was close to the

border. Back in Guadalajara I left all my
friends, my way of living. Sán Quintin
is a small town, a rural place with no
places to go out or play. I was happy because

I was able to see my parents more often.
I lived there for almost 3 years. Right when
I graduated from elementary school at the age of
12, my parents decided that it was time

to come to the U.S.A. for a better education.
We moved to Salinas, CA. I lived there
for two years. Here I graduated from middle
school. By that time my little sister was born.

I was living in Salinas when the most embarrassing
thing happened. I was at school, it was
lunch time, me and my friends were playing soccer.
I stepped on dog poop, but I didn't notice

at that time. When the bell rang, I headed
to my class room. In a matter of 5 minutes,
the poop under my shoe started to smell,
everybody started to talk about the odor

that my shoe provided. I felt bad,
and I went to the bathroom
and cleaned up my shoe. Right after
my birthday we moved to Yakima.

I lived with my aunt for 3 months.
We moved to a house by 9th St. We got
here during winter. It was difficult for my
parents to find a job, so they decided to

move back to California. I decided to
stay here with my Uncle Mario to finish
high school. I passed a lonely Christmas
and a new year. My parents would send

me money every two weeks. Here in
Yakima I met new friends. I had the
chance of meeting Gastón and his family
and a lot of great teachers, like Ms. Salatino,

and Mr. Garcia. Gastón and I became
good friends. After school we would
go to run and play soccer at Washington
Middle School to get in shape for try outs

for Davis soccer. We finally made it on the
team. A year had passed since my mom came
back to Yakima to live with me. My dad stayed
in Somerton, Arizona, where he has a good job.

Dream or Story?—My Life

María de Jesús Garcia

Everything seems to go wrong; I get blamed for everything that goes wrong in her life. María do this, María do that. It doesn't seem to end.

"María! Ya estás fregando los trastes?"

Como quisiera que un día, un solo día no me culpara o me dijera algo.

"María!" My mom yells once more.

"Ya voy!" Todos los dias igual. Lo digo en mi cabeza porque me puede ir mal.

"Ahorita que venga y no has terminado de fregar los trastes, vas a ver." She says as she walks out the door.

"Don't listen to her, she is an old woman and she is going through some tough times," Horte, my older sister tells me.

"How am I going to do that if it's an every day thing? I would understand if she did it once in awhile, but it's not. It's every day, non-stop." I respond angrily.

"Think about it, you only have about two years before you can leave," she states, trying to give me a sense of hope.

That reminded me of the time when we had to leave San Diego to come to Washington. Someway, somehow we ended in Los Angeles at a park. I remember I cried that day because I didn't want to leave, but what choice did I have? I was a little girl then. It was the beginning of the summer and we were told to pack our belongings because we were going to leave. It was a BMW, the type of car we traveled in. On the freeway I heard a man say, "We have to go back, porque 'La Migra' está allá." Back then I had no idea what that was. It was at that point that I started to realize that my father would not be joining us. It wasn't until we got to Washington that I opened my eyes in believing that he would never be back.

"I wish I could, but I can't." I say.

"Why not?"

"Because I just can't, I can't find the guts to do it. The only way I will do it is when I go off to college.

At the age of four, it was time for me to go to school. Like any other kid, I was excited. But it was a whole different story once I got there. Holding my mom's hand we walked up to the classroom. She was about to leave when I started to cry. I ran up to her hanging on as tight as I could. I didn't want to stay. I wanted to go with her instead. That will be one day that I will never forget. The teacher came out and took me into the classroom. Once in the classroom, I sat in a really soft chair and the teacher gave me a doll to play with. For that whole year, every day I cried, and every day was the same routine. First grade was a good year. I remember the teacher had asked us if we knew how big an ant was. When I showed him the way I thought it was, he and the whole class started to laugh at me. I don't remember my second grade, but my third grade was a good experience. That was the year that I learned how to do Origami, and how to speak some Japanese. Fourth grade I think was the best because I was in choir and I loved it. We would always go to different places and sing especially during the holidays.

"So what are you going to do?" Horte asks.

"Nothing. All I can do is listen to her and ignore her until I can leave."

"Well, talk to her or tell her something."

"*No soy capaz de decirle nada.*" I tell my sister. "I mean, I understand that she is going through some tough times, but she should at least cut me some slack. I know she stresses about money and bills and sending money to my grandparents but, I don't know, she just gets mad so easy, and there's not much I can do. Y para más, yo soy la que cocina, limpía y tengo que tener todo en orden, *and it's hard.* There is no way that she will understand that I have homework and other school commitments before I can do housework. I know I have to help her out, and I do try but she cannot see all of the good things I have accomplished. I know I'm the oldest here at the house and I am also responsible for what goes on, but that's a big load after the things I have to do. Sometimes I wish to go away for some time and see how she would handle it all. Anyway I have to wash the dishes," I finally say.

"Well, I'll come back later, aver que," she responds on her way out.

"Okay."

The water runs slowly and peacefully as my mind wanders of to another place.

To the place where the journey begins. After many years, my parents finally decided to go back to the United States. It was a long trip, but we did it. Like any other illegal family, we too, crossed the border. Many stories go about the crossing of the border, from swimming the Rio Grande to the hot deserts of Arizona. It was different for us, in that I don't remember which way we came through. But I do remember something. I remember that my dad was holding my hand while my other hand was holding the fence right behind me. It was like sliding, but not really. It looked like a dam or something of that sort because we were up on top by the edge of the fence that separated the dam and the outside world. The people that were down there had big plastic bags on their legs trying not to get wet by the water that was there. The water was maybe up to their ankles. or up to their knees, I couldn't really tell. After that scene in my life I don't remember coming out of that fence. The next thing I remember is still holding on to my dad's hand, but this time he is urging me to hurry up. At that particular moment I have no idea why we are there or why my dad is making me walk so fast. Right there on the ground, I see a frog or a toad. I don't know I can't tell the difference, but I do see people sitting down on the floor all dirty. Those people, some of them were sitting next to the fence and others on the other side against something else. I find it strange that this is all that I can remember of our trip here, to America.

"You're going to get in trouble if you don't finish the dishes before mom gets here," Lalo, my little brother says. Hearing his voice makes me go back in time to the place where he was born. *It is there in San Diego that I can call home. Nobody was home one day except for my little brother Eduardo. When he woke up from his nap I remember I had to change his diaper because, well you know. When my mom got back she was so proud of me because of what I had done.*

For a kid to be able to go somewhere at the age of four or five is unusual. I remember that I used to go to the store all on my own. I would get sent to a store that was pretty far to buy things we needed. At this place there were a lot of little stores—barber shops, restaurants, apartments, and a self-serve laundry mat. At the laundry mat I remember playing on the roof. Since there were apartments, there were also stairs to go up. My sisters and I would always go up there and play. At that place there was a store that sold candy and other things, and every time we were there we would buy candy. Being there so many times, the owners knew us all by name.

I wish things would go back to the way they were, when I didn't get in trouble all of the time. The day I was born would be good. *My mother told me that I was born in La Loma Municipio de Coahuayana, Michoacán, México. The first three or four years of my life I spent* in México. My mother always told me stories that I used to go to the store and buy things, but I don't want to believe her because it makes no sense. How can a two-year-old, maybe three, go the store and buy something? I didn't have time to enjoy my time in the state I was born, because from there we went to Tijuana, México. It was there that I started to have my first actual memories. Still, in that age range, I remember playing with my sisters and some other kids. The skateboard had a rope tied to it and somebody would have to pull it. Anyway, it was my turn so I got on it. I remember getting on the skateboard and my older sister started to pull me. Some other kid, Tony, wanted to get on it, but my sister told him that it wasn't his turn so he started to cry. Cuando recuerdo eso me río porque en esé tiempo eramos un poco pobres y todos, digo los niños estabamos mocositos. Since I am already talking about skateboards I remember that both my sister and I were on one. Who knows how it happened? But we fell and I got my knees all scraped up and I don't remember what happened to my sister.

Another memory that I have about Tijuana is that there was a lady that my sister and I would go see every once in awhile. That lady lived across the dirt because there were no roads at the time. Later on, my sister told me that that lady used to make dresses for her. Maybe she did then for my younger sisters and me, but I wouldn't have any knowledge of knowing so. We moved from that place to where we lived closer to the school and to a store. One time my mom sent me to the store and all I remember is seeing a HUGE dog. I don't remember going in or out of the store, but I remember the dog. He seemed to look like a skyscraper because he was really tall. The thing that attracted me was his golden color. There is one memory that is still unclear in my mind. It was after a rainy day that the ground got all muddy and wet. I remember playing mud ball in a fight with my older brother and sister. That event had bothered me for so long that I decided to ask my mom if it was true. To my surprise me dijó que estaba loca y que eso era un sueño que tuve. Until this very day I choose to refuse that, that so called dream is just a dream and not a real memory.

The last memory I can think of while we were in Tijuana is that one day my mom told me to go the school and take my older sister and brother their lunch. La escuela estaba arriba de una montaña, más bien un cerro de tierra. No era grande pero para mí, como era pequeña era enorme. No recuerdo si estaba cargando algo o no. Ya que llegué allí me encontre a un niño, le pregunte, ¿Que dónde quedaba la clase de Leo o de Baby? my older sister (we all called her Baby when we were smaller). He pointed out some classroom and I started to walk. I don't remember much after that. I don't even remember getting home or how I got there. My grand Aunt Elvira lived in a huge house and what I remember about it is that in her living room she had this huge television set that would be an antique now days. I'm not sure if it was before or after dinner that all of the kids had to go outside and play. It may have been that my memory only allows me to see *myself in that event, or that I just simply don't remember the other kids. Out in that gigantic place that she had, there was a place where she had some chickens and some other animals. That place smelled good to me, it smelled clean and fresh, but to other people it might have smelled bad. When they called us to go eat we washed up and got ready to eat fish. I don't remember what kind of fish it was but I do remember that I almost choked. I must have swallowed a bone because my mom gave me a lot of tortillas or bananas for the bone to go down. I must have scared my mom half to death because of that bone.*

I do have to give my mom credit for all of the things she has done for me. She has always been there when I needed her and I know she will always be there. She always tells me to study and work hard so I won't have to depend on others. My mother wants me to do better than her and to be successful and for that I thank her.

Life wasn't always easy. That I know, after some time and experience.

My older sister and brother became rebels when we first came to Yakima, Washington. My sister skipped school and my brother was different. Perhaps it was that we left California so suddenly and we left our friends behind. It was around this time that I decided that I was not going to be like them. I wanted to show my mom that I would be different and that I would become somebody. I was good in school and I got good grades. It was in middle school that I decided to become a lawyer to help people. I also wanted to give my younger brother and sisters a good example. The example that if I could do it they can, too. If I don't give the example, who will? High school has been a great experience and I treasure it the most. My mother didn't finish her education because she had to help my grandmother. Together, as well as with the help of her older brothers, they had to come up with money to get the things they needed. Mi madre también lavaba y planchaba ropa ajena para poder tener comida en la mesa and for that I am very proud to say that without her I would not be where I am today.

I do know one thing, and that is that I will make it through no matter what.

Part VII

About the Authors and Vocabulario de los Abrecaminos

Contributor's Information

Clementina Abúndiz: Born on March 5, 1984 to Maria and Eudoro Abúndiz, God has been good to her and her familia. Cleme, as her family calls her, enjoys spending time with her familia, reading, hanging out with *real* friends, and attending church. She also loves singing in her church choir, helping others, and being there for her true friends. Cleme loves her nieces Nissi Yvette, Canela Zafiro, Laurel Topasio, Margarita, Kaila Elise, who's on the way, and her nephew, Leví Jared, dearly. As an abrecaminos student, a senior at A.C. Davis High School, her graduation date is June 6, 2002. Both excited and scared, Clementina can't wait for her next *etapa* in her life as a college student at Central Washington University. Go Wildcats!

María de Jesus Barriga: I came from Aguililla, Michoacán, Mexico three years ago. Aguililla is a very small town. I am a senior student. In Latino Lit we write poems about our dreams and tell stories about our lives. Also we study and write about our ancestors. I was born in Yakima, Washington in 1982 because my parents had to migrate to the U.S.A. with the hope of a better future. We moved to Mexico when I was a year old and I came back to Yakima on my own on December 23, 1998, at the age of 16. My struggle started since that date when I left my home, the little town, and my family, siblings, and friends for better opportunities of education.

María Guadalupe Barriga: I graduated from Davis High School and now I'm a student at Yakima Valley Community College. I came from a big family. I'm the ninth of eleven children. When I was at Davis I had the privilege of being a student, and I learned the way to become an abrecaminos, and to climb the Machhu Pichhu Mountain. I was born here in Yakima, Washington, but I was raised in Mexico. When I was 17 I came to the U.S. I was raised in Aguililla, Michoacán. I returned to the U.S. in 1997. I have been working and studying.

María Rosa Barriga: I'm the student who wanted to become an *abrecaminos*. I want to make a way where there is no way. I came here looking for a life. I didn't come here looking for America. I wanted a better life. I'm only 18 years old. I never thought that the great America was so hard to discover. I'm from a nice place called Aguililla,

Michoacán. I was born in 1983 when everything was easier than before. I had to leave Aguililla because all my sisters were here. I was the only one left in Michoacán, so they decided to bring me over. Now I'm becoming an abrecaminos. I like it. It's beautiful to make a way where there's no way. I'm making a way for those who don't know how to make one. In my writing I'm trying to make those "vagabundos" walk in the right way, to make them see the real life, *no fantasias en donde pasan viviendo tanto tiempo.*

Estakio Beltran, winner of the Raymond Carver Writing Contest at Davis High School, is a son, dreamer, student, and gymnast. Graduate from the abrecaminos. Currently he is writing his own book, which is in process, and working as a gymnastics coach in Spokane while attending Gonzaga University. He says, "I'm going to write the stories of the voices that speak to me. The whispers in my ears. *El sonido del viento punzando sobre mis tambores.* Give me, give me your stories. I want to hear your cries and share them with a world that ignores you. I am going to write so that people don't forget me. I am going to leave no doubt of my existence."

Bertha Campos: I'm a student at high school. I'm abrecaminos. I write stories in my free time. I like to read interesting stories and poesía. I have four brothers and four sisters. I'm 17 years old. One other thing, I'm from a small town in the mountains of Michoacán, México. I was born in 1984. My family lives in Yakima and I arrived in 1999. I don't have a dad because he died in 1989. My mother is working right now in Alaska. My sisters and brothers take care of each other while she is gone. I'm trying to write my feelings of the heart.

Pedro Campos: I'm 19 years old. I was born in Mexico. I lived there almost 16 years. I arrived in the U.S.A. in 1998. I have been three years in this country. I studied English in this school. I want something for my future. I'm looking for something new, ideas and goals. It's because I feel sad when someone arrives in this country and he doesn't speak English. I learn about the life. It's hard for me because my father died when I was a child. I was almost 5 years. Now my mother is working hard for me for my future. She is working a lot to support me. She is working in Alaska right now. In my writing I'm trying to say, if you are like me, or a girl, you need to study for your future. It is not only for you, it is for your family.

Rosalinda Campos: I'm a student of the abrecaminos. I write poems and tell stories about my life. I am from Michoacán, México. I was born in Cruz de Campos. My family is big. I have four brothers and four sisters, and now we live in Yakima, Washington with my brothers. My Dad is dead. My mom is working in Alaska. My hobbies are playing volleyball and listening to music, *y lo que más disfruto es estar con mi familia,* the thing I enjoy most is being with my family.

Antonia Caro: I'm 18 years old. I came to Yakima about four years ago. I'm from Guadalajara, Jalisco. I went to Ignacio Ramirez Secundaria in Mexico. I used to be on the volleyball team which I enjoyed a lot. It was my favorite hobby. I'm the second youngest of five children. I'm a junior at Davis High School. My goals are to get better every day in speaking English, getting better grades and going on to college to become a lawyer. I try to express my feelings, my thoughts, and also I am trying to make my voice be heard through my poems.

Maria Caro: I am from Jalisco, Mexico and I am 20 years old. I like to write poems because it is one form of expressing the feelings and I can practice my English. My favorite hobbies are to play volleyball and read interesting books. I never thought I was going to write poems. I have discovered the fun things, and the beautiful, which is to write poems. I'm trying to write my way of thinking, and my point of view of being and thinking.

Erika María Cruz: I'm 17 years of age and a senior. I'm proud to say that being an abrecaminos has helped me mature and see life with different eyes, the eyes of the heart *(el alma)*. I am a person who is ready to overcome any challenge that comes to me because the abrecaminos way and Jesus have helped. I really am thankful for knowing these qualities. Also, Miguel, my boyfriend, who helped me get close to my religion and understand what life is worth. And thanks to my family for the times they have been there for me. In my writing, I'm trying to wake up a story that has been dead or sleeping for a long time, and I need to know what lies beneath those lies.

Uziel Estrada has been a student for 11 years. Over the years he has experienced things he never expected in his growing up. He loves school, especially going to Davis High School. He enjoys cruising in his Silverado pickup every day of the week, especially during the weekend. He also is engaged in church activities. Uziel thinks that anybody with a dream or a goal can make it come true by working hard and putting your strengths forward. I think I am a wonderful guy, but many people don't notice it because they never met me before. But everybody that meets me, they always take something into their hearts from me. In writing I'm trying to say something brief and special about me. There's tons more of information of me, but I think you can tell who I am.

Cesar Farias: I write poems about my life and my struggles. I wrestle and play soccer for the school teams. I was born in Coalcoman, Michoacán in 1983. We migrated to Washington to have better opportunities. I live with my parents and some of my brothers and sisters. I write my life stories to get where I want to get and make my parents proud. I want the rest of the world to see that I try hard. I work hard to be somebody and to let others know my story. I can be stronger and walk with my head held high, in front of me, proudly.

Blanca Flores: I'm a senior at Davis High School. I'm 18 years old. I like to play basketball and my favorite team is the L. A. Lakers. My favorite player is Kobe. I'm an abrecaminos and write poems and stories. I've learned a lot in the class called Latino Literature. I'm the oldest of five girls. I was born in Los Angeles, California. We lived there until I was 11 years old. I've been living in Yakima, Washington for six years. I plan to move back to California after graduation. I'm trying to let people know a little about me so they can understand my writing.

Francisco Galeana: Things for me are very different in life after being an abrecaminos. Life and love is more like form, and the relationship with family and *naturaleza* is better. I love every day a little more. My mom and I like to bring happiness to the ones who love me and don't like to have problems with anyone. I like to be confident with my friends and have a lot of fun with them. In my free time I like to go to places where there are a lot of trees and plants. I like to have plants in my house and take pictures of them and make poems about nature. I'm trying to express myself and help others with it. I'm trying to tell others what I feel in my head, and so others transfer good, positive energy.

María de Jesús García: It was recently that I started to open up to people, to share my life with them. I noticed that if I don't become more open, no one will pay attention to me. Most of the time I spend with my family. *Vengo de una familia humilde pero decente. Nosotros, no todo el tiempo hemos tenido todo, pero lo poquito que tenemos nos gusta compartir.* In school I have played volleyball and I am currently on the Dance Team. Not only that, but I also participate in clubs that I feel will help me better my skills with communication. I only have one goal in life and that is that I will go through every obstacle that gets in my way to get ahead.

José Garibay: I'm 18 years old. I'm from Michoacán, México. I arrived here in the United States when I was 16 years old. I wanted to come here because I wanted a better education or a better job. My family is in Mexico—my Dad, my sister, etc. My mother died when I was 14 years old. I would like to talk about my favorite things that I like to do. I like to play soccer and I like to run, too. I'm studying right now at Davis High School. I have a literature class with a teacher who is an abrecaminos. My friends are abrecaminos, too. I was living in Arizona before and then I moved here with my sister. I like this city, and I like everyone who likes me. I'm trying to express my feelings and I would like to talk about my life and my mom because I love her even though she is dead. I still love her.

Martha Gamboa: I will be attending the University of Washington in the fall. In my spare time I enjoy listening to Ja Rule, P. Diddy and Bad Boy's Family. I also enjoy playing my cello in the Davis Orchestra. I was born in Torrance, California, but I was raised in L.A. I grew up in the big city where there is non-stop traffic. I always tried to stay out of trouble. We moved to Yakima, Washington where I became a young writer. My writings are about all those around me. When I can see what they go through I learn from them. I like to write in a way that you can see what I'm trying to say, and be able to feel it.

Eloisa Gonzalez: I am an abrecaminos who has learned to take the path of no other, my own. Through my journey, I have learned to discover myself in every poem, interview, and story I have written. I was born June 20, 1984, in Santa Ana, California, but raised in Huntington Beach, California. In the summer of 1996, it was necessary for my family and I to move to Yakima, Washington, due to family matters. Currently, I am a 17-year-old high school student who attends Davis

High School. I will be graduating this June of year 2002, and will be transferring to Gonzaga University in Spokane, Washington in the fall of 2002.

Josie Guapilla: I'm a senior at Davis High School. I'm an abrecaminos. In this class we all have the same goal, and that goal is to make our own discoveries. We all have learned to discover what has not yet been discovered. I was born in Santa Ana, California. At age 11 me and my family moved to Yakima. In my writing I'm trying to write what I feel at this moment.

Bertha Gutiérrez: I am 18. In the fall I'll be attending Grays Harbor Community College. I got a scholarship because of basketball. The first time I picked up a basketball I was hooked. I grew up with the guys so the girls made fun of me. I didn't care because all I wanted to do was play basketball. While the girls made fun of me, the guys thought I was cool, because I played like them, or better. It got better. In middle school the cute girls got cut and I made it. I became captain of the team. Now in high school, I run the team, through hard and easy times. I've always given my best. I told my sister it would be easy for her to get into college because of her grades, because she had such good grades. On the other hand, in order for me to get into college it would be because of this stupid basketball. Now I am eating my words. Hope you enjoy my story.

Marco Gutiérrez: I was born in Cocula, Jalisco, Mexico in 1985. I spent four years living in Guadalajara, Jalisco, Mexico. My parents were working in U.S.A. and my brothers and I were living with my grandma. We had it too hard in a small town called San Quintin, Baja California, Mexico, six hours from the U.S.A. boundary. We couldn't see our parents too often, but they visited us once a year when they could. In 1997 my parents decided to bring us to Salinas, California. After two years we came to Yakima. I am now part of the "abrecaminos family," where we write poems and stories about our experiences and hardships in our lives. We write about America's best writers and controversial women. We write so we can all be heard. I played soccer for Davis last year. I'm a hard worker. I try and let the readers know the truth of my writing. I let them know how I feel, and what I think and I uncover myself and put it in the writing.

Claudia Guzmán: I am an abrecaminos and a chain breaker. My favorite thing to do is write and read. I enjoy going out with my friends and talking on the phone. I love spending time with my family and having long conversations. In my writing I'm trying to be the voice for those who don't have one. I could say things that wouldn't come out the same orally. Expressing myself through paper is a way of breathing, letting it all out, uncensored.

Erika Hernández: I have 18 years old. I was born in 1983. I'm from Michoacán. I'm part of the class, Latino Lit. We write poems and tell stories about our lives. One of my favorite sports is to play basketball. Part of my time is to be with all of my family. One of my dreams is to have my mother back, to be together. She died in a car accident when I was little. I want to be a lawyer. In my writing I'm trying to do the best to be the person who I am, to be part of the abrecaminos in this class and forever.

Eleazar Herrera: I'm a senior at Davis. I was born and raised here, but I still consider myself *Mexicano*. My teacher helped me realize that. I managed to learn more about the history *de mi tierra*, of my land, things that make me happy. I'm trying to say that I lost my grandma so fast, that she never saw me get married as she always wished to see.

Abraham Mancilla: It's my last year in high school in Yakima, Washington, my last year in high school, that is. I represent a group of people here at school, and I am proud to say that I am a Latino, Mexican, Hispanic person. I am a jazz musician. I play gospel, Latin, funk and just about anything the ears enable one to hear. I was born in Apatzingan, Michoacán in 1984. June 29 was a special day. It made a mark in history. I am currently 17 years of age. I only lived in Mexico for about four months. I'm seeking a path where I can leave footprints that will lead people to success. I want to lay out music that will make people dance. I want people to say, "Wow, what was that!" in amazement to my God-given talent. Don't worry, my people, there'll be a way where there wasn't a way before. I walk the path for all who seek the same dream as I. My name is Abraham Mancilla. I'm trying to let the reader know a little about what I'm about and what I want to accomplish. My writing is based on my life—what I do, what I think, what happens to me, and music. I am an *abrecaminos*, especially to other people. I just make a *camino* for myself.

Cristal Manjarréz: One of my favorite classes is Latino Lit. I like to write poetry and I'm very interested in the study of human cultures, especially Hebrew culture and Judaism. That is one of my biggest passions in life. As a Mexican woman I consider very important the fact of conserving our values and carrying our dignity wherever we go. And don't forget that we all have been created equal and we are God's children. In my writing I'm trying to explain the point of view of a young person who lives between two cultures.

Michelle Martinez lets her emotions escape onto paper. She writes stories and poems that reflect herself in one way or another. When she is not writing, she likes to read. Horror stories are her favorite. She is attending Yakima Valley Community College. She is finding her way of life through the support of her parents, sisters, brothers and her boyfriend, Ryan. She says, "In my writing I'm trying to keep the fire in my soul alive. I am lucky to find that fire in my writing. I feel so much passion for my writing because it brings my emotions alive on paper."

Roberto Méndez: I am in a beautiful class for Latino students. I like that because I learn more about poets that I never heard. I have lived in the U.S.A. for three years. I am from Oaxaca, Mexico, a small city. I was born there in 1983. I had to come here because my mother is living here. When I was in Mexico I wanted to know how the life is here. A hobby that I have is playing soccer. I have played soccer all my life, and my dream is to be a professional soccer player. I'm trying to say something about my life. I think that my writing is about my life and how I have lived.

Liliana Mendoza: I'm a sophomore student proudly attending Davis High School. I came from the dangerous streets of Fresno, California where I was raised until the age of ten. My family and I moved to Yakima, Washington due to my parents' divorce. My talent in writing was discovered in this small town, therefore I don't regret coming. I set my mind into poetry when my father died in October 2000. He wasn't my biological father, but he raised me from the age of one and grew to love me like one of his own. At the time I was too young to realize it, but I know he's watching over me. Now that I can't show him my love, affectionately I dedicate all my poems to him for loving me like his real daughter, just the way I'll always love him.

Laura Mendoza: I was born on Valentine's Day in 1984. I am currently a senior at Davis High School, and I'm 18. I was born in

Santa Ana, California. I moved to Yakima when I was in third grade. My family and I had to move because we no longer had enough money for food. My goal after graduation, in June 2002, is to go to college and receive a degree in education or law. I wish to someday become a great bilingual attorney or teacher.

Lilia Nava: I'm from Puebla, Mexico. I'm a senior, ready to graduate from Davis High School. I'm 18 years old. My daily activities are that I go to Beauty School in the morning for half a day, and for the rest of the day I go to Davis. At the end of the afternoon I go to work until 11 p.m. My dreams are to graduate from A.C. Davis High School, graduate from Professional Beauty School and after that my plans are to go to college for business and finish my degree. And then I'll help my parents like when they helped me when I needed it. In my dreams there's also my baby. He is the one that gives me fuerzas to write my testimonio. All I wish is to accomplish all my dreams for my son.

Arturo Obisbo: I was born in Michoacán, México. When I was four I moved to California. That was in 1989. We lived there for a couple of years and then moved to Yakima. I like to play sports and have fun with my friends. I live with my parents and little sister. My inspiration for writing has been my family and also my teachers, especially Mr. Grimes, who always pushes you to the limit. I wrote this poem in his class called *Braided Lives on Turtle Island*. I try to express my hard times in life that I have gone through and maybe help people by the poems that I write.

Gastón Pérez Padilla: I'm 18 years old. I was born in a small town in Madrid, Colima, Mexico. My family and I moved to Yakima because my Dad was working here at Yakima. I like to participate in church. Today I'm singing and playing guitar for St. Joseph's Church. My favorite hobby is to play guitar and to write songs. I consider myself a poet and a musician. I believe that one of the biggest things is love. I think love is the main part of this world. In the future I would like to be an engineer in computer systems. My family is my biggest support. I like to sing for my girlfriend. I'm trying to communicate my thoughts and also I like to give something from me.

Paloma Pérez Padilla: I am from a little town called Madrid, Colima, Mexico. I'm the youngest in my family, from a beautiful couple, Cesar

T. Pérez López and Blanca E. Padilla Velazco. They, and my brother, are all for me. I'm a junior now and I hope to get ready to go to college next year. My favorite hobbies are running, exercising, and everyday seeing the sky, because that makes me feel free of my problems, and to forget all that happened in that moment. In the future I would like to be a business administrator, something that is not going to be impossible, maybe hard, but not impossible. I also would like to be a model and open my own business of clothes, and at the same time administrate it. My mother does all of these things now, so I know how. If there is somebody who I have to be thankful to, it is to God for giving me the opportunity to enjoy my beautiful family and this life. In my writing I'm trying to talk about what I don't share with a friend or family because writing and playing guitar is how I express what really is inside me, in my heart.

Jessica Padilla was born on July 18, 1983 in Toppenish, WA to Jose Anjel Padilla and Elisa Padilla. When she was barely 3 months old her parents left to Mexico and lived there for five years. Then they moved to Yakima in 1989. She has lived here for twelve years. Jessica is the third one in her family. She is 18 years old. She lives with her mother and her sisters and brothers. Her father left the family in the house. Jessica's mother had to work hard to keep food on the table for seven kids. It was really hard for her to do it herself. Jessica will see her mom working hard enough. When she was 16 Jessica started working at a warehouse with her mother and sister to help her mother out, but it was temporary so she went out looking for a job. It was kind of hard for her because wherever she went they would tell her that she had to be 17 years old to work, but after looking hard enough she got hired at Taco Bell, where she is currently working. Jessica goes to school in the morning and toes to work after school from 5 to 10 at night. She enjoys working very much. It helps her get things out of her mind. Her favorite year in elementary was first grade. Mrs. Quevado was the nicest teacher. She has to say that her way of teaching changed her way of listening at school. Currently she goes to Davis High School and plans to graduate this year and go to nursing school. She wants to get a secure career before she plans on getting married and having kids. This summer Jessica wants to go to Mexico for vacation and see her aunts and uncles whom she hasn't seen for years. She also has a dream of buying a house in Mexico.

Maribel Padilla: I am 16 years old. I have been living in Yakima for three years. I came to school because I want to graduate and then if it's possible I want to go to college and get a career. In my free time I like to study English and sing in English so I can improve my language. At school I like to study and do the best, and at lunch time when I see my friends I like to talk to them and play, or with some of them we just talk about our classes. At home where I have my mother, my father, two brothers and two sisters, we play and sometimes we just remember our town and the people who we left in Michoacán. One other thing, I am from La Cuestito, Michoacán, Mexico, a very small, but beautiful town. I was born in 1985, but at the age of 13 I came with my family to the U. S. That's why I'm studying and writing poems in my Latino Lit class. This is a thing I like to do. I try to get the information about me and about what I'm writing about, but most of the times, I am trying to explain the importance about the thing I'm doing.

Maria Trinidad Padilla: I am currently a senior at A.C.Davis High School. My graduation date is June 2002. I came to the United States on October 1998. I started school on April 15, 1999. I used to live with my father and my two sisters, but my mother and my other three siblings were living in La Cuestita, Michoacán, México. This is my *querido pueblo natal,* where I was born on July 22, 1980. *Thanks God, I could almost see all my family together.* My older two sisters are already married. One is in Mexico and one is in California. I am the aunt of three cute boys. I am very happy to have them with me, because it was very challenging being with just my dad. I really missed them a lot. When I started school, I was 18 years old. I started in 9th grade. I was afraid thinking that I was the only person who didn't speak English. I didn't know that there were people like myself. But when I saw that I was going to have a lot of opportunities to learn a myriad of things, including a new language, I started to study so hard, doing all my homework assignments and attending classes. When I saw my first diploma for Student of the Month in May 1999, I felt so happy. At this moment I promised my parents that it wouldn't be the only one that I would get, but rather I would get more recognition. At this moment I have received 23 academic awards, which demonstrate my dedication as an abrecaminos in achieving academic success and getting to the top of the Macchu Picchu Mountain.

In my writing I'm trying to let the readers know that for an ABRECAMINOS like me, a migrant coming to the United States, not knowing English, there is nothing that could stop me regarding education. I am trying to be someone productive for my community. As a nurse or a paramedic, I would be able to help adults who are suffering, assist little kids who have diseases, or comfort the elderly, who have always been supportive of my studies. I will also be the first person in my family to go to college.

Oswaldo Placencia: I was born in Guadalajara, Mexico in 1982. I moved to the United States when I was nine years old. Now I'm going to Davis High School. At Davis I make jewelry and play for the soccer team. My goal is to play on the national team to win a World Cup. That's my biggest dream. I'm living with my parents right now. I have four brothers and one sister. That's all the family that I have here. All my other relatives are in Mexico. In my writing I'm trying to let people know what I want to do. My dreams are on this piece of paper. My goals and plans of what I want to do. This is my life and my future.

Monica Pola has lived in Yakima her whole life. She attends Davis High School and is in the eleventh grade. Monica has been on both the dance and cheer teams. Monica has learned a lot about herself and her heritage from being in Latino Literature and being an abrecaminos. Monica tends to dream about what she has, what she wants, and about what she needs. Monica wants to graduate from high school and continue her education to become something she could be proud of, and be able to say, someday, that she has worked hard, and that it paid off.

Rosa Robles: Here in Latino Literature I've learned how to see the world in a different way, with my eyes open. I'm seventeen. Before, I was afraid to speak my mind, defend my beliefs. Now I'm not. I have learned that nothing else, not the opinions or truths of others, is more true than what I believe, and have to say myself. It is like I have now opened my wings. I have climbed to the top of the mountain, Macchu Picchu, and I am not going back down. I try to free my thoughts, my inner self, and my heart. Like "rompe cadenas."

Mayra Rodríguez: My passion is to finish school and become a successful person. I'm 17 years old and a sophomore at A. C. Davis High School. I like to do math even though I get confused from time to time. Never have I stopped loving numbers. I also like to read, to be able to enter one's mind, see his or her way of thinking, or discover someone's way of life. This is profoundly interesting to me. I'm smart and considerate of the people who surround me. I'm a person that admires other people's courage, effort and determination. I have learned to value people in their unique ways. I take my memories from my home, which I will never forget, and I make them into stories I wish to share with you. In my writing I'm trying to find my true self. I write so people can hear my voice, and that way have them see how people really can overcome any obstacle.

Oscar Rosales: I'm originally from Guadalajara in the Mexican State of Jalisco. I'm a senior at Davis. I'm the youngest of three kids and have spent the bulk of my life trying to walk in my brothers' shoes, always trying to be just like them. Yet I had to learn that no matter what, I'll never be like them. I have to be myself, and do what I can to dictate my own path through life. It is something we all must do. My hobbies include reading, art, listening to music basketball, and watching Seattle Mariner games. I'm also involved in wrestling, and was involved in football and track and field during my freshman and sophomore years. My future plans involve going to college and majoring in either social sciences or psychology. I also hope to start a business someday.

In my writing, I'm always trying to get the reader's attention, as well as trying to link all my writing together. The methods I use in trying to attract the reader often include strong words, or strong imagery. Different readers have different reactions to my tactics. Some may be appalled, while others don't have quite the same reaction. Also, I try to link all my work together by trying to spread out the main theme. I almost never give away everything in just one piece. I intentionally try to make my writing like a jigsaw puzzle and have the reader put everything together.

Antonio Ruíz: This is my third year living in the U.S.A. I came here with all my family, my parents, and my brother and two sisters. But after a month, my parents went back to Mexico and my brother, my two sisters and I stayed with my grandparents. It was very difficult to live with my grandparents. They didn't let me go out with my friends. Sometimes I felt envious to tell my friends that I couldn't go with them. After living one year with them, my brother, my two sisters and

I decided to rent a house and live an independent life. My two sisters and my brother had a job and they were going to school at the same time. It was better to live without my grandparents. After two months of living by ourselves, I got a job and started working to support myself. Since that moment, I'm more confident. My parents just came from Mexico to visit us. I'm so glad to see them after so long. I wish they could stay, but they have to go back to Mexico and leave us alone again. I'm looking back in my writing, to explore and to say things about my life that I wouldn't be able to say or write before. Also to discover a part of me that I haven't discovered yet.

German Ruíz: I am an abrecaminos who emigrated from Mexico a few years ago. Running away from my ordinary life, I decided to enjoy living with my family, who have been here since 1991. I became a student at Davis when my mother made me come to school when she didn't let me go to Chicago. By that time, I didn't want to attend school, because in Mexico, I was expelled from the school. That's why I came to the United States, and now I am in my last year of high school. I will come back next year to finish with some requirements. After that I am planning a trip to Mexico to meet those places that I don't know. I'm trying to show how I see life, and how I am living it between Mexico and the U.S.A. We don't want to forget women because they teach us how we have to see and live our lives.

Octavio Saucedo: I'm 18 years old and I came from Mexico when I was a little child. We moved from Mexico because my Dad needed a better life and a job, and wanted to give us an education. We live in a normal house, me and my sister and two brothers and parents. My free time I like to go to the park and have fun with my friends. I also like to go to movies. I can really enjoy spending time with my family and I also spend most of my time with my g.f. because in this life we need love from a woman that you love with all your heart. I try to give an example to all the teenagers in the whole universe.

Yoshikovasha Segura: Although I have already graduated, I am still in school getting as much as I can for free. My goal the rest of this year is to learn more Spanish for my future plans. In my past I was an Exchange Student to Australia. I've also been strongly involved in my school clubs as well as Jazz Band, Band, and Choir. When I'm not in school I am usually roller skating, hiking, snowboarding, skiing, windsurfing, playing video games or volunteering. In this next year I want to take another year off and go to Mexico with my fiancé, and then continue studying to be a nurse for many countries in need. My dream is to gain knowledge to help people and start my own family. I'm trying to express what problems I encounter along the way, while I'm trying to reach my dreams in my future.

Manuel Santos: I was a student from Davis High School. Now I am on my way to the real world and discovering the mysteries of knowledge. I was a naive person with little experience. I was a runner and swimmer in high school. I was a Student of the Month four times. I liked the things that I used to do. I was going to reach my goals but I could not. I am going back to Washington State University to get my G.E.D. I speak Mixteco which is my native language in Oaxaca, Mexico. Kunayaya means abrecaminos, or open the door. I am proud of my native language. Not too many people speak it. Many people want to vanish it. I will speak my language the rest of my life, and the way I am I will keep it.

I'm trying to recover my knowledge that I have lost. This is what I wrote. I speak Mixteco and proud of it. My village is called San Antonio de las Mesas. It is on top of the mountains. There are about two hundred who live there. When I was in my country I never had the opportunity to go to school. I first went to school when I came to the United States. I was 17 years old when I first went to school. I did not know how to speak Spanish or English, nor did I ever write any language. I had to learn like a little child. I have to hear everything at the same time. Sometimes I did not know what to do. I was confused about what school was. There were times when I wanted to quit school but something from my heart motivated me and said, don't quit school. All the three years I was in school I had a very hard time because I did not have a job and my Mom in Oaxaca wanted some money. Running every day helped me to get tough. There are many things that I need to learn and to do. I have many goals I can't get because of my living situation. I hope that all things I dream about will become true.

Ricardo Torres: My name is Ricardo. I am from the graduating class of 2002. I plan on attending a four year university next fall. In my spare time I play basketball and draw. Playing basketball and drawing are the only things I find comfort in when I'm going through a stressful situation. I was born on a rancho called El Capulín, in Michoacán, México. I moved here when I was about a year old. My parents moved here to seek a better life. And here I am, now seeking the better life. I am very proud of being Mexican. I can say I've been Americanized, but I still represent to the fullest. One of my favorite quotes is, "Life is a mystery to be lived, not a problem to be solved." I feel as if a lot of people live and look at life the wrong way. They seek things that aren't really there. They turn life into one big problem trying to find different solutions. In my writing I try to interest the reader as much as possible. I want to write things where the reader can say, "Oh, I know what he's talking about;" or, "Oh, I can relate to that." I want the reader to be able to understand me clearly. I want them to know the type of person I am after reading a piece of my work.

Tatiana Whizar Toscano: I'm a student at Davis High School in a small town called Yakima, WA. I was born and raised in Tijuana, Baja California, Mexico in October 24, 1983. I have a huge love in my life, which is Tae Kwon Do. Tae Kwon Do is an Olympic sport and my dream is to represent Mexico in the 2008 Olympics held in Beijing, China. I have been practicing Tae Kwon Do for ten years and had the amazing opportunity to represent my country, Mexico, in the 2000 Junior World Championships held in Killarney, Ireland. When I was 16 years old, I left Tijuana, my family, and my school for Tae Kwon Do. I lived in Mexico City and trained three times a day each week. I was part of the National Team. That is why Tae Kwon Do is my passion. In my writing I'm trying to express all the feelings I have kept inside all my life. Also my writings keep all the good and bad memories of my life alive.

Vocabulario de los Abrecaminos

abrazo: Embrace. Wrap your arms around all of it. Get as much of the story as you can.

abrecaminos: We call ourselves the *abrecaminos*. *Abre* means to open. *Caminos* means paths. Open the ways. Many paths. Each person who makes a way makes many paths. We don't know how we're going to make our road, we only know that's what we are going to do. Make a way. Make ways. We're not the only ones. *Somos muchos.* The concept of the abrecaminos was a gift from the poet Inés Hernandez Avila. It has turned into one of our guiding principles. It is to be an example. We are all examples. We never stop working or searching. We open paths that help others to be successful. You can be the *abrecaminos* in your family, just by helping others. My mother is an *abrecaminos*. A person with hope to win. *Siempre hay un lugar donde puedas encontrar un abrecaminos.* There's always a place where we can find an *abrecaminos*, too. You have to have the desire to be an example for other people. This person makes a path where there is no path, and makes it easier for more people to go through. Rigoberta Menchú is an *abrecaminos*. You can be one, too. This is who we are. We make a way. Be an *abrecaminos* and get to work. A chain breaker. For me, Gloria Anzaldúa is an *abrecaminos*.

abuelito/a: Grandfather. Grandmother. An *abuelo* is considered the head of the family in our culture. We honor our grandparents by showing respect to their lives. *Apá grande.* The grandmother is one of the chief teachers.

acarrear: To haul, carry. *Acarriar agua.* Among their chores, *quehaceres*, many of the mothers of the writers hauled water from wells or rivers during their childhood years. See the interview by Blanca Flores with her mother.

aclarar la garganta: Clear the throat. This is what I have to do when I write; what is necessary in order to write my truths. See *bocón*. Speaking one's truth has a cost to it. It is a heavy responsibility, too.

acostumbrado/a: To be in the habit of. Our mothers have a difficult time getting used to this culture, getting accustomed, comfortable.

aislados: Isolated, alone.

alma: Soul. The Aztecs have two words for soul. *Tonal*, or *alma*; and *nagual*, or other self, like a plant or animal spirit. Our souls guide us in our lives. You better listen to your soul. You better get hit in your soul.

a menos que: Unless.

andadas: Tracks. *a la andadas*—to the journey. But be careful: *volver a las andadas* is to go back to the old ways, to backslide. This is different than getting stuck. See *atrapada*.

andador: One who walks. *Abrecaminos* are *andadores* walking into new lives.

ánimo: *Alma*, spirit, soul. Self-encouragement. This is real important to the *abrecaminos*. Courage, valor, fortitude.

apodo: Nickname. Latinos love nicknames. Everybody has one.

archetypal symbols: Images that exist in each person.

atrapada/o: Trapped, *estancado*. *Abrecaminos* get stuck *a veces*, sometimes. They don't give up.

ayudar: To help, to assist. We help each other learn. It's part of the way of the *abrecaminos*. The writing helps even more. There's so much *pode*r in our stories.

Aztlán: Mythical homeland of the Aztecs.

baboso/a: Slug, slobberer, stupid. He will talk stuff that will make him sound stupid. This is someone who has not yet understood the purpose of his life. *Una persona que sale con puras babosadas.* He wants to act childish and does not understand.

barreras: Barriers, obstacles, chains. A word often used by parents of *abrecaminos* during the interviews. An *abrecaminos* is one who breaks the *barreras*. This is for life or death. Crossing the land. If you make it, this is where you could find life, but sometimes sorrow.

barrio: Neighborhood, district, another word is *colonia*. The *barrio* is my home. The word gets changed in the United States.

bilingual: *Abrecaminos* speak more than one language. It's an advantage we have. It doesn't always show up on test scores. *Es una cosa importante en el mundo cotidiana.*

bocóna/o: Big mouth. Traditionally, not a positive word. Many people think this is a bad thing. But sometimes it's necessary. Sometimes I have to take the risk to speak out, to speak up, and risk being called this by others, in order to speak my truth.

bromas: Jokes. A way to laugh, show you care, seeing people laughing and being happy. *Persona humorosa.*

cadena: *Abrecaminos* break chains to help us go forward. *Romper cadenas.* Chains also connect us to others and ideas, too. It's a paradox we explore. See *paradoja.*

caer bien: Likeable. *Me caes bien.* Agreeable.

caminar la plática: Walk the talk. *Todos los seres humanos tendemos a imitar los patrones de conducta de las personas a las que admiramos.* Path of the *abrecaminos.* Progress, not perfection. *Sólo algunos se comportan como se los pides, pero todos hacen lo que tú haces.* Tough path for a writer.

camino: Path, way, Also, *sendas.* A way of being. No one knows where the road goes or ends. The way we go.

canción: Song. The story of my life is a song. This is one of the things I must keep practicing.

cántaro: Large narrow mouth pitcher or jug, *hecho de barro y se utiliza para acarrear agua.* We will remember the daily chores of our mothers because we have interviewed our mothers and saved their stories for our children's children. Not just any pitcher, vessel into which votes are placed.

cierracaminos: One who closes roads. Goes with closed minds. The opposite of being *abrecaminos.*

change: Comes in small, disjointed steps, taken as opportunities arise. See Jim Rigney.

charra/o: Cowgirl, cowboy. See Paloma and Gastón's interview with their mother. One of her accomplishments was to be a *charra.*

Chicano/a: Mexican-American. Persons who followed Cesar Chavez called, and call themselves, *Chicanos.* Not limited to these. Children of Mexican parents who are born in the United States, *nacieron en este lado de la frontera.*

chismes: Gossip. Someone who gossips is *chismoso/a.*

cholo/a: Gangster. A person that has no manners, and doesn't care about anyone and anything but himself. A person insecure in his ways, seeking to fit in with others who do the thinking for him. He is afraid of his thoughts. *Alguien que busca su futuro en las calles.* He just thinks he's all bad, with his pants almost to his knees, and he thinks he acts very cool. *Vato loco.* He fights for his territory. For me, it's stupidity. *Es un miembro de una pandilla.* He fights for a color and dress and is always in the streets painting the walls. Surrounds himself with his friends to feel that he belongs.

cholito/a: Term of endearment.

cliché: Worn out images. See *Frases trilladas.*

Colima: Many of the Mexicans who come to Yakima are from this State. Many come from the capital city of Colima.

¿como le ha ido?: How's it been going? We can all greet each other this way. *En cualquier idioma.*

comienzo: *Cada día un nuevo comienzo. Unos de los principios de ser abrecaminos.* Beginning.

compa: The best friend of a guy. Or a compadre of a guy or a woman. Friend. Partner.

connection: *conexión.* Everything on earth is connected. Circle of life. The widening gap between rich and poor, the availability of information, the population growth in the Third World, the mechanization of agriculture, rampant urbanization, bigotry, global convulsion. See *Las noticias de poesia.* See *migration.*

consciente: Aware. *Darse cuenta de.* You must wake up, you must see beyond the literal, before you can begin to take responsibility for your own life. *Tiene la capaz.* You are able to respond.

consejos: Advice, counsel. Much of the most important things learned by the *abrecaminos* comes from their mothers, fathers, persons who leave a large impact. It can be negative or positive.

consuegro/a: Parents of both families help young people understand marriage. They do this together. This is something I don't see in the United States, all of the parents helping us get used to marriage. Here there is much more divorce. See *suegro.*

contradecirse a si mismo: To contradict oneself. What writers need to learn to do. Not to confuse themselves, or their readers, but in order to build a hotter fire. Octavio Paz, *en una carta al joven poeta José Carlos Becerra, ...luchar contra sus dones, me gustaría que su escritura fuese más veloz, menos río, más conjunción de realidedes simultáneas.* Write against your gifts, write with more velocity, more furiously, give us more simultaneous realities.

coraje: Courage, spirit, anger. La fuerza de salir adelante, de hacer algo, las ganas. Having enough guts to do what others wouldn't. When you stop the injustice, when you step up. *Fuerza que llevas dentro para ir más allá.* Different from *valor.* See *valor.*

correveidile: Traditionally: *corre ve y dile.* Run and go tell. Go between. In daily use, it's chismes, gossip, and small talk. But this is sacred work for bilingual people. Children act in this way for their parents every day as they interpret the daily world for parents, and anyone who negotiates the differences between cultures and political differences, acts in this way. Malinche is the first historical correveidile in Mexican history.

corriente: current, trend, the flow. *Que corre. Sin impedimento, curso de aguas,* the flow of life.

coyote: He is someone that helps you slip across the border from Mexico to the U.S. *El coyote es muy astuto y sabe lo que esta haciendo. Persona que pega por detras. Malero.* He can be good or he can be bad. There are coyotes in the desert. *El coyote es mi nagual.*

cumplir: To accomplish, to carry out, to finish what we begin. *Este es el processo de los abrecaminos.*

crossing: A way of reaching out, a way of listening, a way of transformation.

cruzar: Atravesar un camino. *Crossing, we pierce into the heart of the mystery of things.* See *rio*, see *puente.*

cuachalota/o: Messy person.

cuñado/a: Brother-in-law, sister-in-law.

curandera/o: Folk healer, psychologist. Someone who heals pain the old way. My grandma was a *curandera.* The *curandera* knows the earth, the culture, the *yerbas.* She has a better understanding of life. Healer of body and of heart. She knows more medicine than any doctor. *La curandera vendrá a curar el hechiso que tengo por dentro.* Every traditional mother is a *curandera.* Ultima is the *curandera* in Rudolfo Anaya's novel *Bless Me, Ultima.* The practical test for the curandera is always with the people. She who makes a difference with the people, is the one who carries the real medicine. What is good in the culture? What is bad in the culture?

chilango/a: Person from the Capital, from Mexico City. A negative, pejorative connotation.

dar la cara: To show your face, and stand up for your beliefs. Feeling strong, empowered, keeping one's responsibilities. It means different things, to me it means don't be afraid if you have nothing to hide. To me it means to show yourself *pocho*. "Gringoized Mexicano." Salir de donde estás escondida y enfrentarse con las realidades. Giving your face to somebody you're talking with, and not being disrespectful looking somewhere else. *No tener miedo de nada y enfrentar todo con valentía.* To face the problems.

democracy: OK, jobs, good jobs. But first, it's an idea. 3. A social condition of equality and respect for the individual within a community. Greek *demos*, common people. Not a corporation. Participatory.

derechos: Rights. *Descubrimos nuestros derechos cuando escribimos.*

despedida: The goodbye, means *fare thee well.* We say goodbye to many things, including old ways of being *abrecaminos.* We have no regrets. This is all part of the process of moving into new paths, new ways of being.

dicho: Es un refran que se refiere o hable de cosas, personas o animales y nos enseña algo. *Every time an old person dies a library burns.* Like that. De tal palo tal astilla.

dinero: Money. Money is not everything in life. *Lana. Jando. Feria. Plata.*

don: Gift, or talent. These are tricky. If we don't take care of these we can lose them. Also, a title of respect. We often use the word before great writers, like *Don Octavio Paz.*

duality: Bicultural people come to know two cultures. This results in what Robert Coles calls "Astonishing duality." Students are often intensely interested in learning about culture. They have a heightened sense of wanting to be connected to America and to their native culture. The task is to belong to both, to learn to keep what is healthy and good and discard what is negative. No stereotypes here: there are greater differences within a culture than there are between cultures. Another risk in duality is that to be both also means that one is not wholly either. The question of belonging anywhere is always the question.

Doce Pasos: Twelve Step Program. The path of clean and sober. *Palabra por palabra.* The journey from the head to the heart. Cada día nos enfrentamos a muchos oportunidades para actuar responsablemente, para tomar decisiones razonables. This is not just about leaving drugs and alcohol behind. Many of us have lived through some dangerous moments, *casi morimos físicamente. Pero aquí estamos, comenzando un nuevo día.* For new horizons, whatever the situation. *Nuevos horizontes.*

330

duende: Elf or goblin. Federico García Lorca says the *duende* is the spirit behind the dance, it's the magical performance, it's what makes the flamenco dancer get up on the table and flame into art, *una bailarina flamenco que tiene duende.* Black sounds. Deep song. It's the power of literature to charm and transform our lives when something of great risk is at stake. *See* Lorca's essay on *Duende.* Owner, yes, in the ordinary world.

dueños: Owners.

elogio: Praise. *Alabanza. Encomio. Aplauso, abrobación.* The opposite of *reprensión, reprimenda, regaño constante, censurar, bronca, sermón. El elogio libera, la critica esclaviza.* See *muertes pequeñas,* the little deaths.

embarazada: Pregnant, expecting.

enojo/a: Angry. Anger, *enojo,* exists like motivation. *Petroleo.* We can convert it to fuel the journey. But it can go bad on us, too, like poison inside a snake.

escuchar: Listen. We listen to each other's poems. This changes everything. Listening is a way of being in love. Listening is a way of loving. In fact, it is making love.

enfadar: To annoy, to anger.

esfuerzo: Effort, animo, vigor. *Fuerzas.* I didn't know how strong my mother was until she told me her story.

esperanza: Hope. It keeps us going, but it can be a burden, too. It means two things in Spanish: to hope and to wait for. Sometimes it's all we have. Esperanza Cordero is the main character in Sandra Cisneros' novel *House on Mango Street.* She doesn't like her name, but she's a writer, and her life changes completely because she writes her story. She writes poems, too.

estrella: Star. You are like a star, out of reach, but worth following and trying to reach. Los ideales son como las estrellas. Sabemos que nunca podemos alcanzar, pero como marineros en alta mar, podemos trazar nuestros caminos siguiendolas. Jim Rigney uses this poem to connect *abrecaminos* anywhere to a visionary path.

estricto/a: Strict, severe. Sometimes our parents are too strict.

equity: *Equidad, imparcialidad.* The law of the land. When there is equity in the schools, anyone would be glad to swap programs with any other. No limits on expectations. Change practice, attitudes follow. Decisions made as close to the students as possible. Teachers are important. They need to put their practices on the table. It's about outcomes. Work that is never finished.

exhilio: Exile; *expatriación; acción y efectivo de abandonar uno su patria. Destierro. Emigración, éxodo. Opuesto de retorno, vuelta.* For many it's the tension between the extremes, living between exile and return.

entrevista: Interview. When we "interview" our mothers, we also get "inner views" of ourselves. The interviews bear witness. Our parents were the first abrecaminos. They were not given the word, but they made the paths, they made the ways.

familia: Family. It means a condition of love with anybody. It doesn't need to be relatives. *Para mi es como una comunidad de amor, confianza y apoyo.* It means you can work in a group or with someone else. When you're in school, that's your family, too. *Lo es todo, significa lo mejor paa mi, consejos, amor es todo lo que encierra esta palabra. Integridad, unidad,* love and respect.

fé: Faith. Travelling to the state capitol to talk with legislators about changing the law making it possible for students without papers to attend college without paying out-of-state tuition, and reviewing the *Vocabulario de Abrecaminos,* one of the *Abrecaminos* writes in faith. *Can't accomplish anything without faith,* he says.

flaquezas: Weakness to many people. *Abrecaminos* make a *principio* from this word. *Sacamos fuerzas de flaquezas.* We turn our weaknesses into strengths. What Tatiana wrote in her card returning from Tae Kwon Do competition in Florida: *Es verdad: las derrotas hacen el ganador.*

floricanto: Flower and song. This is the Spanish equivalent of the Nahuatl compound, *xocicuicatl,* meaning poetry. See *Floricanto Sí, A Collection of Latina Poetry.* Aztec scholars make the connection between poetry and truth in Aztec society.

fracaso: Failure.

frases trilladas: The wheat that makes the bread is the word a writer looks for. Words that feed us, words that make us strong, build bridges, they change the world. Writers separate the wheat from the chaff. The chaff is left-over, and over-used. *No sirve. No hay comida en frases trilladas. No puede hacer poemas de frases trilladas.* Trite, hackneyed. See *cliché.*

fresa: Strawberry. Metaphor for snob, twink. Also the dentist's drill.

frontera: Border. A line that separates us, sometimes politically. What people don't know is that inside that line there is another world, *otro mundo*. That's where some abrecaminos make their home. *Son barreras que se ponen en nuestros caminos,* and sometimes it's hard to take them out of our paths. The borders are hard for immigrants to cross. *La frontera está en Nogales y Texas.*

Frozen barrel: An original image of Uziel Estrada, describing the process of losing one's dreams. See his poem on Sor Juana.

ganas: Desire. Willpower, drive. The strength that comes deep from our souls that gives us the impulse to go on, and fight through the struggles that come, to be someone in life, and as *abrecaminos,* we will become. *Es la voluntad, la esperanza que une tiene en la vida.* This is the power to put something, sometimes ourselves, into other worlds. Desire, hunger. Very powerful. A gift that we learn to use.

garrapata: Tick. Jim Rigney says, "As time goes on I find that I have been more of a *garrapata* than a builder of bridges. The tick does not have the power or force of the bull, but by golly the bull always knows the tick is there, always knows it is there, and does little to aggravate it and set it off again. Driven, not deterred."

garganta: Throat. *Aclarar la garganta.* Clear the throat. Discover your voice. Speak your truth. Poets do this. So do *abrecaminos.* A way of breaking chains.

gavacho/a: The white insides of the orange peel. Sometimes it can be un poco *amargo,* or bitter.

golpe: Blow. There are *golpes*—blows in our lives. We take our hits. If we don't deal with them, they come back with their sharp teeth in the form of *remordimientos* and kick us again, and harder, when we're not looking.

gozo: Joy, pleasure. *Para mi es una energia de disfrutar algo.* We take joy in living each day. *Cuando se goza no se olvida.* Good feeling given or caused by people you love. *Un sentimiento que que experimentas al probar, tocar, tener algo entusiamos por un o largo memento.*

Green Card: A compact wall that is built by the fear of the insecure. And blindness. A pink piece of legal paper *por el cual mucho gente ha muerto.* Lots of people have died because they didn't have the Green Card. *Permiso para trabajar.*

Guadalupana/o: *Es tener sangre India pura y tener orgullo de lo que vale cada ser humano. Para mi es tener alma y corazón.* It means life to me. A woman gives birth, and, in a way, she gave birth to God. We are all the sons and daughters of *La Virgen Morena*. The mother of Mexicans.

guia: Guide. To life, or to be a writer. *Personaje que conduce a otras y les enseña. Quien enseña o dirije a otro.* Dante had Virgil. The *Abrecaminos* have Neruda. The guide knows the spiritual paths to other worlds. Sometimes the guide knows the path of clean and sober.

hecho poético: Poetic fact. Images that follow a strange inner emotion, made of poetic architecture. Something added to nature, beyond natural or metaphorical description. Visionary. Again, read Lorca. Invoke the *duende*.

heartbeat: Can you hear the heartbeat? *¿Puedes escuchar el latido del corazón?* Manuh Santos, whose work appears in this book, taught us how to say this in Mixteco: *Zohu nima quizihi.*

echame aguas: Be my eyes. Look out for me. Watch my back.

herencia: Inheritance. *Algo que pasa de alquien a tí, heridar algo que sea material o espiritual.* Memories, thoughts, emotions, possessions left behind by others, sometimes having to deal with consequences, too. What is left, what is transformed in the future. *Son las cosas de valor,* or ghosts that haunt us like in *Como Agua Para Chocolate.*

hijos: Children. The children are the gift of God.

hocicona: A slanderous name for a woman who speaks her mind. Gloria Anzaldúa turns the word upside down and embraces it in the name of liberation. Read the letter poems to Anzaldúa by the *abrecaminos* for a variety of responses. *Hocico* is a snout or muzzle; *hocicar* is to run smack into difficult problems. *Darse de hocicos* is to fall flat on your face. Freedom takes many paths.

House Bill 2330: Would have qualified undocumented students for resident tuition if they have lived in Washington for at least one year and have graduated from a state high school. Introduced by Representative Phyllis Kenney in 2001, Governor Gary Locke said he would sign the bill when it got to his desk. Students, teachers, parents and administrators from all over the State went to the State Capital in Olympia to lobby for this bill. The *abrecaminos* were there, too. The bill failed to get out of committee by one vote.

humilde. Humble. My mother is a humble person. See the interviews with the mothers.

imagines de mujeres: There's more to us than Malinche or Guadalupe, *virgen o mala mujer. A dentro de la Malinche hay muchos imagines: abrecaminos, amante, político, madre, bilingüe—multi-lingüe, multicutural.* There is Sor Juana, Rosario Castellanos, Sandra Cisneros, Anzaldúa, our mothers, Laura Esquivel. *Somos muchas.* Julia Alvarez. Ask your bookstore to get the books. Ask your teachers.

identidad: Who I am and how I know it. What I search for in my writing.

Iku ka nuhu: Mountain in Mixteco. Manuh Santos taught us this when we were writing our way to Macchu Picchu. *Ihini* means *inside. Iku ka nuhu ihini* is the mountain inside, as we were taught by Manuh. See *Macchu Picchu.*

I.N.S.: Another wall for some of us. Dream stoppers. *Otra barrera. La migra.*

inspiración: Inspiration. This is the work of literature and poetry. Poetry transports, or carries one to another world. Inspired is related to enthusiasm, which comes from the Greek *enthus. When the gods give us breath.* Literature is often a necessary, practical ingredient in transformational work.

invisible: Sometimes we're so invisible we're visible. That's what Inés Hernández Avila wrote about women. That's why we write, so we can see ourselves more clearly. But I don't think it's just about women. It's true about everybody, especially teenagers. *Abrecaminos* are sometimes invisible. Sometimes we're so far out front we think we're behind. Lots of people think we're behind. If we're the ones opening the way, how could anyone see us? How could they know?

jamaica: Flower of hibiscus, for making *agua de jamaica,* a delicious sweetened fruit drink at many parties. Blood-red, translucent.

jefe/a: Leader. Affectionate term for parents or spouses.

jornada: Journey. We say *jornada sagrada*, meaning sacred journey. It's how we live our lives and how we study, too. Another word is *peregrinaje*, or pilgrimage.

Latinos/as: Spanish-speaking people of Western Hemisphere with language and cultural roots via Spain. Some of the struggle for liberation takes place here. Rigoberta Menchú is a *Latina. La lucha empieza con lenguaje.* The struggle begins with language.

lagrimas: Tears. When my poems make others cry, I know I'm getting warm. When they make me cry, I'm getting close to God. This tear is for her. *Hay lágrimas de tristeza y lagrimas de alegria.*

lana: Metaphor Mexicans use for money. See *dinero*. Wool in the dictionary.

liberación: Liberation. The work of the writer, work of the *abrecaminos*. Get out of our rooms, stop languishing, *pare la languidecía. Haga algo.* See a poem by Luis Rodríguez called The Calling/El Llamado.

listen: *Escuchen. Con oidos atentos. La llave, que es esential, es escuchar en nuevas manersa.* Listen with your whole body to everything. Listen like an athlete in top form. When I listen to someone tell their story, I help bring him, or her, into power. See *escuchar.* See *oir.* Note the differences between *escuchar y oir.* The human being listens with his *oidos,* his ears that can also hear his heartbeat.

lobby: *foyer, vestíbulo, ejercer presión sobre, grupo de presión.* Pressure.

loneliness: My point of view is this: when you live in a little town, you learn how life is, and the *loneliness,* and what is poverty—because loneliness is your friend. When you are alone, and you talk with it, you can feel the loneliness in your body. Your body can get lonely when you don't have money to buy food. This is poverty, too, and even poverty is your friend. But only those of us who have lived these moments understand. See *pobreza.*

love*: Amor. Hay cuatro palabras de amor en griego*: "Storge", or affection; "philia", or friendship; "eros", or sexual/creative; and "agape", or unconditional love. You need love of yourself. Otherwise your love is *seco,* your love is *muerto.*

luchadores/as: Fighters. *Somos luchadores.* This is how we get to the top of the mountain. This is how we realize our dreams. Before there were *abrecaminos* there were *luchadores.* Our parents were *luchadores* and *abrecaminos.* It makes sense to *luchar* for something, not just to *luchar.*

llegar: Arrive. This is a spiritual journey. *Cuando lleguemos. Nunca llegamos.* But if we never arrive, we're always arriving.

luna: Moon. The moon understands my mind.

luz: Light. *Toda obra de arte es generadora de luz. Despiertate.* Wake up. Find the light, *porque la oscuridad es también olvido. La luz es, el poeta Carlos Pellicer dice, es un rechazo de la sombra, sino más bien una absorción de ésta.* Light rejects the darkness by absorbing it. A *principio* of the writing done by the *abrecaminos* in this book.

luz en oscuridad: *Poesia.* Poetry. *Tomás Rivera, unos de los abuelos de literatura Chicana escribió, —…que una vez le dijo a la raza que leyeran los poemas en voz alta porque la voz era la semilla del amor en la oscuridad.* "…at one time he told the people to read the poems out loud because the spoken word was the seed of love in the darkness."

machismo: A macho is a man who thinks he can do everything, but the woman can't. Why do men think that? They are *machistas*. What is the word for *machista* in your culture? On the other hand, a macho is someone who can, and will, take care of his family honorably.

Macchu Picchu: This is the mountain we climb to be a man. Or a woman. Or, the boy dies so the man can be born. Or another way: Let the boy live, but let the man be stronger. We go up this mountain. We write our poems. This is the way of the *abrecaminos*. We only carry what we need. Break chains and get up that mountain. This is a place in the heart. Pablo Neruda wrote, *Sube a nacer conmigo, hermano,* in his poem, *Las Alturas de Macchu Picchu. Rise up to be born with me, my brother.*

majadería: *tonteria*. Stupidity, foolishness. *Majadero*. Someone who is crude, vulgar, *tonto*. A fool.

malhechores: Bad guys.

maltrato: Bad treatment, abuse, of women. What can happen when there is no relationship. See Rosa Robles' poem on Malinche.

Malintzin: Figurative mother of all *mestizas*. Translator, advisor, mother of *Hernán Cortés*. She came to be known as *Doña Marina*, as well as the derogatory *La Malinche*, the traitor, and *La Chingada*, the violated, and worse, whore. Visionary realist.

mano izquierda: Left-handed. The true hand of poetry.

mentira: Lie. I can't lie to myself. Sometimes I need you to help me see the truth.

mestizaje: Mixture. Native American with European. The being different in more than color and textual features. Knowing that *Raza* is but a title and standing within a stereotyped group. For being mestizo is but a lighter shade of brown, and we often forget that we are all of color. It's more complicated than *European father and Indian mother.*

migrant: *Migrante*. Spiritual traveler. Sebastião Salgado says, *...most migrants leave their homes filled with hope: refugees usually do so out of fear.* See *migration*.

migration: Humanity on the move. The Brazilian photographer Sebastião Salgado says, *few people uproot themselves by choice. Most are compelled to become migrants, refugees, or exiles by forces beyond their control....they set off with the belongings* *they can carry, making their way as best they can. Most head for cities, the most ambitious set their sights on the United States or Europe.*

mirada: *Instinto, intuición. Para escritores—la mirada es todo para ver el otro lado de la realidad.* Intuition, the other side of reality. What writers need to learn to trust in order to go there.

me doy cuenta: To get the point. I realize. I wake up.

mocoso: Snot-nosed brat.

mochila: Backpack. We don't put anything in our backpacks we don't need. We take anything out that weighs us down, *qué es pesado.* We can't get up the mountain of Macchu Picchu if we're carrying bad stuff in our backpacks.

modo: Way, manner. *a mi modo de ver.* You have to have this.

mojados: Wet ones. Slang for persons who cross the border illegally.

molcajete: It is a kind of a small pot made of rock. It is used to grind tomatoes, peppers, cilantro, mixed with water and salt to create a hot sauce called *salsa. Molar*—grinder for different spices and herbs.

morder: To bite. *Asìr algo con los dientes.* If you get bitten twice it turns to remorse, guilt, *remorder.* It's the second bite that gets you, because you don't just feel it once, you feel both both bites. *Abrecaminos* deal with their problems the first time. There is less post-traumatic stress that way.

muertes pequeñas: Pablo Neruda writes about the little deaths in his Macchu Picchu poems. He says that we get them each day. *Nosotros exploramos de dónde vienen los muertes pequeñas en nuestros poesia.*

movimiento mundial: Movement. The people of the world are moving. The governments can't keep up. *Alteración, inquietud.* See *corriente.*

muertes pequeñas: Key image in Neruda's Macchu Picchu. *Cada día una muerte pequeña…* Each day a little death. *Pueden ser chismes, rumores, palabras de abuso. Muertes pequeñas pueden venir de amigos, familia, maestros, y otra gente familiares. Pueden empezar en sociedad. Cada sere humano conoce la verdad del poder negativo. Haga investigacción de su vida explorando las muertes pequeñas.* Discover your own voice— when you do, you'll start breaking chains, you'll begin to take back your power.

mujeriego: Womanizer, player. Skirt chaser.

mundo: World. So many worlds. And only one world, too. Which world are we living in? This is a question we're constantly asking ourselves.

muñeca: Doll. See *olote*.

nieto/a: Grandchild. Write the story of your mother so that the grandchildren will know who they are.

noticias de poesia: *El poeta William Carlos Williams dice: Es difícil recibir las noticias/de poemas/pero seres humanos/se mueren cada día/miserablemente/por falta se descubren allá.* It is difficult to get the news from poems/yet men and women/ die miserably/every day/for lack of what is found there. See *Asphodel, That Dreamy Flower.*

nubes: Clouds. Sor Juana talked to the clouds. She used her imagination. The work of the imagination is essential for the abrecaminos. One who goes his or her own way will talk to more than the clouds. Ricardo Torres writes that he goes against the grain. This is one way of understanding what we're talking about.

obligación del escritor/a: Writers need to feel safe, and have permission to share or not to share, but it gets complicated. Sometimes writers need to make themselves feel *unsafe*, in order to be heard. *Abrecaminos* sometimes need to use their voices to demand that society acknowledge them and their concerns. Otherwise they might be ignored. *Abrecaminos* begin to feel an obligation to speak out, not only for themselves, but for others who live in silent fear. *Este es una responsibilidad grande de los abrecaminos.*

odisea: Odyssey. Epic journey. *Jornada, perigrinaje. Poema extenso, El poema como el viaje de la vida.*

oir: To listen, to hear. One learns to use the inner ear, listening to music, love, poetry; to listen with one's *oidos*, or inner ear, as opposed to the *orejas*, or outer ear.

olote: Cob, corncob. Many of our mothers played with dolls made of these, and dressed them in pieces of old cloth. See *muñeca*.

olvidar: To forget. It is hard to forget the past, but it is sometimes hard to remember it, too. We must do both.

opresión: *Acción y efecto de oprimir.* All people have been oppressed in some way. Knowing this makes us work harder. Dangerous. Internalized oppression results in people believing the messages they receive and acting harmfully toward themselves. Transferred oppression is prejudicial action toward someone in one's own group or (in the case of racism) a person of color in another ethnic group. People outside of the oppression sometimes deny it exists. *Abrecaminos* believe the hurt caused by oppression can be healed and harmful practices eliminated.

oro: Gold. My parents are worth more than gold. Or, *hechos de oro*, we are made of gold.

orgullo: Pride. To demonstrate that you could feel better and not be hurt. *Egoista. Demostrar realmente lo que sentimos.* A state of mind. Happiness to be shown. Self-esteem. I think pride can overrun those with weak hearts. *Orgullo de ser quien eres: de lo que portas, de tu cultura y de tu gente. Y puedes perder mucho solo por ser orgulloso.*

oscuro: Dark. The dark is only what we don't yet know, what we haven't discovered. In every dark room there is something we are going explore. We will find the light in every dark room. It's a metaphor. *En cada cuarto oscuro el escritor puede sacar la luz.*

pachuco/a: During, and after, theMexican Revolution (1910-1920), many Mexicans came to the U. S. These people had kids in the U. S. and some of these children created their own culture, dressing in "zoot suits." They were known as pachucos. Escuche al ensayo de Octavio Paz: *los pachucos son bandas de jóvenes, generalmente de origen mexicano, que viven en las ciudades del Sur y que se singularizan tanto por su vestimenta como por su conducta y su lenguaje. Rebeldes instintivos, contra ellos se ha cebado más de una vez el racismo norteamericano.* After a half century, this essay from *The Labyrinth of Solitude* continues to provoke and instruct. Later in this essay, Paz writes: *Man is alone everywhere. But the solitude of the Mexican, under the great stone night of the high plateau that is still inhabited by insatiable gods, is very different from that of the North American...* We can still learn a great deal from Don Octavio Paz.

padres: Parents. *Nuestros padres fueron los primeros abrecaminos.* Our parents were the first *abrecaminos*. We hope you can see the love we have for our parents in our interviews. My father was never there for me. Now I find fathers in men everywhere. And this: *Mi padre es me ser, sin él cual, podría perecer, sin vivir mi vida ni la familia defender.* Without him I wouldn't be able to do it.

pajaro libre: Free bird. Sometimes it's one bird at a time, one person at a time.

palabra: Word, *que es el arco de la memoria, según del poeta Rosario Castellanos.*

pandilleros: Gang members. Everybody talks about the *pandilleros.* See *pocho.*

paradoja: Paradox. Like in Oswaldo Placencia's poem about Sor Juana: "...hiding the truth in order to get to the truth." It's kind of like *contradecir* to go against what I say, or to contradict. As an *abrecaminos* I'm always gaining new information, I'm always exploring and going forward. It seems *mentira*, but it's not. It's the truth. See *mentira*.

partera/o: Lady or man who deliver babies. Midwife.

pasado: Past. My life was in the past, but knowing my *raíces*, my roots, I know myself. See *identidad*.

patrón: The *cacique, hacendado*. The man at the *rancho* with the power. One of the reasons behind the *Revolución* was to get rid of the *patrón*. The boss. Not necessarily pejorative, also a word of respect.

pensar: To think. Every second I think of you. *Siempre te tengo en mis pensamientos.*

perder: To lose. We sometimes lose in life, and we have to live with it. Not letting it beat your dreams is what's important. *Perdedores/Vencedores.* See the *Abrecaminos* essay of Crystal Manjarréz.

perezoso: Also flojo, huevón, holgazán. Not the way of the *abrecaminos*. *Abrecaminos son antónimos, polos opuestos, y ellos estudian, cultivan, se aplican, actuan, se dedican. Como esto.*

pertenecer: To belong. It is a wonderful thing to belong to a place. Abrecaminos belong in more than one place. It's beautiful, and it's hard. It leaves us *con un sentimiento de anhelo*, yearning. See *añorar. Pertenezco aquí. No puedo volver atrás, regresan.* I have to keep going.

pesadilla: Nightmare.

pobreza: Poverty. It's a stereotype that we're all poor. It's not true. All writers must come face to face with their own poverty. All readers, too. It's true. We live with la *pobreza*, we write about it. Read our stories. We are rich in our stories and in the way we struggle for justice. See *loneliness*.

pocho/a: Being two races. One who doesn't speak Spanish but whose parents are Latino. A person of two backgrounds who doesn't enforce one of those backgrounds like Spanish/English, or follow his Mexican beliefs. Person of both cultures who fail to incorporate languages and cultures. Multi-cultural. Mexican-American. Children of mixed marriages born in the U.S. Caucasion and Hispanic. Often used pejoratively. Listen to people carefully, though. *Pocho* makes its own culture, with its own sense of pride. Often out front of the traditional cultures. Students studying popular Mexican-American culture in the universities are encountering discoveries in music, fashion, language and relationships.

poesía: *Palabra de fuerza, potencia inalcanzable, que sobre pasa las fronteras y derrota todas las barreras.* It's the inside power we must show to cross borders and break chains. For me, it means part of my heart, desquitamos nuestro coraje cuando lo escribimos en poemas, is part of my life. A metaphor that deals with your perspective, imitating your world, the sight that you have everyday when you are trying to send yourself forth in the world. Poetry brings the abrecaminos to life. A poet should be able to live and understand all the different worlds.

poeta: *Somos poetas. Pertenecemos a literatura. Es otro mundo, un mundo que transende, sobrepase, y transporte.* The poet is a solitary. The poet has to find her own way, or his own way. Sometimes magical things happen. The way of the poet is a free way with very strict rules.

por si a caso: Just in case. What's your back-up plan?

principiante: Beginner. *Yo soy principiante.* Another way of being in the world. A pilgrim. Someone who goes on a journey. Everything is always new to the *peregrino.*

principio: *Comienzo.* Beginning. A principle. The *principios entre* being a writer and being an *abrecaminos* are interesting to me. Sometimes they're the same. *A veces son diferentes. Necesitas disciplina para ambos.* Sacred person, sacred place. Sacred journey. *Persona sagrada, lugar sagrado, jornada sagrada:* These are the basic principles of the *abrecaminos.* What are your metaphors? *¿Qué son su metaforas?*

provecho: Benefit, advantage. In the new world the advantage goes to those who are bilingual and bicultural. It's a richer life. Also said at the dinner table: *buen provecho.*

pueblo: Village, town. My mother carries the culture of the *pueblo* in her *corazón.*

puente: Bridge. Most often a metaphor, as in the book: *This Bridge Called My Back.* Ask your librarian to order the book.

¿Qué onda?: The most popular greeting among young Mexicans. *What's happening?* But it's more: *¿Qué tiene profundidad?* Say it before starting a conversation. *Es una costumbre para los cholos, también.* To me, it's the way a poorly educated person talks.

342

querer: To want, desire, love. To like is not the same as to love. *Desear.* Desire. There is a famous *dicho, Querer es poder,* that means to want to do something is to be able to do it. Note: *querer* is also used to mean to love, such as: *Te quiero mucho.* And this: *Queremos. Tenemos. Podemos.* We want to, we have to, we can.

quinceañera: *Es cuando dejas la niñez y entras a ser mujer.* At 15, the traditional passage from being a girl to becoming an adult woman.

raices: Roots. *El llamado viene de aquí, buscando nuestros raices.* The calling. We're called to our roots, and our roots call back. Our mothers' stories will never be forgotten. *Estamos aquí. We're not going anywhere. We know who we are.*

racismo: Racism. See *opresión.*

ráfaga: Gust of wind, flash of light. Inspiration of the poet to *amalgamar, mezclar, y incrustar los momentos de modernidad.* The poet's job is to open the doors of time itself, to make this thing, *haz de palabras.*

ranchero: Farmworker. A person who works at a farm doing hard jobs. Also a farm owner.

rancho: A house in the countryside. Windy Point Ranch. A ranch of dirt and rocks, but everybody likes living there. Only three or four houses. *Una casa sola con una familia o más viviendo en el cerro. La Lechuguilla, La Guacatera,* these are places where there are a lot of animals, at the most, 20 houses. *La Barranca, El Capire. La Cofradia.* Everybody knows each other, a small community. A very small town where you don't find hardly any utiliities like gas, grocery stores, clothes stores, etc. Many of us come from *the ranchos en Jalisco, Colima, Guerrero y Michoacán.*

raza: *Tu cultura, tu familia, tu lengua, tu color, tu sangre. Mi raza son los Hispanos.* José Vasconcelos, minister of education in Mexico during the 1920's, called us the *Raza Cósmica,* the new race of people for the world. One group fighting together for rights and freedom of their world. It's not a street gang. *La raza es nuestro orgullo, las culturas de nuestros padres.* Not one or the other, but the best of both.

realismo maravilloso: More commonly, perhaps misleadingly called, **magical realism.** Extraordinary reality. Daily life is wild, marvelous. Reality is full of wonder. *Asombrado.* To live in this world, *este mundo asombroso. Asombroso.* Gabriel Garcia Márquez is often considered the father. His father is Juan Rulfo.

refránes: Sometimes called *dichos,* or proverbs. The popular sayings that brighten the talk. The wisdom can be profound. It can also serve to maintain the status quo. *Flies won't enter a closed mouth.*

reir/reirse: To laugh, to laugh at. *Humor Mexicano es seco.* You have to read between the lines. We can't tell everything. Read this book carefully.

respeto: Respect. One of the strongest values taught in the Mexican family. Children are taught to give respect to all. A person who fails to give respect is seen as being *mal educado,* poorly educated.

revolución: There has to be a revolution in every single person in the world. So you can realize life. *Si no hubiera revolución en nuestras vidas, no tuvieramos ningún sentido.*

riesgo: Risk. The world is full of risks, but *podemos elegir enfrentarlos con miedo o con ganas.* Only when I take the risk do I have the possibility of taking a new path.

río: There are many rivers to cross. It's a different river depending which side you're on. Rio Bravo on one side, Rio Grande on the other. We also cross the Wilkamayu and the Urubamba writing our way to Macchu Picchu. It's a border, it's a metaphor. Octavio Paz says once you cross the river you're different forever. Each crossing changes you.

rumbo: Path, direction. *Mi rumbo is con los abrecaminos. Mi rumbo is con la verdad, con raza, con poesia, conociendo los raices de mis padres.* To have your own path. A way you choose, where you can truly find yourself. *Es el camino o destino que tu vida sigue hacia tu futuro. Rumbo* is a direction. *El camino del destino.* Having *rumbo* is knowing where you want to go. See *corriente.*

sano: Healthy, wholesome; whole, intact. *Vivimos puro y sano. Es uno de los principios de los abrecaminos.*

searchers: *Buscadores. Escuchen a Tomás Rivera:* I wanted to document the spiritual strength, the concept of justice so important for the American continents. Within those migrants I saw that strength....spiritual justice...it was there....And the migrant workers still have that role: to be searchers. That's an important metaphor in the Americas. *No viajamos solos.*

se porta bien: He or she behaves himself, herself. The Mexican parents always says this to their children, *te portas bien hijo,* when they leave the house. To behave poorly is to be *mal educado.* This is one of the fundamental *principios* of the Mexican family.

senda: *Camino*, path.

sentir: To feel. I want to feel the love within me. I don't want to be afraid to feel anything. I want to feel like the wind. *Quiero siento como el viento.*

ser: To be. *Otra manera de ser.* Another way of being. This is a line from Rosario Castellanos. It's one of the *principios* of the *abrecaminos.* All writers swim in these waters.

silencio: *La habilidad de poder comunicar con nosotros mismos, Dios y la naturaleza de una forma profunda. Através del silencio se llega a la iluminación.* Silence brings us powerful knowledge, but we must learn to break the silence, too. You need to talk sometimes. You need to speak out or they will take advantage of you.

soledad: Solitude, loneliness. *Estar solo no es malo, es un rato para reflexionar lo que has echo en tu vida.* It's not bad. You learn what you've done in your life. Before you can live with someone else you have to live with yourself. Sometimes it's hard for our mothers, being here, so far from our *pueblo.*

soltar: To let go, set free. Chain breakers need to let go of certain things that keep them from going forward. Each *abrecaminos* must find these things out for themselves.

sueños: Dreams. *Unos de los principios de los abrecaminos.* The poet William Blake commands us to dream dreams, see visions, speak in parables.

suegro/a: Father-in-law, mother-in-law. See *consuegro.*

susurro: Whisper, also *cuchicheo.* Sometimes our true voices begin this way, in a whisper, but we know. We have a responsibility to tell our stories, to speak our truths.

susto: Fright, scare. Sudden, and intense.

testigo: Witness. *Soy testigo.* The poet is a witness.

tierra: Land. So much of the land they gave us didn't have any water.

testimonio: Testimony. But more: a narrative central to La Raza. Called …*the margin at the center.* Carlos Maldonado from Eastern Washington University, helped the *abrecaminos* deepen their work in family history. "Bearing witness in the act of testifying, in the legal or religious sense. In testimony, it is the intentionality of the narrator that is important. The situation of narration in *testimonio* has to involve an urgency to communicate, a problem of repression, poverty, struggle for survival. *Tesimonio* is not fiction. We are meant to experience both the speaker, and the situation and events as real. It doesn't focus on the inner self, but on communal experience."

tomar medidas: To take steps. There are things that you have to do differently if you want to get up the mountain.

Tonantzin: Aztec goddess of earth. Tonantzin had her sanctuary on the hill at Tepeyac, and the Indians made pilgrimages there to worship her. The site of the Shrine of Guadalupe today.

traducir: To translate. Many of the *abrecaminos* translate for their parents. In addition, many of them have translated their own work in this book. Some translate from English to Spanish. Others translate from *inglés al español*. They are their own *traductores*.

trastesitos de barro: Little plates, cups and pots made of clay. See interviews by Maria and Antonia Caro with their mother.

tristeza: Sadness. My hands are covered with sadness. We have an expression, *la tristeza de la vida*, the sadness of life. *La vida no es toda una alegría. Hay que conocer la tristeza para apreciar la alegría.*

truth: *La verdad. La verdad no peca, pero incomoda. Hay veces en que* we have to say the truth. It makes people uncomfortable. The truth is something we say with *certeza y sinceridad.* See *verdad.*

umbral: Threshold, doorway. That point in our lives we are just getting ready to walk through. Rosario Castellanos is the poet who leads us through this challenging and exciting time.

único: Only one. Learning to be unique like each one of us is. *No es fácil.*

verdad: Truth. *Buscando luz en cada cuarto oscuro.* See *poesía.*

valor: *Tener que enfrentar obstaculos que se te presentan y no tener miedo.* Courage, worth, value. *Es cuando te sientes con las ganas de hacer algo y nada te detiene y lo haces sin mirar atras. Como un sexto sentido que sale para expresar algo o hacer algo.* Also, being able to believe in yourself. To know something and stand for it.

venganza: One of the chains broken by the abrecaminos. Writing a strong poem is the best revenge.

vida: Life. *La vida cotidiana.* Daily life.

Yakima: Located in eastern Washington State. Also *Yakama*. A city, county, river, valley, nation. Home of the *Yakama Nation*. A destination point *por muchos Hispanos*. Many Mexicans originate from the states of Colima, Michoacán, and Jalisco, start new roots in Yakima. Home of the *abrecaminos*.

Each story has its own untold story. Each teacher in our English as a Second Language and Language Departments, Jerry Cole, Julie Salatino, Jim Rigney, Maryann Piñon, Jorge Rodríguez, Kerry Chama, Gabriela Botello, Lenin Caltenco, and José Garcia, is critically responsible for the teaching, and support of, Manuh Santos. What they have given of themselves to Manuh, from his first days in the Newcomer Program, they give daily, through their teaching and humanity, to hundreds of students who experience the best of what an open, North American culture offers them. In addition, José Garcia, Julie and Steve Barker have shown the truth of the Mexican proverb, *mi casa es tu casa,* making education possible against the greatest of odds. Miracle work is practical and can be seen. The fact of certain stories presented here is a result of their work. These teachers know how they have been abrecaminos to the abrecaminos. Jim Rigney's importance as a bilingual educator comes from deep intelligence. He is without peer. I am a witness to his support of the abrecaminos. Jorge Rodríguez is my Spanish teacher.

This book owes its existence to the abrecaminos who opened the way for *With My Hands Full/Con Mis Manos Llenas* (Blue Begonia Press, 1999), and to supporters of the book and the abrecaminos throughout the state of Washington, and all over the Northwest. These include The Yakima Herald-Republic; Lynda Mapes, The Seattle Times; Ricardo Sanchez, Director of Latino Educational Achievement Project; Ed Esparza, Hispanic Academic Achievement Program; Rick Simonson, Elliott Bay Bookstore; Judith Roche, Literary Director, Bumbershoot One Reel; Karen Garrison, former principal, Davis High School, now Education Professor, Heritage College; Dr. Larry Petry, former Superintendent of Yakima School District #7, now Dean of Students at Heritage College; The National Migrant Conference in San Diego; Bernal Baca, and Mario Campean of Yakima Valley Community College, who organized readings and taught the book in their courses; Alice Lara, who put books in each of the Yakima Schools; Doug Johnson and Tom Moore, who taught the book in their classes; Carol Perry at Sunshine & Wisteria Bookstore; and Carole Folsom-Hill of Casa Hogar, as much a prophet, as she is a Director. I would also like to remember the abrecaminos work of Dr. Gloria de Martinez and Raul (Torito) Torres. Charles Potts published poems and reviews in *The Temple.* Tino Gallegos reprinted poems in the *Texas Law Review,* keeping them alive after the book went out of print. Carlos Maldonado, from Eastern Washington University, has given presentations on *Testimonios* helping us understand the Latino tradition of witness. I am grateful to all of the abrecaminos who continue to teach me how difficult and important it is to take responsibility for one's story. *As difficult as it is necessary.* These include Alma Varela, Javier Vargas, Omar Ramírez, Gavicel Antunez and Gabino Salazar. Ines Hérnandez Avila's work with images of Latinas is present in both books. Felipe Garrison, poet and essayist from Central Washington

University helped with the reading list during the early development of the course.

Arturo Obispo is a student of Barry Grimes. His poem, *Unknown Passage*, opens this book. The poem is about poetry as much as it is about story. Poetry is the discipline responsible for transportation.

Rex DeLoney, Katie Hall, Marty Lovins, and Rob Prout teach the abrecaminos in their art classes. Abrecaminos learn about liberation and stories in art classes, too. Each abrecaminos has a teacher somewhere, who helped them with their story in ways no one knows about. Each book has its own rules. When the energy of *Seeking Light/Buscando Luz* threatened to overwhelm my capabilities, Terry Martin's vision appeared. Jackie Prout brought her matching energies. Karen Bodeen, a spirit, is the poet's muse. She makes the vests. Today she's making a quilt. Rob Prout showed me another way of photographing the abrecaminos; another way of integrating image and text; another way of saying the word collaboration, *co-labor*. Teachers are people who say things twice. It's the only joke I know. Teachers who I learn from mix practicality with vision. The process is mystical, but it can be observed by anyone. That is the paradox. If anyone's eyes can't see it, then it isn't true. This page is for those who make and give. *How we are called is how we use our privilege.*   —Jim Bodeen

What We Did

Sometimes it's silver particles on film. Sometimes it's ones and zeros on a memory chip. Either way the process is seeking light.

The process this time is seeking light together—involving the kids in the search. Photographing in their homes we are the searchers and they are teachers. Family albums and old snapshots provide the questions that will illuminate their past.

Preparing portraits of the abrecaminos, they show us which photos find that light: "Yes...yes...no...no, not that one...too dark...too mean...too sad...yes this one, I like this one."

Digital feedback—immediate—helps them find where the light falls just right on the face and in the eyes. Digital feedback helps Jim and I see their light. We find it together.

Digital feedback tells me now if I got the light. If I don't find what we want we go back in. We don't lose the moment.

What Jim and I do with cameras, what Jim does with words, what these kids do with their journeys—seeking light, finding light.

Rob Prout
Memorial Day, 2002